8TH EDIT

D0965144

THE

MELALEUCA

WELLNESS GUIDE

Presented to the

Healy Heights

Family Library

By the Members of the

Rotary Club of

Bend High Desert

Portions of this book were compiled or written by D.S. Church, Ph.D.

Published by:

RM BARRY PUBLICATIONS
P.O. BOX 3528
LITTLETON, CO 80161-3528

Toll-Free **1 (888) 209-0510**
Local (303) 224-0277
Fax (303) 224-0299

Web Site: **WWW.RMBARRY.COM**

E-mail: **INFO@RMBARRY.COM**

ISBN 0-9665924-6-8

Printed in the United States of America

TABLE OF CONTENTS

INTRODUCTION

The Melaleuca Wellness Guide

We hope you enjoy this newly updated and greatly expanded version of the popular *Melaleuca Guide* book. Since 1995, the *Melaleuca Guide* has been the most authoritative and comprehensive resource for users of Melaleuca, Inc. products. Actually, earlier versions of the *Melaleuca Guide* go back as far as 1986, shortly after Melaleuca, Inc. was founded, and over 700,000 copies of different versions have been sold.

Of course, the people who have been involved with publishing this book over the years have always strived to provide information to help readers of the book achieve *wellness*. In keeping with this mission, and in keeping with Melaleuca's emphasis toward wellness, we've decided to change the title slightly to *The Melaleuca Wellness Guide*.

You will find that this latest version has been greatly expanded. In fact, this version has 65% more information than the previous edition. We've added nine new chapters as well as some additional information in the appendix section. We've also added over fifty new health conditions in the "Healthy Body" section which respond well to Melaleuca products. We've included new chapters on horses and farm animals, and greatly expanded the chapter on cats and dogs. We've expanded the "Healthy Home" section to cover almost twice as many applications for Melaleuca products around the house. A new "Healthy Garden" section covers a number of horticultural applications for Melaleuca products. And our new "Alternative Uses" chapter covers some unusual applications for Melaleuca products submitted by our creative readers.

We've also added informative chapters on maintaining prostate health, coping with menopause, nutrition for the eyes, depression, boosting the immune system, and head lice.

We're confident you will find this newly updated and expanded *Melaleuca Guide* to be the most complete resource for Melaleuca users ever—and worthy of its new name, *The Melaleuca <u>Wellness</u> Guide*.

CHAPTER ONE

THE MELALEUCA STORY

by Richard M. Barry

Portions of this chapter have been taken from "Built On Solid Principles: the Melaleuca Story" by R.M. Barry. The book is a fascinating, in-depth portrayal of Frank VanderSloot, his mission, and how this former Idaho farm boy, once rated as lacking in leadership qualities, led Melaleuca, Inc. to phenomenal success in just a few short years. Informative, captivating, and truly inspirational, this fascinating portrait of a business founded on principles and integrity is a "must read" for anyone who wants to understand the company and the people who are drawn to it.

The story of Melaleuca, Inc. as we know it today actually began about fifteen years ago when a gifted American businessman had the insight to recognize the vast potential possessed by the unique substance we now call *Melaleuca oil*, and the foresight to evolve a business strategy based on its therapeutic properties. That man is, of course, Frank VanderSloot, founder of Melaleuca, Inc.

The early days of the original company, Oil of Melaleuca, Inc. were beset with difficulty. At the time, Frank VanderSloot seemed an unlikely candidate for such a venture. He was already a successful man. His personal abilities had enabled him to rise above his simple origins in rural Idaho to become Regional Vice President of Cox Communications, Inc.

Initially, he was called into Oil of Melaleuca, Inc. by the Ball brothers who wanted a man of his prestige and prowess at the helm. They finally managed to convince Frank of the vast, untapped potential of this wonderful substance from Australia. After some investigation, Frank was sold on the product, and decided to join the Balls in the business, which had already been operating for several months. He intended to help out the Ball brothers for eighteen months and pick up his bonus check to pay off his new house-end of story.

It didn't quite work out that way.

On his first day at work, VanderSloot heard the tape of a radio interview given by one of the Ball brothers. This tape was being sold as a marketing tool, and when he listened to it VanderSloot was astounded to hear, among other claims, that *Melaleuca oil* was being touted as a cure for herpes and gonorrhea. VanderSloot immediately ordered the tape to be withdrawn, but it was too late. The very next day, he was informed that a representative of the FDA was waiting to see him in the reception area.

In his speech at the Melaleuca Caribbean Cruise of 1999, Frank describes the incident very wittily. At first Frank was not worried. He went into the reception area, leaned across the oak desk and offered his hand to the FDA officer. Frank says, "Have you ever extended your hand to someone to shake it and they didn't shake it? It's not a good feeling. And that's what happened. I reached my hand out and instead of extending his, he reached into his back pocket and pulled out a wallet. A big, black wallet, and did what I know he'd done a hundred times before. He did a little flip with it. He flipped it open and it went 'thud!' right on that oak countertop and I was staring at the ugliest badge I have ever seen in my life. It said 'FDA'—and some other things on it—United States Government. He said: 'I'm Ed Edmunsen and I'm here to close your doors if you don't cease this illegal and unethical advertising.'"

With a gulp, Frank ushered the man into his office to be told in no uncertain terms he would not be allowed to operate while making such claims.

"I said, 'Hey, well, you'll be happy to know, sir, today's my second day on the job and yesterday, my first day, I took that tape off the market. We're not selling it anymore. And besides, the guy that you're after is in Australia.'"

Frank later consulted an FDA expert to find that none of the literature could be used to promote Melaleuca. Whether the claims were true or not, in strict FDA terms, legally they could not be advertised.

Everything that could go wrong in a business did, though it was through no fault of Frank or the Ball brothers. Not only did the FDA totally clamp down on any advertising claims for the product, but the company's business plan floundered mainly because it was saddled with weaknesses inherited from an MLM-type structure.

The death knell was sounded with some more bad news. Frank had initially been attracted away from his secure job by the exciting potential of the oil itself. A partner in the business, an Australian plantation owner, had promised a world monopoly on the supply of high-grade oil. Given the enthusiasm that Frank had for the product after researching its benefits, the promise of a world monopoly had been a major clincher. It seemed too good to be true. And, in fact, it was. The Australian planta-tion owner's promises turned out to be false, and their world monopoly melted away.

Plagued with problems and unforeseen legal complications, VanderSloot and the Ball brothers made the inevitable decision to close the company.

Rather than see this as a failure, VanderSloot seized upon the demise of the original company as a starting point for an entirely new company. In doing so, he used the new company as the platform to launch an ideal so basically American that it seems innovative only because so many modern businesses have lost sight of it. Namely, that the Free Enterprise system does not have to be exploitative to succeed. To initiate his strategy, one of the first things VanderSloot did was to formulate a Mission Statement—*"Enhancing the Lives of Those We Touch by Helping People Reach Their Goals."*

From the beginning, Frank VanderSloot was adamant that the 'new' Melaleuca should help people to reach their goals in such a way that no one should get hurt, either in the business or by the business. This credo, coupled with his insistence on diligent legal and scientific research, led to the impeccable Melaleuca product line—"quality products made from natural substances supported by intensive research."

Perhaps the key to the heart of Melaleuca lies in VanderSloot's determination to "build a business to last a lifetime." Frank was a shrewd businessman and experience had taught him that continued growth needs two essential resources: product and personnel. In the case of Melaleuca, where the Marketing Executives are drawn from people with homes and families—and full-time jobs—the only factor which will attract people and keep them is belief. It is impossible to foster this in people unless the products are the best and the morals of the company are beyond reproach.

Wary of the pitfalls of inventory loading and the multitude of traps in the MLM structure, VanderSloot evolved his now-famous system of Consumer Direct Marketing. Quite simply, it meant that any average person could gradually work towards financial independence, risk-free, without quitting his or her day job, spending vast amounts on products, or working countless hours processing customer orders on a monthly basis.

Listening to Frank VanderSloot's Melaleuca speeches over the years, it is possible to see how much his own personality has grown along with the company—a classic case of a man growing to fulfill the role he's defined for himself by sharing his heart-felt values. Though a fuller analysis of the man and his novel business methods are beyond the scope of this chapter, they are, in fact, covered in depth in a fascinating book *Built On Solid Principles: The Melaleuca Story.*

Frank's accomplishments are many. Not only does he serve on the Board of Directors of the prestigious United States Chamber of Commerce, but Idaho State University named him Business Leader of the Year, to mention but a few. Typically, VanderSloot shrugs off the glory of such successes, saying, "There were many people besides myself who contributed to Melaleuca's success."

Nevertheless, inadvertently, Frank tapped into something that is the model for new millennium business success as touted by America's top economic experts.

Charles Handy, "the philosopher for the world of business and management," foresaw in his book, The Age of Unreason, the collapse of the 45-year job and the paternalistic company which is taking place around us now. His blueprint for success in the next century provides a radical break with the 'take-no-prisoners' attitudes of 1990's business practice. Handy says: "The old-fashioned models of corporate control and contracts of employment are meaningless. Organizations have to be based on trust."

Similarly, Peter Drucker, one of the most perceptive observers of the American business scene stated: "The kind of organization [that will succeed] will be built around family and regional ties that, unlike American business, are personal rather than impersonal."

The fact is Frank VanderSloot must have gotten something right—the growth of Melaleuca has been staggering. In comparison with other product-based companies, there are no unseen pitfalls, no 'trickle-downs' from upper Executives making a fortune at the expense of those lower down the scale. The system works for everybody. Melaleuca's Marketing Executives have become a market force to reckon with and, as their scope and power have grown in keeping with the demands of the market, so has Melaleuca.

Despite these changes, the basic principles of Melaleuca have remained untouched. Time itself has shown that it is these very principles that have enabled Melaleuca to flourish at an amazing rate when traditional companies are going under. That these principles are touted by experts as "cutting-edge" may give rise to a chuckle. Melaleuca's principles were not formulated in an oak-paneled room in Princeton or Harvard. They are simply the down-home values Frank acquired from his hard-working Idaho father. It is these simple truths that empowered Melaleuca to rise above the shaky start of Oil of Melaleuca, Inc. and chart a path through the shark-infested waters of the 90's business world into the bright future of the next century.

It also attests to something that Frank VanderSloot believes we all possess: the ability to affect the lives of others in a positive way. He says: "We don't have to do great, newsworthy things to have a great influence on this world. We only need to live a life others can follow. It is impossible to measure the impact that one life can have on thousands of others."

VanderSloot calls this principle ...

THE POWER OF ONE

The success of Melaleuca is living proof of this principle for, in VanderSloot's case, his main influence—an influence that is prevalent everywhere in the 'Melaleuca philosophy'—came from his father.

Peter Francis VanderSloot is typical of the millions of "quiet Americans" who formed the backbone of America in the 1950s and, in many ways, enabled it to rise to its status as the leader of the economic world. They did this simply by being who they are: simple, working folk who work. And how they work. With only a third-grade education, Peter VanderSloot labored up to sixty hours a week on the railways, sometimes away from home a week at a time. He spent his whole life just feeding his kids and providing a home and values that would serve them in the future.

There is in such people a quiet wisdom which is the way of those who tend animals, till the soil and wake each morning without complaint, ready for a day of toil. Frank imbibed this wisdom from his father wholesale-and is eternally grateful for it. He says: "If I had not had the influence of my father in my life...it's doubtful that Melaleuca would exist as it does today."

Life on a small farm is not easy. Rural Idaho in those days was very poor. Work was hard to come by and it was mostly just logging. Such environments breed common sense, and Mr. VanderSloot, Sr., instilled his values in Frank not by preaching sermons but by practical example. For example, when he wanted Frank to have the education he had missed himself, he gave Frank a milk cow! Frank would milk that cow morning and night. He'd churn up the milk with a hand paddle and, making sure to keep his brother away from the final product, Frank would sell the cream for a few dollars at the market. Amazingly, Frank used this money to finance his college education. And, in keeping with the hard lesson learned, he actually paid for his own college expenses by living in and watching over a Laundromat.

It was quite an eye-opener for Frank seeing people at college with new clothes when all his were bought at the Salvation Army thrift store, but he was never jealous. In fact, it reinforced his first lessons: keep out of debt, work hard and, as he never heard his father tell a lie, always be honest.

For those approaching the Melaleuca organization for the first time or even those within it, it is important to understand VanderSloot's assertion that he is "not especially gifted." In his early years, he actually hated standing up in front of people and failed a leadership-attitude test because of his shyness. But through the example of his father and other key figures in his life, he came to realize the importance of self-esteem and the impact that the right kind of influence can have on the future of a so-called "average" person.

After the demise of Oil of Melaleuca, Inc., VanderSloot had to work late into the night to salvage a viable business from its shipwreck. He was not simply struggling with facts and figures. Rather, he was determined to develop a business that was built on the solid foundation of his home values. Also, it had to be a business that was readily available to not just a gifted few but to anyone with the desire and determination to succeed.

In picturing Frank at this stage, it should be remembered that when he began with Oil of Melaleuca, Inc., he was already a very successful businessman. As Regional Vice President of Cox Communications, Inc., a Fortune 500 company, he'd served his time in the 'war trenches' of modern business and had come out tops. The fact is, once the initial shock of the Oil of Melaleuca, Inc. failure had settled, he realized that he now had the chance to start something new, something that had been hovering at the back of his mind for years.

He embarked on a quest for knowledge. He consulted marketing gurus, direct-sales experts and FDA attorneys. From them he took what he thought was the best and incorporated it into his own methodology. What he came up with was a risk-free plan with a low monthly production requirement well within the scope of any American household.

The plan was elegant in its structure, economically sound—and innovative. VanderSloot was no longer in pursuit of a dream but possessed of a viable strategy to facilitate it. It was to become no less than the 'Melaleuca Way.'

THE MELALEUCA WAY

"Give a man a fish; it feeds him for a day. Teach him how to fish and he can feed himself for a lifetime." VanderSloot's idea was not to give away opportunity but to empower people to make their own. And from the well of this simple philosophy have sprung many statements and slogans which are at the heart of the Melaleuca experience:

- "No one must get hurt from what we do."
- "The magic is in helping others reach their goals and not in trying to reach our own goals."
- "No amount of wealth will bring true happiness if it is gained unethically."
- "We are not a multi-level company...Multi-level marketing has been used to con [people] into money-making schemes. We have never done that."
- "We don't have a right to be here unless we are marketing the best products for the best prices at the best value of anybody in this nation."
- "Don't quit your job."
- "We're telling about Melaleuca, not selling it."
- "The marketing and delivery of exceptional products at reasonable prices has been the key to our success."

Hundreds of thousands of people are now taking advantage of the opportunity to compete against the huge conglomerates. Marketing Executives are pulling customers away from these giants in tens of thousands by using Melaleuca's unique Marketing Plan.

However, when VanderSloot hears his Executives enthusing about his "wonderful Marketing Plan," he gives them a few home-truths. "I feel that sometimes there's a tendency for people to perceive that it's the Marketing Plan that brings us our success. It is not so." His conviction is deep on this matter. "Without having the best products that money can buy, we don't really have an excuse to be here."

THE BEST OF SCIENCE AND NATURE

It is for this reason that he was determined that, in the future, Melaleuca would use only those products that were the very best in nature, as supported and guided by scientific research. VanderSloot sought tirelessly to form relationships with pharmacists, nutritional experts, allopathic and homeopathic doctors, herbal experts, and scientists from all fields. His aim was to sort out the product wheat from product chaff.

As an illustration of how VanderSloot spent his time during this period, here's an example of one of his contacts. Frank located a doctor who was something of an expert on tea tree oil. For more than ten years, this man had been using the oil in his practice to treat a wide variety of complaints. Frank spent the entire day with the doctor, extracting every scrap of information he could about the uses of tea tree oil and the various mixtures used to treat different complaints. They must have been mutually impressed with each other because when Frank established Melaleuca, Inc., the man became a loyal customer. So much so that in 1986 the doctor published his first book about Melaleuca products. Then, in 1995, the doctor greatly expanded his book and called it the *Melaleuca Guide*. It is said that the test of time is the true judge of all things. If so, his books have passed with flying colors, since over 700,000 copies have been sold. In fact, a historical footnote is that this worthy doctor has since moved on to other things. However, the book in your hand at the moment, *The Melaleuca Wellness Guide*, is a new and radically-revised book, but is still based on all the tried and tested product knowledge from the original *Melaleuca Guide*.

THE PIONEER PRODUCT: MELALEUCA OIL

To create the exceptional product line he needed for the new company, VanderSloot had to have a dependable supply of high-grade *Melaleuca oil*. He went to great lengths to secure a crop which could propagate a superior tree line. No two strains of the *Melaleuca alternifolia* tree provided the same quality of oil. His investigations took him to Australia. The best stands of *Melaleuca alternifolia* trees are in an area called the Bungawalbyn Reserve.™ The Bungawalbyn varieties produce genetically-superior trees that give the highest quality oil. The properties of the tree were so highly thought of by the local Aborigines that the very word *Bungawalbyn* means 'healing ground.' Thus, VanderSloot was able to secure exclusive rights to oil harvested from natural stands; these Bungawalbyn trees had never been treated with herbicides or pesticides.

Under Melaleuca's incentive, the growers sought out more robust and higher-yield trees, took seedlings from them, and from this superior line began establishing plantations of trees. The enthusiastic participation of the Australian growers was ensured by Melaleuca who supported them through years of poor yields, and the growers responded with a greater diligence in producing the highest-quality yield possible.

As research on *Melaleuca oil* progressed, it became obvious that its medicinal properties were directly proportional to its quality of oil. Higher grades of the oil have greater levels of the therapeutic agent Terpinen 4-ol and less of Cineole, which can be irritating to sensitive skin.

Other companies were selling substandard grades of the oil as "pure oil of *Melaleuca alternifolia*." Some of these oils have very little, if any, medicinal value. VanderSloot wanted to make sure that Melaleuca sold only the highest-quality oil available, and that customers could clearly see what grade they were getting. He decided to place the grade designation right on the label, and hence the name "*T36-C7*" for the standard high-grade oil, and "*T40-C5*" for the ultra-rare grade oil. These pure oils have been shown to be superlative treatments for stings, burns, skin rashes and a host of topical applications. Because the higher grade of the oil comes from trees with rare genetics and the supply is limited, it is more expensive.

Melaleuca recently raised the standards for both grades of their oil to "*T36-C5*" and "*T40-C3*," which demonstrates a commitment to making the very best oil available as growing and harvesting techniques continue to improve. The standard high-grade oil is used in a wide range of Melaleuca products, most notably in skin care, hair care, dental care, and medicine chest products.

Even though reputable organizations the world over have validated *Melaleuca oil's* effectiveness and safety, VanderSloot is always cautious about its claims. By 1996, over six million bottles of the oil had been sold. Nevertheless, when describing its uses, Frank insisted on erring on the conservative side, saying, "It's clear that *Melaleuca oil* has some very unique and unusual properties. Many people have experimented and reported very favorable results on conditions such as cold sores, canker sores, candida, chicken pox, herpes, thrush, etc. Several studies have been done on some of these conditions that appear quite promising. But more research needs to be done to verify its efficacy before being able to make legitimate claims in regard to these conditions."

The book is not yet closed on *Melaleuca oil.* In some ways, it is still a mystery and, as of yet, not all of its properties are fully understood. New research is expanding its possibilities every day. One thing is certain—as new uses are discovered for this wonderful substance, Melaleuca will ensure that any potential benefit is passed on to customers.

BEYOND MELALEUCA OIL

Nearly 30% of Melaleuca's revenues go into product quality. Compared to this, traditional manufacturers only spend about 10% for the same purpose. By pouring revenue back into product development, Melaleuca has been able to provide an ever-widening range of new products, many of which are not based on *Melaleuca oil* at all.

Melaleuca's research and development team continually searches for natural ingredients with known restorative or curative powers. Having found such an ingredient, Melaleuca will either closely examine any former research on it, or they will initiate fresh research. As a result of such investigations, Melaleuca now distributes a line of products which use ingredients that go far beyond the original flagship product, *Melaleuca oil*. Nowadays, many of the products are not based on the oil at all but on other natural botanicals—plants and herbs whose health-promoting properties have been known for years and whose viability has been established by further testing. These include household products that are safe to both the health of the user and that of the environment, and a wide range of personal care and cosmetic products.

Americans are slowly becoming aware that protecting our health and the environment is not just the province of the fanatical few. The gap between the violation of nature's delicate balance and its rebound effect on humanity is growing narrower every year. Melaleuca's household and personal care products offer a solution where the giant corporations have simply turned a blind eye. This has created a competitive edge for the company as it attracts more and more people who realize they can now exercise personal and environmental responsibility without sacrificing effectiveness.

UNLOCKING NATURE'S SECRETS WITH SCIENCE

As Melaleuca expands, there seems to be a peculiar sense of appropriateness in the direction taken. Following its establishment of safe household and personal care products, Melaleuca's move into the area of nutrition and personal health aids seemed a natural step. "We have found that mother nature has provided a natural solution for almost every health problem that confronts us. Our task is to use science as the key to unlock the secrets that nature has to offer," states VanderSloot.

As Melaleuca R&D uncovers fresh developments in natural health, the flexibility of their infrastructure facilitates their ability to investigate and incorporate such developments into an enhanced product line. This is accomplished on a time scale which would be impossible for the gigantic corporations. Not only does this put Melaleuca on the cutting edge, but the speed at which it takes place does not compromise safety or quality.

FRUCTOSE COMPOUNDING

Given some of the negative factors of modern life—stress, pollution, over-processed foods—it is even more essential that our body receive an adequate supply of vitamins and especially minerals. A healthy diet which includes the recommended intake of fruits and vegetables does not always provide the necessary nutrition. If the minerals are not in the soil, they won't be reproduced in the food. Thus, the degeneration of soil quality and the practice of over-processing food has given rise to a peculiar phenomenon—people who overeat and are still malnourished.

Furthermore, nutritional research has also shown that even when there is an adequate mineral supply within certain foods, it doesn't necessarily mean that the body will receive the full benefit. This anomaly came to the attention of nutritionists in Egypt, Libya, and Iran in the 70's, where children were suffering from horrible symptoms of zinc deficiency—severe growth retardation and dwarfism—even though the local foods contained an adequate supply of zinc.

The explanation is that the zinc attaches itself to certain acids in the food and is passed right through the body as "waste," without even getting to the cells. This happens, though to a lesser degree, with the minerals in our diets as well. The problem is solved by using an innovative process which binds a mineral to fructose, a substance found in fruit which is very readily absorbed by the cells. By using this "fruit sugar" messenger to carry the minerals piggy-back style, the mineral is passed through to the tissues and its full benefits can be utilized by the body.

This patented process called "fructose compounding" is exclusive to Melaleuca. No one else has this cutting-edge technology, which is one of the features of Melaleuca's *Vitality Pak*, a health product delivered to the customer's door in the shape of fifty-five vitamins and fructose-compounded minerals.

THE CASE OF BOBBI MCCAUGHEY

Melaleuca's emphasis on using only those quality products which have been validated and well researched has had some interesting repercussions in the community at large. Not the least of these is the case of Bobbi McCaughey, the Iowa woman whose claim to fame is the delivery of seven living children at one birth.

To fully appreciate the magnitude of this feat, it has to be remembered that formerly in cases of multiple births, all or some of the children died. In fact in two previous cases of septuplet births, all the babies died.

When Bobbi had recovered from the news that she was pregnant seven times over (if, indeed, she ever will recover!), the primary concern was her physical robustness. Could she withstand the severe assault of this incredible event?

Her pastor's wife, Ginny Brown, is a Melaleuca Marketing Executive. Ginny suggested that Bobbi use *The Vitality Pak*. Of course, Bobbi had to have her doctors look over the specifications of *The Vitality Pak*. They examined the ingredients closely before approving them. Bobbi embarked upon a regimen of three *Mel-Vita* and *Mela-Cal* tablets, and three *ProVex-Plus* capsules daily. The most distinctive advantage of *The Vitality Pak* is the high absorption of minerals due to Melaleuca's patented fructose-compounding process.

Bobbi says, "We thought it would be a great help during the pregnancy and that it would be much more usable—as far as being absorbed by my body—than a regular prenatal vitamin would be."

A pregnant woman has very special nutritional needs. For instance, Bobbi was supposed to eat 4,000 calories a day, but she could not eat that much. "I needed to eat something every forty minutes and I just couldn't."

Zinc and calcium are especially needed, even during a normal pregnancy. In this case, the situation was even more extreme—Bobbi was carrying seven babies. So it was absolutely essential that she had the right nutrition. But, for the first five months of the pregnancy, she was so sick she could hardly eat at all. Once she got to the hospital she was able to eat a little bit more, but she says, "But then I had hospital food, so I didn't want to eat any more! So it was good to have something that was really able to boost the vitamins and minerals I didn't get from the food."

The circumstances of a pregnancy seven times over needed very special precautions. Bobbi was told by her doctors to stay in bed for the last five months of the pregnancy. This immediately introduced other possible problems—blood clotting in the legs, reduced muscle tone, and loss of bone mass. Also, a common aspect of multiple pregnancies is that blood pressure can rapidly escalate to abnormal proportions. The doctors who had examined the ingredients of *The Vitality Pak* told Bobbi to take three *Mela-Cal* and three *Mel-Vita* tablets every day, and she never had any problems with blood pressure.

Ginny, knowing that it might be difficult for the McCaughey's to pay for the vitamins in such quantities, called Tish Poling at Melaleuca, and Tish discreetly arranged that the McCaughey's would get everything they needed from Melaleuca without any intrusive publicity.

When Bobbi was asked how she felt during this period, she replied, "I felt really good. It wasn't until probably the last week and a half that I really felt terrible. By that time, the contractions had started and I was on other medications to stop them."

Of course, Frank VanderSloot was proud that Melaleuca's vitamins and minerals had been used in such a medically-sensitive situation. He said, "We're really pleased that the McCaugheys decided to use our vitamins, and that the result has been so great. Our hopes and prayers are with them as they prepare for the wonderful experiences ahead."

Well, the results have become worldwide news. Bobbi did deliver her seven bouncing bundles of joy—the first woman in known history to do so. Of course, Bobbi's major feat attracted worldwide attention. One day, when Bobbi was back in the hospital post-delivery, the phone rang. Ken McCaughey picked up the phone. A voice said, "Mr. McCaughey, you have a phone call from the President of the United States."

The McCaugheys were astonished. The President had phoned to offer his personal congratulations. Bobbi's marathon feat had even caught the imagination of the President of the United States!

Naturally, the credit should go to Bobbi and her team of doctors. Still, there is no doubt that Melaleuca's policy of credible testing and high-quality product meant that *The Vitality Pak* was well up to their standards.

A comic side-light to the Bobbi McCaughey case took place during one of Frank VanderSloot's talks. While addressing a roomful of people, Frank mentioned that Bobbi had been taking *The Vitality Pak*.

"All of a sudden," Frank said, "from the back of the room, a woman screamed, 'OH MY GOSH!!' It seems she was a new customer and she'd just started taking *The Vitality Pak* herself. She was concerned that somehow that was what caused the seven babies!"

Partly because of Bobbi McCaughey's experience with *The Vitality Pak*, Melaleuca has now introduced *The Vitality Pak Prenatal*. This new formulation is specifically designed for the nutritional needs of a woman during her pregnancy.

THE ACCESS BAR

As we move into the first century of the new millennium, the greatest change in health care is the trend towards prevention rather than cure. In particular, lifestyle has been designated as a major causal factor in disease.

Exercise is a key element in a healthy lifestyle. Obesity is a major concern, and lack of exercise is a main contributor to strokes and heart attacks. *The Access Bar* was developed specially to ensure that the maximum possible benefits were obtained from exercise.

Through Melaleuca's practice of networking with cutting-edge doctors, they became aware of Dr. Lawrence Wang's studies into fat metabolism. Dr. Wang, Ph.D., is the Professor of Animal and Human Physiology at the University of Alberta, Edmonton, Canada, and a member of the prestigious Royal Society of Canada.

His research into fat metabolism led him to a substance called adenosine which exerts a blocking effect on the burning of stored fat during exercise. Adenosine, a by-product of activity, leads to the familiar sensation in fatigued muscles, expressed in the old exercise slogan as "feel the burn." It is adenosine which is indirectly responsible for that burning sensation and muscle soreness after exercise. Normally, exercise burns off glucose, not fat, but by utilizing a natural substance which inhibits the effect of the adenosine, Wang was able to increase the direct burning of fat, not glucose, during exercise.

This led to the *Access Fat-Conversion Activity Bar,* a product made from natural substances which has become a mainstay for both athletes and casual exercisers alike. Taken approximately fifteen minutes before exercise, the bar ensures that the body will burn less glucose and more fat. Fatigue and soreness are minimized and exercise can continue for longer periods. This simple, safe exercise bar ensures that maximum benefits can be attained during any exercise routine.

THE EVOLUTION OF PROVEXCV™

Melaleuca's interest in formidable health issues did not stop with obesity. In 1995, Melaleuca announced that they were committed to becoming a world leader in research and development into a group of substances known as flavonoids. This was in direct response to the enormous medical problem of heart disease and the related medical and lifestyle factors associated with it.

The results have been quite amazing. VanderSloot remarked: "We never dreamed that when we said we would become a world leader, we would actually become the world leader in the development of products to reduce the risk of heart disease."

Melaleuca's interest in flavonoids had been aroused by a peculiar phenomenon known as the French Paradox which came to the attention of the public in 1990. The way in which the story develops is a prime example of Melaleuca's product development methodology.

Apparently, the French consume 2.8 times the amount of lard as Americans and 3.8 times as much butter. The French are also a nation of very heavy smokers. Yet, despite the fact that they have higher blood cholesterol levels and higher blood pressure readings than Americans, the French have only one-third the rate of heart attacks.

Subsequent research led scientists to attribute this odd paradox to the French's habitual consumption of red wine with meals. This led to further studies into the constituents of red wine, aimed at pinpointing the connection between the wine and their lowered incidence of heart attacks. Over the years, many such experiments gradually eliminated different factors until, finally, something concrete was established. It seems the lowered incidence of heart attacks in the French was due to a substance in grape skins and seeds known as flavonoids. Flavonoids are present in red wine and purple grape juice.

The basic causes of heart attacks had already been well established by earlier researchers. It stems from two factors—the buildup of "oxidized" cholesterol on artery walls, which causes the artery to become restricted, and the "stickiness" of blood platelets which may cause a blockage in the restricted artery.

The buildup of "bad" cholesterol has been shown to be minimized by antioxidants such as Vitamin E. Also, as early as 1974 it was demonstrated that aspirin can reduce artery blockage by inhibiting platelet clotting.

This simplified explanation indicates that any attempt to reduce heart attacks has to be a two-fold attack—one, to produce an antioxidant that reduces the oxidation of "bad" cholesterol, and two, to reduce blood platelet "stickiness" in a similar manner to the action of aspirin.

Aspirin has one major drawback. Most heart attacks are induced through stress, and it was found that aspirin's effect is minimized in the presence of adrenaline, which is released during stress—the "Catch 22" of using aspirin for this purpose.

Melaleuca, in responding to the challenge of this new area, formed an alliance with Dr. John Folts, the man who had conducted the original research into the beneficial effects of aspirin. Folts had already spent several years researching the effects of flavonoids on platelet stickiness. He believed that flavonoids were the key to the 'French paradox.' Folts says, "Focusing on flavonoid supplements was the next logical step. Everyone has been asking when they'll be able to get the same benefits [of red wine] from a pill."

Melaleuca's goal was to develop a flavonoid-based dietary supplement that would be effective at preventing heart disease. Initial research revealed that flavonoids extracted from plants are not absorbed completely by the body. At first this was very disappointing news.

Other manufacturers of flavonoid supplements were touting them as being effective against heart disease based on tests which were done in test tubes only. Melaleuca's research had been done in living subjects and clearly showed that the claims made by the other manufacturers were greatly exaggerated.

The researchers set out to solve the problem of absorption so the benefits of the flavonoids could be utilized by the body. After almost two years they discovered that a particular mixture of flavonoid extracts combined with a special blend of enzymes greatly increased the absorption of the flavonoids. This was the breakthrough they had been looking for. This led to the development of the first flavonoid-based supplement which has been proven (in living subjects) to be effective in curbing the two primary causes of heart disease.

"WHEN THE TRUTH IS ALMOST TOO GOOD TO BE TRUE"

This was the title of Frank VanderSloot's September 1997 President's Message, which was a direct response to the results of Dr. Folts' research. These results, to put it mildly, were overwhelming. A ripple of excitement fluttered through the Melaleuca world as the breakthrough product, known as *ProVexCV*, was made available to Melaleuca Marketing Executives at the 1997 Convention.

Frank VanderSloot, in accordance with long-established Melaleuca principles, asked for restraint. He urged his Marketing Executives to refrain from any publicity until Dr. Folts and his researchers could publish their findings in appropriate medical journals.

Melaleuca's success with *ProVexCV* is not a lucky accident. Melaleuca is ever sifting through the enormous number of natural remedies to all kinds of illnesses. The larger corporations simply will not take time to investigate natural remedies. One reason for this is they cannot be patented. And smaller companies simply don't have the funds to pursue the kind of research that led to *ProVexCV.* So Melaleuca has carved out a huge niche for itself in the marketplace as the leading manufacturer of beneficial natural products.

In his February 1997 address, Frank VanderSloot illustrated the importance of R&D: "If any company, large or small, comes out with a great product, rather than competing with it, we'll incorporate it into our own product line-and we will challenge our own scientists to improve on it. We did exactly that with *ProVex*—instead of becoming a competitor or follower in that industry, we found a better way, and we became the leader."

Melaleuca, Inc.'s astute methods of uncompromising testing have borne fruit in more ways than one. In the words of Frank VanderSloot, "As our ongoing research continues to uncover more of nature's secrets, we promise to keep you informed. We believe this is a never-ending story, but the first chapter is now complete. Stay tuned for more information."

Well, more information did come and this time it raised a ripple of excitement not just amongst Melaleuca Executives but the world.

The Press has always been intrigued by the idea of the French Paradox—the idea that drinking alcohol could actually promote health is something of a teaser. Unfortunately, this was always its weak point medically.

Then, in November 1998, Dr. Folts delivered a presentation to the American Dietetic Association. In the context of numerous other presentations, this was the one that attracted the attention of the Press.

Folts had experimented with a supplement consisting of carefully researched amounts of grape seed, grape skin, Gingko biloba, bilberries and a specific flavonoid called quercetin. Folts found that his test subjects showed a "significant and encouraging" reduction in the contributing factors responsible for heart disease.

This was the news that sent the Press racing for the door. The news was circulated very rapidly via Associated Press, Reuters, and numerous other agencies. Over 100 articles were generated in different newspapers around the nation and on numerous television news programs. Here was absolute verification that a non-alcoholic substance in pill form could be effective against heart disease.

Folts' talk was a major breakthrough. But for Melaleuca, it was, in some sense, old hat. For, of course, the supplement Folts tested was none other than *ProVexCV*.

Earlier that year, VanderSloot had said, "We have also learned some exciting things about the most effective way to extract the nutrients from grape seeds and grape skins...We have learned exactly how to do it and we are not telling anyone else. And much of what we know is now protected by patent."

A patent? Yes. Melaleuca, Inc. had the foresight to contract with the only manufacturer who knew the special process needed to obtain the maximum result from the grapes. Melaleuca even arranged with the manufacturer to have a special factory built. Melaleuca's contract ensures that they, and only they, are eligible to receive this special extract for the next twenty years.

It is ironic that fifteen years earlier Frank VanderSloot had taken over the reins of a new company based on the promise of another monopoly —the world monopoly of *Melaleuca oil*. Sadly, it turned out to be too good to be true. Now, fifteen years later, Melaleuca, Inc. stands on the threshold of an incredible medical coup. And this time, the monopoly is signed, sealed, and water-tight.

As the new millennium dawns and Melaleuca trembles on the brink of a solution to America's Number One health problem, the future is looking brighter than Frank VanderSloot could ever have dreamed. With an air of barely-concealed excitement, he states:

"I do not know of any company, regardless of size, let alone a Direct Marketing company, that has had the opportunity to take a product of this magnitude to market. A product that is so far advanced beyond anything else in the marketplace…! It's wonderful to be in a position where the truth is almost too good to be true. Thank goodness it is true. I cannot imagine a better situation for us to be in."

Indeed.

The complete 128 page book, "Built on Solid Principles: the Melaleuca Story," is available from RM Barry Publications. Call 1 (888) 209-0510.

CHAPTER TWO

THAT AMAZING TEA TREE OIL!

ABOUT THE AUTHOR

Karen MacKenzie began her investigation into Tea Tree oil in 1989 while working as a researcher for an essential oil company. During this time, she began to develop a strong interest in alternative medicine and nutrition. When, in 1991, she developed an allergy to chemicals in many personal care products and make-up, she was forced to search for chemical-free alternatives. Unfortunately, there were very few alternatives available back then. Her quest led her to begin using Tea Tree oil in a variety of ways with spectacular results, and her allergy eventually subsided.

She began writing about Tea Tree oil to share her experiences with others. In 1996, she founded the Tea Tree Oil Information Service in Great Britain to help spread the word and to assist medical professionals as well as the general public in using this valuable natural gift.

INTRODUCTION

When I initially heard about Tea Tree oil, I could not believe it. It was too good to be true. Why had we not heard about it before? The truth is we had, but then we had chosen to ignore it!

I have traced Tea Tree oil back to its roots in Aboriginal Australia, through its popularity during the Second World War, right up to the present day world-wide acclaim. I have read the research papers, used it for first aid applications, treated my pets, and even cleaned many household accessories and furnishings with it.

I am constantly amazed by its versatility and effectiveness. I would never have believed that an essential oil from one plant could lend itself so successfully to so many different applications. No one but God, through nature, could have created such a valuable broad-spectrum substance, and that is the beauty of Tea Tree oil—it is totally natural.

I wrote this in an effort to bring Tea Tree oil to your attention, so you, like I, could read about its history, study the research work, utilize its many properties, and make up your own mind about nature's potent gift. After all, Tea Tree oil was created for each and every one of us.

PREFACE

Every week we see the same headlines in the newspapers "Head Lice Shampoo Cancer Scare"..."The Age of the Superbug is Here"... "Household Chemicals and Pollution Linked to Cancer"..."Acne Treatment Damages Skin Cells"... and so on.

We are now just beginning to wake up to the fact that the synthetic chemical cocktails we encounter during the course of a lifetime—hairsprays, cosmetics, deodorants, polishes, detergents, toothpastes, perfumes, aftershaves, first aid treatments, medicines, air fresheners, etc. —are systematically weakening our bodies. It is undeniable that our health is beginning to suffer. Where will it all end?

Germs, bacteria, and other parasites are evolving to beat their chemical killers. The "superbugs," including MRSA (Golden staph), thrive. Mystery illnesses are on the increase. Do we then try to make stronger chemicals? You bet we do!

Are we not forgetting one simple, fundamental fact? Bacteria is a basic, one-celled form of life, and these chemicals are harmful to all life—including our own!! When we use harsh chemicals against bacteria we can also unbalance and even destroy our own body cells, too.

I am not denying that synthetic medicine was, and is, a great gift. But it is its indiscriminate use, in addition to all other synthetics and chemicals, that is causing the problem. Over fifty years ago society started to turn its back on nature, and the chemical industry took center stage. We seemed to forget that we were part of nature and that to turn against it, we would be turning against ourselves. It is only now that we are beginning to pay the price.

Now, wouldn't it be marvelous if we could find a safe, non-toxic, non-irritating substance that would play a role in replacing many of the strong chemicals in our cupboards? Well, we have!

Here is a product that is made by nature, for nature. It is a completely natural, topical, clinically proven anti-bacterial and anti-fungal substance. It has anti-inflammatory, immune system strengthening, pain killing, and wound healing qualities. It also exhibits anti-viral, expectorant, and balsamic characteristics.

All this, and it can be used as a powerful antiseptic, parasiticide and insecticide. AND it's also kind to our skin cells. The pure Tea Tree oil of the *Melaleuca alternifolia*, works with the body, not against it. Research shows it has rapid results against the new "20th Century Superbugs" including MRSA.

I still find it ironic that if man had made such a synthetic substance and had spent millions of dollars on the development program, it would have been hailed as the wonder of the century. Everyone would have known about it, and everyone would be utilizing its many properties. But because Tea Tree oil is found in nature, it is viewed with suspicion.

The sooner we all once again wholeheartedly embrace a more natural approach in both medicine and in industry, the sooner we will begin to stem the tide of the so called "superbugs" and "mystery illnesses."

THE TEA TREE OIL STORY

To trace the history of the "healing Tea Trees" we have to start on the North Eastern coastal region of New South Wales, Australia—the only place in the world where the *Melaleuca alternifolia* tree yields the "real" Tea Tree oil.

We then have to travel back centuries, long before Australia was "discovered," and long before scientific evidence began, to a time when Australia belonged to its native inhabitants, the Aborigines. In particular, the Bundjalong Aborigines inhabited the wetlands around the Bungawalbyn Creek and, according to legend, were well aware of the medicinal qualities of their many "healing trees." Although not documented, it is widely understood that they treated various wounds and skin infections with an early form of poultice made from crushed leaves and warm mud from along the banks of the creek. The poultice was excellent for drawing out infection and healing the skin.

These Aborigines also used the healing waters of the pools in the area which were surrounded by the trees. Falling leaves and twigs leached their "magical" healing liquid into the water, turning it a deep yellowish color. The Aborigines bathed and washed in this natural healing "spa" to treat any number of conditions from sore muscles to serious diseases. Maybe this is why they named the area "Bungawalbyn" in the first place. The name means "healing ground."

The "healing trees" did not become commonly known as "Tea Trees" until around 1770 when Captain Cook, along with a botanist named Joseph Banks and the crew of The Endeavour, used the leaves with their distinctive aroma to brew a spicy and refreshing "tea." It is most unfortunate that they did not "discover" and publish the unique healing qualities of the "Tea Trees." But according to the account of that time, they drank the essence in varying concoctions, even alcoholic beverages such as a "Tea Tree beer."

Thus the name "Tea Tree" became popular, especially with the first "white" settlers who colonized the low-lying areas around the Clarence and Richmond Rivers. From the 1790's on, they watched and learned from the Aborigines how to use the leaves and waters in various inhalations, poultices, and rubbing mediums. Because these first settlers rarely had medical or botanical backgrounds, there was no real "scientific" evidence recording the healing qualities of the Tea Trees. The European community was very skeptical of these "anecdotal stories." It could not have helped that the Aborigines were often thought of as primitives from an uncivilized world. In the words of the settlers, "They didn't want to work or better themselves...they were always disobedient and lazy." Thus the healing remedies, along with the Aboriginal way of life, were treated with contempt.

As new settlers arrived, they struggled to clear the harsh native vegetation to make way for settlements and dairy farms. They cursed every Tea Tree for its hardy and persistent hold on its own natural habitat. The Tea Trees tenaciously survived drought, fire, flood, and even frost, and resisted any attempt to destroy them. Fortunately for the rest of the world, the only way they could have been eradicated was by the physical removal of every part of the tree, including the extensive root system.

It is ironic that while the settlers battled to destroy the Tea Trees, they were only too willing to use the healing leaves for poultices and inhalations to stem infection and disease.

It is to our loss that the Tea Tree, although used as an effective "bush remedy" by subsequent generations of farmers, did not reach our attention until the early 1930's. It was not even mentioned in the British Pharmaceutical Codex until 1949, where it was listed as "Oleum Melaleuca." [1]

In Australia it was not until the early 1920's that Arthur de Ramon Penfold, FCS, Chief Chemist at the Museum of Applied Technology, Arts and Sciences in Sydney, extracted the oil of the Melaleuca alternifolia and announced that "yes indeed!" it did have antiseptic and anti-bacterial properties.[2] The accepted anti-bacterial agent at that time was carbolic acid (known as phenol). Imagine the stir it must have caused when it was determined that "an old Aboriginal remedy" was up to 13 times stronger! and was non-toxic and non-irritating—unlike carbolic acid! [3]

When the results were finally published in 1925, there was great enthusiasm among doctors of the time and "Penfold's discovery" was immediately put to the test.

In 1930 the *Medical Journal of Australia* published an article, "A New Australian Germicide," by Dr. E.M. Humphrey.[4] It stated "that what he found most encouraging was the way that the oil from the crushed leaves of the *Melaleuca alternifolia* dissolved pus and left wounds and surrounding areas clean." He tested and enthused about this great substance, highlighting Tea Tree oil as never before.

He noticed "that the germicidal action became more effective in the presence of living tissue and organic matter, without any apparent damage to healthy cells."...

He suggested "that it would be particularly good for applying to dirty wounds caused in street accidents." ...

He also found "most encouraging the results on nail infections. Particularly those infections that had resisted various treatments for months which now were cured in less than a week!" ...

"The pus solvent properties of Tea Tree oil made it an excellent application for the fungal nail disease paronychia, which if left untreated could result in the deformity and even eventual loss of the nail." ...

1 "Oleum Melaleuca," *British Pharmaceutical Codex,* 597-598, 1949.
2 Penfold, A.R. and Grant, R. "The Germicidal Values of Some Australian Essential Oils and Their Pure Constituents," *Journal Proceedings of the Royal Society of NSW,* 59:3, 346-50, 1925.
3 This was determined by the Rideal-Walker co-efficient, a method used at that time to determine the germicidal properties of compounds.
4 Humphrey, E.M. "A New Australian Germicide," *Medical Journal of Australia,* I, 417-418, 1930.

He urged the dental industry to "take seriously the antiseptic properties for infections of the gum and mouth." ...

He noted that "just two drops of Tea Tree oil in a tumbler of warm water made it a soothing and therapeutic gargle for sore throats in the early stages."...

He wrote that "it would probably be effective for most of the infections of the naso-pharynx."...

That it "was an immediate deodorizing medium on foul-smelling wounds and pus-filled abscesses."...

And, "if it was added to hand soap it would make the soap up to sixty times more effective against Typhoid bacilli than the so-called 'disinfectant soaps' of the day."...

He felt "that if an ointment could be made from the oil it would help to eradicate several parasitic skin diseases."...

He concluded "that it was a rare occurrence because most effective germicides actually destroyed healthy living tissue along with the bacteria."...

The Scientific and Medical worlds were intrigued. More research was funded and articles began appearing in additional publications such as the *Australian Journal of Pharmacy* [5] and the *Australian Journal of Dentistry*.[6] World-wide appetites were whetted. Articles were presented and published in the *Journal of the National Medical Association* (USA) [7] and the *British Medical Journal*.[8]

As the reputation of Tea Tree oil spread, there was a great deal of anecdotal evidence about its effectiveness in a wide range of topical applications, both medical and veterinary. From diabetic gangrene in man [9] to diseases of poultry and fish, it was recognized as a safe, effective, non-toxic, non-irritating, antiseptic disinfectant.[10]

If Penfold was the "Founding Father," Humphrey was certainly the "Metaphorical Mother." His enthusiastic writings opened up a multitude of medical and practical uses for Tea Tree oil. Others have tried, tested, and approved of its healing properties, but thanks to Penfold and Humphrey the world would no longer be denied the miraculous healing powers of the Aborigine "healing tree," the Tea Tree— *Melaleuca alternifolia*.

5 Anon, "Tea Tree Oil," *Australian Journal of Pharmacy*, p274, 30th March 1930.
6 MacDonald, V. "The Rationale of Treatment," *Australian Journal of Dentistry*, 34, 281-285, 1930.
7 Anon, Journal of the *National Medical Association* (USA), 1930.
8 Anon, "Ti-trol Oil," *British Medical Journal*, 927, 1933.
8 Anon, "An Australian Antiseptic Oil," *British Medical Journal*, 966, 1933.
9 Halford, A.C.F. "Diabetic Gangrene," *Medical Journal of Australia*, 2, 121-122, 1936.
10 Penfold, A.R. and Morrison, F.R. "Some Notes on the Essential Oil of *Melaleuca alternifolia*," *Australian Journal of Pharmacy*, 18, 274-5, 1937.

A GROWTH INDUSTRY

By the start of the Second World War, Tea Tree oil from the *Melaleuca alternifolia* had earned its reputation as a miracle healer. It was medically recognized world-wide for the successful treatment of a whole range of conditions including:

- Ear, nose and throat infections: tonsillitis, gingivitis, pyorrhea, etc.
- Gynecological infections: candida, thrush, etc.
- Nail infections: paronychia, tinea, etc.
- Skin infections: impetigo, pediculosis, ringworm, etc.
- And a wide range of other contagious and non-contagious fungal, bacterial and parasitic infections (It was considered especially effective for pus filled and dirty infections.)
- Dental nerve capping
- Hemorrhages, wounds, first aid, etc.
- Not to mention all of the many and varied veterinary applications.[11]

A bottle of Tea Tree oil was a standard Government Issue in Australian Army and Navy first aid kits, especially for those soldiers serving in tropical countries. It was initially used in munitions factories to inhibit the high air-borne bacteria count. Then it was found that, by adding it to the machine cutting oils, it substantially reduced infections, especially those from abrasions caused by the off-shoot of metal filings. The production of Tea Tree oil was considered of such great importance that bush cutters were exempt from doing national service.

Surgeons, doctors, dentists, vets, and even housewives were utilizing its many healing properties. The Australian division of Colgate-Palmolive manufactured a Tea Tree oil "germicidal" soap that was very popular for a number of years.

During this meteoric rise in popularity, the actual Tea Tree industry was very modest indeed, with just over twenty steam distillation units (stills) in the Bungawalbyn area, and those were mostly small family run businesses. The cutting and harvesting was completed totally by hand, mainly from trees growing wild in the swampy bush lands. Successful harvesting depended wholly upon manpower against the harsh elements of the Australian climate and the many hazards of working alongside the carnivorous and poisonous wildlife. Inevitably demand became far greater than supply. Throughout the war years all available stocks of good quality Tea Tree oil were taken under government control. There was little or none left for the developing marketplace. Scientists concocted cheaper synthetic alternatives. Although not as effective as Tea Tree oil, for their germicidal qualities, they were much more readily available. In the post war era the pure oil of the Melaleuca alternifolia was almost impossible to buy.

11 Penfold, A.R. and Morrison, F.R. "Some Notes on the Essential Oil of *Melaleuca alternifolia,*" *Australian Journal of Pharmacy,* 18, 274-5, 1937.

Right up until the middle of the 1940's the pure Tea Tree oil was still highly regarded and sought after. It had been the heyday of the Tea Tree oil industry.

During the earlier years, as the popularity of Tea Tree oil was growing, so too was medical technology. In 1928, Scottish biologist Alexander Fleming first observed the effect of penicillin on bacteria, and the antibiotic was "born." By 1941, the drug was developed and on its way to becoming established. By the 1950s it was heralded as the new "wonder drug." It was the age of synthetic and semi-synthetic medicine. Infections that were usually fatal were now virtually wiped out—tuberculosis, pneumonia, and venereal disease to name but a few. There was now hope where there had been despair. The new drugs went from strength to strength. Everyone wanted them, and everyone got them. Antibiotics were the theme of the day, and man rejoiced in the fact that he had finally triumphed over nature. The Tea Tree industry went into steep decline as natural remedies were classed as quack cures. Modern medicine was being built on synthetic chemicals and, for more than a decade, they reigned supreme.

Unfortunately the developing drug manufacturers were not interested in natural or preventive medicine, or indeed actually curing non-pathogenic diseases. The "BIG" money was in controlling symptoms so that the sufferers would be using a drug for the rest of their lives. Yes, there were side effects, but there were more drugs to control the side effects. Big money spawned big power. The press was courted, and the diminishing herbal medicine sector was held firmly down. Fortunately, as the saying goes, "You can fool some of the people some of the time, but you can never fool all of the people all of the time."

In the 1960's the "hippie" revolution started. Suddenly there was a growing awareness and unease concerning the whole scenario. Chemical pollution, animal testing, cover-ups, the addictions to synthetic drugs, and the hazardous side effects all added to the rumblings of disquiet. Then came a bombshell—an emergence of the "superbugs." Virulent strains of pathogens had evolved and were becoming immune to the antibiotics. It was clear that within the next few years these new strains could infect the population as before. With the dubious environmental and social implications all this held, once more, people were beginning to look for alternatives. "Natural" remedies were gaining in popularity, and before long the "Herbal Renaissance" had begun.

Like the tenacious hold those newly discovered Aboriginal "healing trees" had had on their natural habitat, so too the Tea Tree oil of the *Melaleuca alternifolia* was waiting in the background, forgotten but not gone. New research work was funded and the popularity of the Tea Tree was once again starting to flourish.

The first signs of the Tea Tree revival appeared when Dr. Henry Feinblatt published his work in the *Journal of the National Medical Association* (USA) in January of 1960. It was a favorable study about the action of a "Cajeput-type oil for the treatment of Furunculosis"(boils).[12] Two years later, Dr. Eduardo F. Peña (USA) completed a successful study of 130 women entitled "*Melaleuca alternifolia* Oil—Its use for Trichomonal Vaginitis and Other Vaginal Infections."[13] In April 1972, Dr. Morton Walker published the results of a study entitled "Clinical Investigation of Australian *Melaleuca alternifolia* for a Variety of Common Foot Problems" (Tinea pedis, Bromidrosis, corns, bunions, etc.) in the *Journal of Current Podiatry*.[14]

As word spread from journals to newspapers, a slowly increasing demand for both information, and indeed for the oil itself, started to grow. Articles appeared in such publications as the *Perfumer & Flavorist*[15] the *Planta Medica*,[16] the *Manufacturing Chemist*,[17] etc. The perfume and cosmetic industries and the botanical and medical faculties were just beginning to take a renewed, albeit cautious, interest.

The ups and downs of what was little more than a bush industry meant that during the 1970's the Tea Trees were still being harvested by hand from the snake and spider infested wet-lands around the Bungawalbyn Creek.

The cutters used machete-like knives to hack off the leaves and the terminal branches, which were then transported out of the swamp to the stills. Many of the wide-tired trucks could not even attempt to make a track through the dense undergrowth, so the cutters themselves manually carried their yield out of the swamps to the awaiting transport. On a good day, one skilled worker could cut and load a truck with up to one ton of leaves and twigs.

Arriving at their destination the cuttings would then be emptied into a container over one of the large distilling vats. Using a simple wood fired steam-distillation method, these vats were fired up and allowed to reach boiling point. The resulting steam would pass through the leaves and twigs, bursting the oil bearing sacs and vaporizing the oil. The vapors then were condensed, mixed with the distillation water in the collection tank, and the pure oil was siphoned off into drums. Each standard vat could quite easily be filled by one skilled cutter and yield around 7-10 liters of pure oil. Depending on the quality of the cuttings, the process could be repeated several times until the last drop of oil had been fully extracted.

12 Feinblatt, H.M. "Cajeput Type Oil (Tea Tree oil) for the Treatment of Furunculosis" (boils), *Journal of the National Medical Association* USA, 52: 32-4, 1960.

13 Peña, E.F. "*Melaleuca alternifolia*: Its Use for *Trichomonal vaginitis* and Other Vaginal Infections," *Obstetrics and Gynecology*, 19:6, 793-795, 1962.

14 Walker, M. "Clinical Investigation of Australian *Melaleuca alternifolia* oil for a Variety of Common Foot Problems," *Current Podiatry*, April 7th to 15th, 1972.

15 Beylier, M.F. "Bacteriostatic Activity of Some Australian Essential Oils," *Perfumer and Flavorist International*, V4, 23-5, 1979.

16 Low, D., Rowal, B.D. and Griffin W.J. "Antibacterial Action of the Essential Oils of Some of Australian Myrtaceae," *Planta Medica*, 26, 184-189, 1974.

17 Pickering, G.B. "Cedarwood Oil Compounds, Silica Gel Separation and Tea Tree Oil as Nutmeg Substitute," *Manufacturing Chemist*, 27, 105-6, 1956.

As demand was once again on the increase, so too, the Tea Tree industry itself started to rapidly expand, and inevitably the natural stands of Tea Trees were being systematically destroyed along with the associated eco-systems. It was obvious that something had to be done. So by the start of the 1980's farms were set up. Tea Trees were now being cultivated on the fertile farmlands and the oil was produced on a semi-commercial scale. From the late 1980's sustainable plantations were established and mechanical cutting was introduced. Tea Tree oil production was substantially increased to meet the ever-growing demand for high quality oil.

During this time new research work was being funded, and in 1985, Dr. Paul Belaiche completed three studies at the University of Paris, France on the use of *Melaleuca alternifolia* for the treatments of (1) Candida albicans, (2) Cystitis (urinary tract infections), and (3) Paronychia (Pus infections of the skin and nail bed). All three trials proved a success for the continued use of Tea Tree oil, and his results were supported by a number of doctors.[18,19,20]

More and more positive studies started to appear, like one on oral pathogens in periodontal disease by Walsh and Longstaff, published in *Periodontology* in 1987.[21] And another in 1988 by Williams and Home, "The Composition and Bacteriocidal Activity of the Oil of Melaleuca alternifolia."[22] And two others by P.M. Altman; "Australian Tea Tree oil," in 1988[23] and "Australian Tea Tree Oil—a Natural Antiseptic," in 1989.[24] Over the next few years there began a whole plethora of Tea Tree studies, some pilot, some in-vitro, and others clinical. Applications were being tested and tried all over the globe.

In October 1990, Bassett, Pannowitz, and Barnetson published a clinical, double-blind comparison of the efficacy of 5% Tea Tree oil to 5% benzoyl peroxide in the *Medical Journal of Australia*. The results prompted the comments, "Both had a significant effect in ameliorating (improving) the patients' acne...encouragingly fewer side effects were experienced by the patients treated with Tea Tree oil."[25]

In 1994, a study by Buck, Nidorf, and Addino, "Comparison of Two Topical Preparations for the Treatment of Onychomycosis: *Melaleuca*

18 Belaiche, P. "Treatment of Vaginal Infections of Candida albicans with the Essential Oil of Melaleuca alternifolia- Cheel," *Phytotherapy,* 15, 13-14, 1985.

19 Belaiche, P. "Treatment of Chronic Urinary Tract Infections with the Essential Oil of *Melaleuca alternifolia* - Cheel," *Phytotherapy,* 15, 9-12, 1985.

20 Belaiche, P. "Treatment of Skin and Nail Infections with the Essential Oil of *Melaleuca alternifolia* - Cheel," *Phytotherapy,* 15, 15-18, 1985.

21 Walsh, L.J. and Longstaff, J. "The Antimicrobial Effects of an Essential Oil on Selected Oral Pathogens," *Periodontology,* V8, 11-15, 1987.

22 Williams, L.R., Home, V.N., Zhang, X. and Stevenson, I. "The Composition and Bacteriocidal Activity of Oil of *Melaleuca alternifolia*," *International Journal of Aromatherapy,* 1:3, 15-17, 1988.

23 Altman, P.M. "Australian Tea Tree Oil," *Australian Journal of Pharmacy,* 69, 276-78, 1988.

24 Altman, P.M. "Australian Tea Tree Oil - A Natural Antiseptic," *Australian Journal of Biotechnology,* 3:4, 247-8, 1989.

25 Bassett, I.B., Pannowitz, D.L. and Barnetson, R.St.C. "A Comparative Study of Tea Tree Oil Versus Benzoyl Peroxide in the Treatment of Acne," *Medical Journal of Australia,* 153:8, 455-458, 1990.

alternifolia (Tea Tree oil) and Clotrimazole" was completed. It concluded that Tea Tree oil was as effective, if not more so, as the Clotrimazole treatment for nail bed fungus.[26] Medical practitioners were beginning to notice the "good effects" on a variety of ailments including abrasions, abscesses, acne, athletes foot, canker sores, chicken pox, dandruff, eczema, hemorrhoids, head lice, infections (ear, nose, and throat), psoriasis, stings and bites, shingles, wounds, etc.

Since the beginning of the 1990's a scientific research team, led by associate Professor Tom V. Riley (including C.F. Carson and K.A. Hammer) at the Microbiology Department of the University of Western Australia, has published many papers and letters, and is continuing to study the anti-microbial properties of *Melaleuca alternifolia*. Their most notable laboratory based studies and subsequent papers include the following:

In 1993, a review into the history and unique anti-microbial properties of this ancient aboriginal oil.[27]

In 1994, two studies were published. The first was a study into the unique anti-bacterial properties of Tea Tree oil.[28] The second was a positive study into the effect of Tea Tree oil on the bacteria that can cause acne and related problems.[29]

During 1995 four studies were published. The first, and most important to mankind, was an in-vitro study into how Tea Tree oil can inhibit and destroy the bacteria that has become immune to methicillin, an antibiotic normally used to combat the *Staphylococcus aureus* species of gram-positive bacteria. Hospitals all over the world are finding more and more isolates of *Staphylococci* that are becoming immune to the once effective drugs. This study successfully showed that all sixty-six isolates were susceptible to the oil of *Melaleuca alternifolia* even at a quite low dilution.[30]

The next study that year detailed a broth micro-dilution method that could effectively be used to detect the susceptibilities of *E. Coli* and *Staphylococcus aureus*.[31]

The third in 1995 was a study into eight of the major components that make up the unique composition of Tea Tree oil, including Terpinen 4-ol

26 Buck, D.S., Nidorf, D.M. and Addino, J.G. "Comparison of Two Topical Preparations for the Treatment of Onychomycosis: *Melaleuca alternifolia* (Tea Tree Oil) and Clotrimazole," *Journal of Family Practice*, 38, 601-5, 1994.

27 Carson, C.F. and Riley, T.V. "Antimicrobial Activity of the Essential Oil of *Melaleuca alternifolia* (A Review)," *Letters in Applied Microbiology*, 16, 49-55, 1993.

28 Carson, C.F. and Riley, T.V. "The Antimicrobial Activity of Tea Tree Oil," *Medical Journal of Australia*,160, 236, 1994.

29 Carson, C.F. and Riley, T.V. "Susceptibility of *Propionibacterium acnes* to the Essential Oil of *Melaleuca alternifolia*," *Letters in Applied Microbiology*, 19, 24-25, 1994.

30 Carson, C.F., Cookson, B.D., Farrelly, H.D. and Riley, T.V. "Susceptibility of Methicillin-resistant *Staphylococcus aureus* to the Essential Oil *Melaleuca alternifolia*," *Journal of Antimicrobial Chemotherapy*, 35:3, 421-4, 1995.

31 Carson, C.F., Hammer, K.A. and Riley T.V. "Broth Micro-dilution Method for Determining the Susceptibility of *Escherichia coli* (*E coli*) and *Staphylococcus aureus* to the Essential Oil of *Melaleuca alternifolia*," *Microbios*, 82, 181-185, 1995.

and Cineole, etc. This is extremely useful for all sectors of the Tea Tree industry, helping to determine the best possible composition of an oil for medicinal effectiveness, etc.[32]

The final study that year took a critical look at the toxicity of Tea Tree oil, opening the way to discovering which components cause a reaction in those who are susceptible.[33]

In 1996, an in-vitro study showed that Tea Tree oil could inhibit the pathogenic bacteria that inhabits the skin's surface but could, in turn, still maintain the essential skin flora. This had good implications for using a low dilution in personal care products and skin creams.[34]

Also in 1996 an important study into the effectiveness of Tea Tree oil against the various gram-positive *Streptococcus spp. Streptococci* bacteria is implicated in many lesser (group B) and major, sometimes fatal, (group A) infections including Strep Throat and the flesh eating *Necrotizing fasciitis* (Type II).[35]

In 1997, their in-vitro study found that Tea Tree oil could inhibit the fungi *Malassezia furfur* (formally known as *Pityrosporum ovale*) which can contribute to dandruff and other various skin conditions.[36]

Their work in 1998 found that commercial Tea Tree products were as effective an anti-fungal agent as a Tea Tree dilution for inhibiting superficial *Candida albicans* type infections.[37]

And in the last year of this century, one of their in-vitro studies suggested that Tea Tree oil may also have a place in combating bacterial vaginosis.[38]

Two projects due to be completed soon are research into the anti-inflammatory properties and the anti-viral activity of Tea Tree oil. Various trials, projects, and medical collaborations are also in the pipeline. At last, mainly due to their invaluable in-vitro studies, things are really starting to move and are actually gathering momentum. Hopefully this will give Tea Tree oil the much needed credibility with those who choose not to see the healing of generations of people as proof of efficacy.

32 Carson, C.F. and Riley, T.V. "Antimicrobial Activity of the Major Components of the Essential Oil of *Melaleuca alternifolia*," *Journal of Applied Bacteriology,* 78:3, 264-9, 1995.

33 Carson, C.F. and Riley, T.V. "Toxicity of the Essential Oil of *Melaleuca alternifolia* (or Tea Tree Oil)," (Letter) *Journal of Toxicology-Clinical Toxicology,* 33:2, 193-4, 1995.

34 Hammer, K.A., Carson, C.F. and Riley, T.V. "Susceptibility of Transient and Commensal Skin Flora to the Essential Oil of *Melaleuca alternifolia* (Tea Tree Oil)," *American Journal of Infection Control,* 24:3, 186-9, 1996.

35 Carson, C.F., Hammer, K.A. and Riley, T.V. "In-vitro Activity of the Essential Oil of *Melaleuca alternifolia* Against *Streptococcus Spp.*," *Journal of Antimicrobial Chemotherapy,* 37:6, 1177-8, 1996.

36 Hammer, K.A., Carson, C.F. and Riley, T.V. "In-vitro Susceptibility of Malassezia furfur to the Essential Oil of *Melaleuca alternifolia,*" *Journal of Medical and Veterinary Mycology,* 35:5, 375-7, 1997.

37 Hammer, K.A., Carson, C.F. and Riley, T.V. "In-vitro Activity of Essential Oils, in Particular *Melaleuca alternifolia* (Tea Tree Oil and Tea Tree Oil Products) Against *Candida spp.*," *Journal of Antimicrobial Chemotherapy,* 42:5, 591-5, 1998.

38 Hammer, K.A., Carson, C.F. and Riley, T.V. "In-vitro Susceptibilities of Lactobacilli and Organisms Associated with Bacterial Vaginosis to *Melaleuca alternifolia* (Tea Tree oil)," (Letter) *Antimicrobial Agents and Chemotherapy,* Jan 1999.

TEA TREE OIL APPLICATIONS—AN AMAZING ANTISEPTIC AND MUCH MUCH MORE!

In the early days of Tea Tree oil, back in the 1930's and 1940's, when the scientific evidence was in its infancy, it became clear that Tea Tree oil was a very valuable commodity. Humphrey's paper, "A New Australian Germicide," published in the *Medical Journal of Australia*, was really the catalyst that started the commercial ball rolling. Ever since the very first evidence, new testing methods, superior emulsifiers and more advanced surfactants have all helped us to understand and use Tea Tree oil in a vast array of products.[39, 40]

ANTIBACTERIAL SOAPS

The first commercially blended Tea Tree oil product was an antiseptic soap, which was manufactured by the Australian division of Colgate-Palmolive. The soap all but disappeared after the war years with the rise in synthetic disinfectants. In the early 1980's antiseptic soaps, creams and lotions started to emerge on a wider scale. A positive trial conducted by The Associated Foodstuff Laboratories of Australia in 1983 showed that the bacterial count on hands was substantially reduced by washing with Tea Tree products. Dr. Humphrey had long advocated the use of its superior germicidal action, and many other clinical trials have later confirmed this.[41, 42, 43]

ACNE CREAMS AND LOTIONS

Many people suffer from acne and facial boils at some time in their lives. There have been quite a few positive trials using Tea Tree oil in various products for these conditions. The unique penetrating action of the Tea Tree oil helps to rid the dermal layers of the invading bacteria. A soon to be friend of mine who had four boils on her chin and was at her wits end contacted us to ask our advice. She had been on antibiotics for over three months, but the boils were still thriving. We suggested she use a Tea Tree problem skin lotion, so she went back to her doctor who agreed to take her off the antibiotics. Within two weeks, two of the boils had disappeared and the third was shrinking fast. Within one month she had just a faint mark where the last boil had finally admitted defeat. She was amazed with the results. We had seen it all before![44,45,46]

39 Williams, L.R., Home, V.N. and Asre, S. "Antimicrobial Activity of Oil of *Melaleuca alternifolia*. Its Potential Use in Cosmetics and Toiletries," Cosmetics, Aerosols & Toiletries in Australia, 4:4, 1990.

40 Altman, P.M. "Australian Tea Tree Oil," *Australian Journal of Pharmacy*, 69, 276-78, 1988.

41 Hammer, K.A., Carson, C.F. and Riley, T.V. "Susceptibility of Transient and Commensal Skin Flora to the Essential Oil of *Melaleuca alternifolia* (Tea Tree Oil)," *American Journal of Infection Control*, 24:3, 186-9, 1996.

42 Beylier, M.F. "Bacteriostatic Activity of Some Australian Essential Oils," *Perfumer and Flavorist International*, V4:23-5, 1979.

43 Williams, L.R., Home, V.N. and Asre, S. "Antimicrobial Activity of Oil of *Melaleuca alternifolia*. Its Potential Use in Cosmetics and Toiletries," *Cosmetics, Aerosols & Toiletries in Australia*, 4:4, 1990.

44 Bassett, I.B., Pannowitz, D.L. and Barnetson, R.St.C. "A Comparative Study of Tea Tree Oil Versus Benzoyl Peroxide in the Treatment of Acne," *Medical Journal of Australia*, 153:8, 455-458, 1990.

MOISTURIZING CREAMS AND LOTIONS

Although very few clinical studies have been completed in this area, there is much anecdotal evidence detailing the good effects of Tea Tree oil, applied in creams and lotions, to help alleviate skin conditions such as psoriasis and eczema, etc. A large Australian Tea Tree company has done its own investigations into inflammatory skin conditions with some quite positive results. A couple of the studies, "A Clinical Investigation of a Tea Tree Oil Preparation for the Re-hydration of the Skin in Lower Limb" by Jill Fogharty, and "A Pilot Study into Australian Tea Tree Oil" by M. Abdulla, have been successfully completed. Where local inflammation is present due to skin complaints, stings, bites, etc., Tea Tree oil in dilution was effective in soothing local irritation and pain. The best thing about Tea Tree moisturizing creams and lotions is that, even with a quite low dilution of Tea Tree oil, they can inhibit harmful bacteria while maintaining the resident skin flora.[47, 48]

ORAL/DENTAL PRODUCTS

An article in one of Australia's popular health magazines (*Prevention* January 1992), and written by Dr. William Mayo, stated that Tea Tree oil was effectively used in many oral preparations (toothpastes, mouthwashes, lip salves, sore throat sprays, lozenges, cold sore ointments, etc). There have been many clinical studies on oral pathogens. Tea tree oil is second to none for helping to keep teeth healthy and white, or to guard against mouth infections.

Dr. Andrew Weil, the well-known medical author and physician, frequently recommends Tea Tree oil toothpastes and mouthwashes for a number of oral problems. Some of these include halitosis (bad breath), gum disease, and canker sores.[49, 50, 51, 52]

HAIR CARE PRODUCTS

Tea Tree oil is a very effective ingredient in shampoos and conditioners. It helps to keep the hair and scalp in tiptop condition. It was reported as early as 1939 that Tea Tree oil was an excellent

45 Carson, C.F. and Riley, T.V. "Susceptibility of Propionibacterium acnes to the Essential Oil of *Melaleuca alternifolia," Letters in Applied Microbiology,* 19, 24-25, 1994.

46 Feinblatt, H.M. "Cajeput Type Oil (Tea Tree oil) for the Treatment of Furunculosis" (boils), *Journal of the National Medical Association* (USA), 52, 32-4, 1960.

47 Hammer, K.A., Carson, C.F. and Riley, T.V. "Susceptibility of Transient and Commensal Skin Flora to the Essential Oil of *Melaleuca alternifolia* (Tea Tree Oil)," *American Journal of Infection Control,* 24:3, 186-9, 1996.

48 Shemesh, A. and Mayo, W.L. "A Natural Antiseptic and Fungicide," *International Journal of Alternative and Complementary Medicine,* Dec. 1991.

49 Shemesh, A. and Mayo, W.L. "A Natural Antiseptic and Fungicide," *International Journal of Alternative and Complementary Medicine,* Dec. 1991.

50 Walsh, L.J. and Longstaff, J. "The Antimicrobial Effects of an Essential Oil on Selected Oral Pathogens," *Periodontology,* V8, 11-15, 1987.

51 Shapiro, S., Meier, A. and Guggenheim, B. "The Anti-microbial Activity of Essential Oils and Essential Oil Components Towards Oral Bacteria," *Oral Microbiolog. Immunology* (Denmark), 9:4, 202-8, 1994.

52 Weil, A. *Ask Dr. Weil,* http://www.drweil.com

ingredient in soaps and shampoos. An Australian chemist advertised the use of a 3% Tea Tree shampoo for the treatment of dandruff. Today *Melaleuca alternifolia* has finally been clinically sanctioned as a possible anti-dandruff shampoo ingredient, and shown that, even at a quite low dilution, it can inhibit the yeast that causes the problem.[53, 54]

PARASITICIDE AND INSECT REPELLENT

There are many anecdotal cases of Tea Tree oil soothing pain and itching after a sting or an insect bite. The analgesic qualities together with its powerful solvent action (dissipating the venom) is probably what makes it so effective. It is also thought that the solvent properties help to dissolve the hard outer case of the insect and so making it an effective insecticide/parasiticide, while the Terpenes present in the oil act as an insect repellent.

Tea Tree has been used for a number of years by doctors for the safe removal of parasites. With the growing concern over the safety of prescription lotions, it was refreshing to actually hear a qualified doctor give his approval. The well-known physician and medical author, Dr. Andrew Weil, recommends the use of Tea Tree oil and other oils for the treatment of head lice.[55, 56, 57, 58]

ANTIFUNGAL CREAMS AND FOOT CARE PRODUCTS

Tea Tree oil is very effective on all sorts of foot problems and infections. Many successful trials have been carried out in this area, from athletes foot (Tinea pedis) and ringworm, to warts, even on rough and cracked skin. It is used by podiatrists all over the world.

On his Web site, *Ask Dr. Weil,* the highly respected medical author writes, "Tea Tree oil is the best treatment I know for fungal infections of the skin (athlete's foot, ringworm, jock itch). It will also clear up fungal infections of the toenails or fingernails, a condition notoriously resistant to treatment, even by strong systemic antibiotics."[59]

We have a lovely letter from a parent whose son's feet were so badly infected with Plantar warts that his doctor had said that surgery was the only option. We put her in touch with a podiatrist who we knew used Tea Tree oil on his patients. After a few weeks of treatment, the son was

53 Goldsborough, R.E. "Ti-Tree Oil," *The Manufacturing Chemist*, 57-58-60, Feb 1939.

54 Hammer, K.A., Carson, C.F. and Riley, T.V. "In-vitro Susceptibility of Malassezia furfur to the Essential Oil of *Melaleuca alternifolia*," *Journal of Medical and Veterinary Mycology*, 35:5, 375-7, 1997.

55 Veal, L. "The Potential Effectiveness of Essential Oils as a Treatment for Head Lice, *Pediculus Humanus Capitis*," *Complementary Ther. Nurs. Midwifery*, 2:4, 97-101, 1996.

56 McDonald, L.G. and Tovey, E. "The Effectiveness of Benzyl Benzoate and Some Essential Oils as Laundry Additives for Killing House Dustmites," *Journal Allergy and Clinical Immunology*, 1993.

57 Williams, L.R., Home, V.N. and Asre S. "Antimicrobial Activity of Oil of *Melaleuca alternifolia*. Its Potential Use in Cosmetics and Toiletries," *Cosmetics, Aerosols & Toiletries in Australia*, 4:4, 1990.

58 Weil, A. *Ask Dr. Weil*, http://www.drweil.com

59 Weil, A. *Ask Dr. Weil*, http://www.drweil.com

well on his way to a complete recovery, and without the intervention of surgery.[60,61,62]

PERSONAL CARE PRODUCTS

Tea Tree oil products for personal care are gathering momentum. Dr. Humphrey in his writings of 1930 stated that it was a good deodorant, killing the bacteria that produced the odor. Hammer et al found that, at low dilution, it could be used on the skin and still maintain resident skin flora. Today we have a far wider choice of personal care items, as word of the effectiveness of this wonderful oil spreads far and wide. From deodorant to body lotion, cosmetics, sunscreen, hand cream, to aftershave lotion, after-sun cream and bubble bath, its non-sting healing properties are being utilized as never before.[63,64]

VAGINAL DOUCHES AND GENITAL CREAMS

Unfortunately for us humans, we have many sites that can harbor the pathogenic yeasts and bacteria that cause infection. Central heating, synthetic underwear, tight-fitting clothes, etc., all add to the problem. Fortunately there are many Tea Tree personal hygiene products on the market with plenty of clinical trials to back up the claims that Tea Tree oil can effectively reduce harmful parasites that thrive in dark, warm places on the body. Dr. Andrew Weil claims that, for vaginal yeast infections, Tea Tree oil "is at least as effective as the usual prescription remedy." [65,66,67,68]

INFLAMMATION

Again this is another area where Tea Tree oil has been used for decades by alternative practitioners in the treatment of inflammation and pain. From insect bite salves to rheumatic rubs and sports care products, there is much anecdotal evidence to support its use in this area. The first clinical evidence that Tea Tree oil may be able to reduce

60 Tong M.M., Altman, P.M. and Barnetson R.St.C. "Tea Tree Oil in the Treatment of Tinea pedis," *Australian Journal of Dermatology*, 33:3, 145-9, 1992.

61 Walker, M. "Clinical Investigation of Australian *Melaleuca alternifolia* oil for a Variety of Common Foot Problems," *Current Podiatry*, April 7th to 15th, 1972.

62 Nenoff, P., et al. "Antifungal Activity of the Essential Oil of *Melaleuca alternifolia* (Tea Tree oil) Against Pathogenic Fungi In-vitro," *Skin Pharmacology*, 9:6, 388-394, 1996.

63 Altman, P.M. "Australian Tea Tree Oil - An Update," *Cosmetics, Aerosols & Toiletries in Australia*, 5:4, 27-9, 1991.

64 Priest, D. "Tea Tree Oil in Cosmetics- The Promise and the Proof," (Technical paper) *Cosmetics, Aerosols & Toiletries in Australia*, 9:4, 1995.

65 Weil, A. *Ask Dr. Weil*, http://www.drweil.com

66 Peña, E.F. "*Melaleuca alternifolia*: Its Use for Trichomonal vaginitis and Other Vaginal Infections," *Obstetrics and Gynecology*, 19:6, 793-795, 1962.

67 Hammer, K.A., Carson, C.F. and Riley, T.V. "In-vitro Activity of Essential Oils, in Particular *Melaleuca alternifolia* (Tea Tree Oil and Tea Tree Oil Products) against *Candida spp.*," *Journal of Antimicrobial Chemotherapy*, 42:5, 591-5, 1998.

68 Hammer, K.A., Carson, C.F. and Riley, T.V. "In-vitro Susceptibilities of Lactobacilli and Organisms Associated with Bacterial Vaginosis to *Melaleuca alternifolia* (Tea Tree oil)," (Letter) *Antimicrobial Agents and Chemotherapy*, Jan 1999.

inflammation and associated pain has been found in a study by the College of Dentistry at the University of Tennessee Memphis.[69] The Rural Industries Research and Development Corporation (RIRDC) in Australia has funded further research into this and the results should be published soon.

BURN GELS

There is a great deal of anecdotal (but not very much scientific) evidence that Tea Tree gel helps to alleviate pain and infection when applied to burns. Many leading Tea Tree companies are using the oil of *Melaleuca alternifolia* in a whole range of new and innovative burn gels and impregnated dressings. The water soluble gel helps to quickly cool down the burn while the Melaleuca oil, held in suspension, reduces the pain and inflammation. Healing is accelerated with much less likelihood of infection and scarring—great news for casualty units, fire departments, industry, schools, families, and in fact, anyone who is likely to treat burns and scalds.

Did you know? It was reported that Australian actor Mel Gibson insisted on using Tea Tree impregnated fire blankets on the set during the filming of the amazing fire scenes for the film *Braveheart*, just in case any of the actors or film crew were accidentally burned! Nice one Mel!

HAND AND NAIL CARE

Dr. E.M. Humphrey in the 1930's found that "The pus solvent properties of Tea Tree oil made it an excellent application for the fungal nail disease paronychia, which if left untreated could result in the deformity and eventual loss of the nail." Dr. Andrew Weil claims that Tea Tree oil works better, and is much cheaper, than prescription antifungals for fungal infections of the toenails or fingernails.[70,71,72,73]

COUGHS, COLDS AND FLU

Alternative practitioners have successfully used Tea Tree oil in sprays (for strep throat), inhalations and decongestant chest rubs. There is some evidence available in peer-reviewed journals that can collaborate these facts, but more research needs to be done in this area.[74, 75, 76]

69 Dabbous, K.H., Pippin, M.A., Pabst, K.M., and Pabst, M.J. "Superoxide Release by Neutrophils is Inhibited by Tea Tree Oil," (Supported by NIDR DEO5494) College of Dentistry, UT Memphis, 1993.
70 Penfold, A.R. and Morrison, F.R. "Some Notes on the Essential Oil of *Melaleuca alternifolia*," *Australian Journal of Pharmacy*, 18, 274-5, 1937.
71 Humphrey, E.M. "A New Australian Germicide," *Medical Journal of Australia*, I, 417-418, 1930.
72 Buck, D.S, Nidorf, D.M. and Addino, J.G. "Comparison of Two Topical Preparations for the Treatment of Onychomycosis: *Melaleuca alternifolia* (Tea Tree Oil) and Clotrimazole," *Journal of Family Practice*, 38, 601-5, 1994.
73 Weil, A. *Ask Dr. Weil*, http://www.drweil.com
74 Carson, C.F., Hammer, K.A. and Riley, T.V. "In-vitro Activity of Essential Oil of *Melaleuca alternifolia* against *Streptococcus Spp.*," *Journal of Antimicrobial Chemotherapy*, 37:6, 1177-8, 1996.
75 Coutts, M. "The Bronchoscopic Treatment of Bronchiectasis," *Medical Journal Australia*, July 1937.
76 Shemesh, A. and Mayo, W.L. "A Natural Antiseptic and Fungicide," *International Journal of Alternative and Complementary Medicine*, Dec. 1991.

THE FIRST ANTI-VIRAL EVIDENCE

Most alternative practitioners have known that Tea Tree oil of *Melaleuca alternifolia* has shown signs of anti-viral activity, especially with the Herpes virus (cold sores, chicken pox and shingles blisters, warts, etc.). Now that the first research report completed by Chris Bishop at John Moores University, Liverpool, UK, has been published, others supported by the Rural Industries Research and Development Corporation (RIRDC) are set to follow.[77]

AT WAR WITH THE SUPERBUGS

Methicillin-resistant *Staphylococcus aureus* (MRSA, Golden-staph, Super-staph) is believed to be at epidemic proportions. The last of the synthesized antibiotics are becoming increasingly less effective against it. Tea Tree oil, at a low dilution of less than 2%, is proving to be the one last hope. Unfortunately, because Tea Tree oil cannot be patented or held exclusive, large pharmaceutical companies do not see the need to help with research. Could this mean that they are more interested in profits than in people's health? [78,79,80,81]

CHILD CARE

There are many safe, dermatologically tested Tea Tree products available that are designed for children. It is comforting to know that Tea Tree is still a very effective pathogenic bacteria inhibitor even at a low dilution of 0.25% in some cases.[82]

PET CARE

The beneficial effects of Tea Tree oil apply to animals as well. Skin problems, wounds, insect bites and stings, and ringworm can all be treated very successfully with the oil or products made with the oil. One property of Tea Tree oil in particular is very beneficial to pets—it is a very effective insect repellent. It's a useful treatment and deterrent for fleas, ticks, and mites.[83,84]

---

77 Bishop, C.D. "Anti-viral Activity of the Essential Oil of *Melaleuca alternifolia* (Maiden & Betche) Cheel (Tea Tree) Against Tobacco Mosaic Virus," (Research Report) *Journal of Essential Oil Research*, 7, 641-644, 1995.

78 Carson, C.F., Cookson, B.D., Farrelly, H.D. and Riley, T.V. "Susceptibility of Methicillin-resistant Staphylococcus aureus to the Essential Oil *Melaleuca alternifolia*," *Journal of Antimicrobial Chemotherapy*, 35:3, 421-4, 1995.

79 Carson, C.F., Hammer, K.A. and Riley, T.V. "Broth Micro-dilution Method for Determining the Susceptibility of *Escherichia coli* (*E. coli*) and *Staphylococcus aureus* to the Essential Oil of *Melaleuca alternifolia*," *Microbios*, 82:332, 181-185, 1995.

80 Carson, C.F., Riley, T.V. and Cookson, B.D. "Efficacy and Safety of Tea Tree Oil as a Topical Anti-microbial Agent," (editorial) *Journal of Hospital Infection*, 40:3, 175-8, 1998.

81 Elsom, G. "Susceptibility of Methicillin-resistant *Staphylococcus aureus* to Tea Tree Oil and Mupirocin," *Journal of Antimicrobial Chemotherapy*, V43, 427-428, 1999.

82 Hammer, K.A., Carson, C.F. and Riley, T.V. "Susceptibility of Transient and Commensal Skin Flora to the Essential Oil of *Melaleuca alternifolia*," *American Journal of Infection Control*, 24:3, 186-9, 1996.

83 Carson, C.F. and Riley, T.V. "Toxicity of the Essential Oil of *Melaleuca alternifolia* (or Tea Tree Oil)," (Letter) *Journal of Toxicology-Clinical Toxicology*, 33:2, 193-4, 1995.

84 Southwell, I., Markham, J. and Mann, C. "Why Cineole is Not Detrimental to Tea Tree Oil," *Rural Industries Research and Development Corporation*, Research Paper Series 97/54, 1997.

AGRICULTURAL APPLICATIONS

Although there have not been a great deal of clinical studies on the use of Tea Tree oil in agriculture, its anti-fungal, parasiticidal, and indeed, anti-viral properties can be utilized for use in the greenhouse and garden (see the first anti-viral evidence above). Australian farmers and organic growers have been using Tea Tree products for a number of years.[85, 86]

HOUSEHOLD CLEANING AND LAUNDRY

The solvent properties of Tea Tree oil, which are so useful at dissolving pus and debris in wounds, are also brilliant in household cleaning products and in the laundry. Today, companies all around the globe are utilizing its unique solvent and anti-microbial qualities. There are soaps, stain removers, fabric softeners, laundry detergents and whiteners, copper and brass cleaners, dish detergents, window cleaners, all-purpose cleaners, bathroom cleaners, furniture polish, air fresheners, odor eliminators, floor cleaners, hospital grade disinfectants, etc. Tea Tree oil can also be used very effectively as an anti-microbial surface cleaner. It is many times more "active" than a comparable strength disinfectant.[87, 88]

The household of the 21st Century has a unique opportunity to say "No!" to those harsh synthetic chemicals that are slowly poisoning our planet. While we still have natural, biodegradable commodities like the oil of the *Melaleuca alternifolia* we have a choice—a greener choice that can not only assist in healing our bodies, but can also safely cleanse all around our homes too, quite literally from basement to attic.

A LESSON IN QUALITY

With the spreading world-wide popularity of Tea Tree oil, there was inevitably a growing demand for high quality oil with consistent healing properties. Unfortunately, less scrupulous companies could easily sell an inferior oil, trading solely on the good reputation earned by the pure oil of *Melaleuca alternifolia*. With no quality standards in place, these companies could quite legally mix the pure oil with a cheaper oil, having little or no healing qualities, and market the blend as "Tea Tree oil" or "Melaleuca oil."

Even if the oil is wholly derived from the *Melaleuca alternifolia* tree, this does not guarantee its therapeutic value. Tree genetics, growing conditions, distillation methods, and storage can all affect oil quality to a degree. This is why, in 1967, in order to protect both the consumer and the Tea Tree industry, the Australian Standards Association established a standard for the oil.

85 Small, B.E.J. "Tea Tree Oil," *Australian Journal of Experimental Agriculture and Animal Husbandry,* V21, 1981.

86 Olsen, M.W. "Control of *Sphaerotheca fuliginea* on Cucurbits with a 1.5% Dilution of an Oil Extracted from the Australian Tea Tree," *Phytopathology,* 78:12, 1595, 1988.

87 Altman, P.M. "Australian Tea Tree Oil," *Australian Journal of Pharmacy,* 69, 276-78, 1988.

88 Altman, P.M. "Australian Tea Tree Oil - A Natural Antiseptic," *Australian Journal of Biotechnology,* 3:4 247-8, 1989.

This new standard was based on two of the oil's key components—Terpinen 4-ol and Cineole. As far back as 1925, it was known that Terpinen 4-ol was the main anti-microbial component. Obviously, higher levels of Terpinen 4-ol are desirable. Cineole is the component that gives Tea Tree oil its unique penetrating ability. But high levels of Cineole can be irritating to sensitive skin, so lower levels of Cineole are preferable. Consequently, the Australian Standards Association set the 1967 standard so that Melaleuca oil should have a minimum content of 35% Terpinen 4-ol and a maximum of 10% Cineole.

Unfortunately these new requirements led to an over-production of unmarketable oil that failed to reach the required standard. To save the ailing and discontented Tea Tree industry, the standard was relaxed in 1985 to a minimum content of 30% Terpinen 4-ol and a maximum of 15% Cineole. Fortunately for us, there are a number of reputable suppliers who still sell high-quality oil which falls well within the original (higher) standard.

Please be aware that there are many oils that technically can be called "Tea Tree oil" or "Melaleuca oil." There are over 150 species of Melaleuca trees, some with nearly identical main components, but there is only one Melaleuca alternifolia. To be sure that you have the authentic Australian Tea Tree oil, it must state on the label that it is the oil of the *"Melaleuca alternifolia."* It should also contain more than 35% Terpinen 4-ol and less than 10% Cineole. It is very important to know your supplier and to make sure that the oil you purchase is of a high therapeutic grade. If in any doubt, go back to your supplier and ask to see a detailed specification. A reputable supplier would be happy to oblige. There are reputable companies today that have never lowered their standards and have always sold the pure oil of *Melaleuca alternifolia* that is well within the set guidelines.

This all reminds me of a very apt slogan I once saw:

"Nothing added, nothing removed,
Nature's best cannot be improved."

Tea Tree oil of the *Melaleuca alternifolia* is a uniquely complex substance that continues to delight and surprise us the more we learn about it. It is truly one of "nature's best," and one of nature's most potent, remarkable, and useful gifts.

"That Amazing Tea Tree Oil" is available as an inexpensive booklet to share with your customers. Contact RM Barry Publications at 1 (888) 209-0510 or visit us on the internet at www.rmbarry.com.

CHAPTER THREE

IS YOUR HOME A HEALTHY HOME?

How common household chemicals may gradually
be making you and your family sick.

by John K. Beaulieu

IS YOUR HOME A HEALTHY HOME?

It's alarming but true—scientists and doctors have discovered that there is a connection between our health and the use of common everyday household chemicals. If yours is the typical home, you probably use dozens of cleaning and personal care products, purchased at the local grocery store, which contain chemical ingredients that could be harmful to your health and the health of your loved ones.

Since World War II, there has been a dramatic rise in the number of man-made chemicals we use in our homes. The typical home now contains over sixty-three hazardous products that together contain hundreds of different chemicals.[1] At the same time there has been an equally dramatic rise in the incidence of certain chronic health problems. Research indicates that it is more than coincidence that the dramatic rise in these various diseases has coincided with the increased use of hazardous, man-made chemicals in the home.

HAVE WE ALWAYS BEEN THIS SICK?

Around the turn of the century the cancer incidence rate was about one in fifty. Today, one in three Americans will suffer with cancer, with that number expected to reach one in two early in the next century. Cancer is the number two killer of adults and the leading cause of death from disease in children.[2]

The incidence of central nervous system disorders like Alzheimer's and Multiple Sclerosis increases annually.

Birth defects are on the rise as well. Over 150,000 babies are born with defects each year for reasons unknown. Another 500,000 babies are

---

1 World Resources Institute, *The 1994 Information Please Environmental Almanac* (Houghton-Mifflin, 1994).
2 Paula DiPerna, *Environmental Hazards to Children* (Public Affairs Pamphlets, 1981).

miscarried early in pregnancy each year with an additional 24,000 miscarried late in pregnancy or stillborn.[3] Infertility is increasing and widespread with over 2 million couples who want children and are unable to conceive.[4]

Asthma was also once a very rare disease. Now the condition is extremely common. The asthma rate has tripled in the last twenty years with nearly 20 to 30 million Americans currently afflicted.[5]

Attention Deficit Disorder in adults and children is rising. In 1993, 2 million children took the drug Ritalin so they could sit still long enough to learn. In 1995, that figure doubled to approximately 4 million, and is expected to reach 8 million by the year 2000.[6]

You or someone you know has probably been touched in some way by one of these illnesses. What could be causing these, and other health problems, to rise and afflict so many otherwise healthy people? Although other factors are involved, more and more scientists are linking these ailments to long-term chemical exposure. And, for most of us, our greatest exposure to chemicals is right in our own homes! We breathe chemical vapors from household products in the air; we absorb chemicals into our skin while using household products to clean our homes or make our bodies clean and smell good; and we swallow small amounts of chemicals when we gargle, or when we eat food from dishes that have been cleaned with chemicals and still contain a thin residue. The home is also where over 1.5 million young children are poisoned each year, and most of the time they are poisoned by a cleaning or personal care product![7]

WHY I WROTE THIS ARTICLE

I realize that you are probably not aware of the potential health hazards present in many household cleaners and personal care products. Unfortunately, most people are not. It is for you that I have written this article. I am not a chemist or a doctor, and I am not trying to promote myself as an expert on household chemicals. However, I have done considerable research on this subject because I want to provide the safest, healthiest home I possibly can for my own wife and children. What I learned is so convincing that I feel I must share it with you and others as best I can.

In this article, you will find quite a bit of information on the connection between household chemicals and your health. I have tried to provide information from the most credible and objective sources possible. You may find the information shocking and very disturbing, as I did. But I want you to know that I do not mean to frighten you. I simply

3 H. Needleman & P. Landrigan, *Raising Children Toxic Free* (Farrar, Straus, & Giroux, 1994).
4 Doris Rapp, *Is This Your Child's World?* (Bantam Books, 1996).
5 Mary Ellen Fise, *Indoor Air Quality* (Consumer Federation of America, 1997).
6 Doris Rapp, *Is This Your Child's World?*
7 The National Safe Kids Campaign, *Poisoning* (1996).

want you to be informed so that you can make a simple, rational decision concerning your health and the health of your loved ones.

THIS ARTICLE HAS A HAPPY ENDING

Happily, there is a simple solution to the problem presented in this article. Some conscientious companies now offer household products that are safer and more natural. Most of these people-friendly and environmentally sensitive products work just as well or better than grocery store brands, and in many cases, actually cost less. So, there's really no reason to risk your health, or the health of your loved ones any longer.

Is your home a healthy home? Right now, it's probably not as healthy as it could be. Read on to learn more.

THEY WOULDN'T SELL IT IF IT WASN'T SAFE ...WOULD THEY?

When we pick up a product at the local grocery store, most of us like to think we are getting something that has been tested and proven to be safe. After all, we have laws to protect our health and safety, don't we? Actually, the government has very limited power to regulate manufacturers, or require testing of their products. Here are some disturbing facts:

- A product that kills 50% of lab animals through ingestion or inhalation can still receive the federal regulatory designation "non-toxic."[8]
- Of the 17,000 chemicals that appear in common household products, only 30% have been adequately tested for their negative effects on our health; less than 10% have been tested for their effect on the nervous system; and nothing is known about the combined effects of these chemicals when mixed within our bodies.[9]
- No law requires manufacturers to list the exact ingredients on the package label.[10]

"Personal care product" refers to just about anything we use to clean our bodies or make ourselves look or smell good. The closest thing to a regulatory agency for the personal care industry is the Food and Drug Administration (FDA), and their power is extremely limited. Here are more unsettling facts regarding personal care products:

- The FDA cannot regulate a personal care product until after it is released into the marketplace.
- Neither personal care products nor their ingredients are reviewed or approved before they are sold to the public.
- The FDA cannot require companies to do safety testing on their personal care products before they are sold to the public.

8 Doris Rapp, *Is This Your Child's World?*
9 World Resources Institute, *The 1994 Information Please Environmental Almanac.*
10 Debra Lynn Dadd, *Home Safe Home* (Tarcher-Putnam, 1997).

- The FDA cannot require recalls of harmful personal care products from the marketplace.[11]
- The National Institute of Occupational Safety and Health (NIOSH) analyzed 2,983 chemicals used in personal care products. The results were as follows:
  - 884 of the chemicals were toxic
  - 314 caused biological mutation
  - 218 caused reproductive complications
  - 778 caused acute toxicity
  - 148 caused tumors
  - 376 caused skin and eye irritations.[12]

WARNING:
YOU CAN'T TRUST WARNING LABELS!

You may think you know what is in a product and its potential harms by reading ingredient and warning labels. Think again. Manufacturers are not required to list the exact ingredients on the label. Also, chemical names are often disguised by using innocuous "trade names." So even if the chemical is listed on the label, you may not recognize it for what it is.

Even if the harsh and dangerous active ingredients are listed on a package, oftentimes the remainder of ingredients are lumped into a category known as "inert" (not active) ingredients. This term may lead you to believe that these chemicals are not toxic or hazardous. In fact, many of the 1,000 different chemicals used as inert ingredients are more harmful than the active ingredients. The Environmental Protection Agency (EPA) does not require manufacturers to identify most inert chemicals, or disclose their potential harmful effects. Even suspected carcinogens (cancer-causing agents) are used as inert ingredients in household products.[13]

Regarding warning labels, one New York study found that 85% of products they examined had incorrect warning labels. Some were labeled poisonous, but weren't; others were poisonous, but not labeled as such; others gave incorrect first aid information.[14] And there are absolutely no warnings on products about possible negative effects of long-term exposure. This is unfortunate because most diseases linked to chemical exposure are the result of long-term exposure.

If we don't know what's in it, and we don't know if it can hurt us, how are we supposed to make an intelligent decision about whether or not to bring this product into our home?

---

11 United States Food and Drug Administration, *FDA Authority Over Cosmetics* (Office of Cosmetics Fact Sheet, 1995).
12 Judith Berns, "The Cosmetic Cover-up," *Human Ecologist* 43 (Fall 1989).
13 John Harte, *Toxics A to Z* (University of California Press, 1991).
14 Debra Lynn Dadd, *Home Safe Home*.

WHY AREN'T MANUFACTURERS REQUIRED TO TEST THESE CHEMICALS?

As we've already discussed, the government has very limited power to regulate manufacturers or require testing of their products. The reason has to do with economics and politics. It takes dozens of years and hundreds of thousands of dollars to fully test one chemical. If the government were to require every manufacturer to test every product and prove that it is safe, many manufacturers would be forced to go out of business, and our products would cost about twice as much as they currently do. Besides, who do you think they would test these chemicals on anyway? That's right—animals.

All this would cause a lose-lose situation for politicians. Manufacturers would be angry at them for imposing the expensive testing. And the public would be angry at them for requiring manufacturers to torture and kill all those animals, and for driving the prices of household products through the roof!

Even if a chemical has been tested and found to be harmful, you still may not get the truth from a manufacturer. Just look how long it took the tobacco industry to finally admit cigarettes are addictive and cause cancer. Do not wait for any company to spend hundreds of thousands of dollars to confirm that their product definitely causes cancer. Let's exercise our rights as informed consumers and choose manufacturers who make products with safer, more natural ingredients.

WHICH PRODUCTS? WHICH CHEMICALS?

Chemicals that can cause death, cancer, central nervous system (CNS) disorders, learning disorders, birth defects, respiratory illness, and many other health problems appear in most of the cleaning and personal care products in your home. It may be difficult, however, to tell which health risks a particular product poses. Since manufacturers do not list long-term health effects on the packages and are not required to list the ingredients, it's impossible to learn all the health risks by reading the label.

That's why I have provided a short list of product types and general comments about possible health risks below. Of course, every product is different. Even the same product's ingredients can vary from batch to batch depending on the cost and availability of certain chemicals. The following lists of cleaning supplies and personal care products are by no means exhaustive. The possible health effects do not apply to every single brand. However, based on examination of many grocery store brands, chemicals in the following products cause the listed health problems:

CLEANING PRODUCTS
- Air freshener – toxic; may cause cancer; irritates nose, throat, and lungs.
- Disinfectant – very toxic; causes skin, throat, and lung burns; causes coma.

- Drain cleaner – toxic; causes skin burns; causes liver and kidney damage.
- Oven cleaner – toxic; causes skin, throat, and lung burns.
- Window cleaner – toxic; causes CNS disorders; causes liver and kidney disorders.
- Floor/Furniture Polish – toxic; causes CNS disorders; may cause lung cancer.
- Spot remover – toxic; may cause cancer; causes liver damage.
- All-purpose cleaner – causes eye damage; irritates nose, throat, and lungs.
- Toilet bowl cleaner – very toxic; causes skin, nose, throat, and lung burns.
- Chlorinated scouring powder – toxic; highly irritating to nose, throat, and lungs.
- Dishwasher detergent – toxic; causes eye injuries, damage to mucous membranes, and throat.
- Dishwashing liquid – harmful if swallowed; irritates the skin.
- Carpet shampoo – toxic; may cause cancer; causes CNS and liver damage.
- Laundry detergent – toxic; irritates the skin and lungs.
- Bleach – toxic by swallowing; vapors are harmful; causes CNS disorders.
- Stain remover – toxic; may cause cancer; vapors can be fatal.
- Fabric softener – toxic; may cause cancer; causes CNS disorders; causes liver damage.

PERSONAL CARE PRODUCTS
- Shampoo – may cause cancer; irritates eyes, skin, and lungs.
- Dandruff shampoo – may cause cancer; causes organ degeneration; causes CNS disorders.
- Deodorant soap – may cause cancer; causes asthma; irritates lungs.
- Bubble bath – causes bladder and kidney infections; irritates skin and nose.
- Mousse and hair spray – may cause cancer; causes lung disease; irritates eyes and skin.
- Mouthwash – toxic to children; may cause cancer.
- Breath Spray – may cause cancer.
- Cosmetics – may cause cancer; causes CNS damage; irritates skin and lungs.
- Perfume/Cologne – toxic; may cause cancer; irritates skin and lungs.[15, 16, 17]

15 Debra Lynn Dadd, *Home Safe Home.*
16 John Harte, *Toxics A to Z.*
17 Ruth Winter, *A Consumer's Dictionary of Household, Yard and Office Chemicals* (Crown, 1992).

ONE COMMON INGREDIENT

Although it would take a second book to cover all the ingredients commonly used in the products above, I want to let you know about one, formaldehyde, as an example. Formaldehyde is used frequently in both cleaning and personal care products because it is a cheap preservative.

The following information is taken from a Material Safety Data Sheet (MSDS) which, by law, must be supplied to anyone who uses any chemical product in the workplace. The MSDS for formaldehyde warns: "Suspected carcinogen; May be fatal if inhaled, swallowed, or absorbed through skin; causes burns; inhalation can cause spasms, edema (fluid buildup) of the larynx and bronchi, and chemical pneumonitis; extremely destructive to tissue of the mucous membrane."[18]

All these symptoms and more are caused by formaldehyde. Yet manufacturers can put formaldehyde in shampoo and not list it as an ingredient![19] You will be shocked to learn that formaldehyde is a common ingredient in baby shampoo, bubble bath, deodorants, perfume, cologne, hair dye, mouthwash, toothpaste, hair spray, and many other personal care items.

Before I go any further, I want to state that the amount of formaldehyde in many of these products is slight. Brushing your teeth every day probably will not give you cancer, but the risk is still there. After all, formaldehyde is still a suspected carcinogen, and if all cancers start from the abnormal growth of one cell, then why allow any amount into or onto your body?

BEWARE OF AEROSOLS

Both cleaning and personal care products come in aerosol cans. I want to warn you of the dangers of aerosols in your home. First, they send a fine mist of toxic chemicals into the air that is easily inhaled and absorbed. Second, this fine mist settles, leaving a coating of toxins on surfaces where children crawl and play and adults eat and sleep. Finally, many of the propellants used in aerosol cans are toxic themselves. Vinyl chloride, one of the most common, can cause dizziness, lack of coordination, headaches, blurred vision, nausea, and death.[20]

I read of a young man named Stuart who became dizzy and collapsed while spray painting bookshelves in his basement. When his wife found him a few hours later, he was dead.

These chemical propellants are also highly flammable. A woman named Laurie received disfiguring burns when the hair spray she was using was ignited by her cigarette. Each year 5,000 people receive emergency room treatment for aerosol-related injuries.[21]

Jimmy, 8, used a hammer and nail to puncture an old aerosol can.

---

18 Material Safety Data Sheet - *Formaldehyde*.
19 Debra Lynn Dadd, *Home Safe Home*.
20 John Harte, *Toxics A to Z*.
21 Dr. Ted Ferry, *Home Safety Desk Reference* (Career Press, 1994).

The can exploded, hurling pieces of metal into his face and upper chest, cutting him severely.[22]

When you weigh the short-term and long-term harms of aerosol products, I think the smart conclusion is simply to get rid of them.

TOXIC CHEMICALS AND THE HUMAN BODY

Your body is a very complex, very fragile system of chemical reactions and electrical impulses. When you consider a single cell breathes, uses energy, and releases waste much like your whole body does, you can begin to understand how even small amounts of harmful chemicals can affect the performance of the body's processes. Chemicals enter the human body in three ways: ingestion, inhalation, and absorption.

INGESTION

Ingestion brings to mind the image of a young child opening the cabinet under the sink and drinking something deadly. Well, each year nearly 1.5 million accidental ingestions of poisons are reported to U.S. Poison Control Centers. The majority of the victims are under the age of twelve and have swallowed a cleaning or personal care product.[23] It amazes me how many deadly chemicals are stored under sinks or on bathroom counters and bathtubs within easy reach of young children.

INHALATION

It may surprise you to learn that poisoning by inhalation is more common, and can be much more harmful, than ingestion. When something harmful is swallowed, the stomach actually begins breaking down and neutralizing the poison before it is absorbed into the bloodstream. However, when you inhale toxic fumes, the poisons go directly into the bloodstream and quickly travel to organs like the brain, heart, liver, and kidneys.

Many products give off toxic vapors which can irritate your eyes, nose, throat and lungs, and give you headaches, muscle aches, and sinus infections. This process of releasing vapors into the air is called *outgassing*. Outgassing occurs even when a chemical is tightly sealed in its container. If you doubt this, simply walk down the cleaning aisle at your local grocery store and notice how strongly it smells of toxic vapors even though all the containers are sealed tight.

ABSORPTION

Finally, you need to realize the potential threat absorption poses. One square centimeter of your skin, an area less than the size of a dime, contains 3 million cells, four yards of nerves, one yard of blood vessels,

---

22 Dr. Ted Ferry, *Home Safety Desk Reference*.
23 The National Safe Kids Campaign, *Poisoning*.

and one hundred sweat glands.[24] We've all heard the ads for nicotine patches and analgesic creams. These medicines work by being absorbed into the bloodstream through the skin. Even some heart medicines are administered through transdermal (through the skin) patches.

Any chemical that touches the skin can be absorbed and spread throughout the body. This can even happen when you come in contact with a surface that was treated with a chemical days, or even weeks earlier. I had no idea that my children could be harmed by crawling across the kitchen floor my wife had just cleaned. I thought we were being conscientious, not reckless. Since we no longer have products which contain harmful chemicals in our home, I no longer worry when I see my baby daughter crawling across the floor or putting her fingers in her mouth. I know she is not absorbing or ingesting toxic residues.

HOME IS WHERE THE CHEMICALS ARE

Home is where you are most likely to be exposed to toxic chemicals. After all, you spend 80 to 90% of your time indoors, most of that at home.[25] This fact is important when you understand that in one five-year study, the EPA found that airborne chemical levels in homes were as much as seventy times higher inside than outside.

When toxic household chemicals release vapors into the air, they have nowhere to go. During the oil shortages of the 1970s, builders began making houses as energy efficient as possible. The result has been homes that keep toxic indoor air tightly sealed inside.

Exposure to toxic indoor air may have a devastating effect on your health. One fifteen-year study found that women who worked at home had a 54% higher death rate from cancer than women who had jobs outside the home.[26] The study concluded that the increased death rate was due to daily exposure to the hazardous chemicals found in ordinary products. Some experts argue that 30% of all cancers stem from exposure to toxic chemicals.[27]

Not all of the health effects are fatal, however. According to a special legislative committee of the Commonwealth of Massachusetts, 50% of all health problems are caused, in part, by deteriorated indoor air quality.[28] A hangover is the side-effect of non-lethal ethanol poisoning (getting drunk). How many days do you wake feeling "hung over," with aches and pains or nausea? Perhaps the air in your home is poisoning you. How many bottles of pain-killers have you purchased to rid yourself of headaches, possibly brought on by your fabric softener?

The good news is that by switching to safer, more natural products, you can rid yourself of these symptoms altogether. You can make your home a healthy home.

---

24 Nancy Sokol Green, *Poisoning Our Children* (The Noble Press, 1991).
25 World Resources Institute, *The 1994 Information Please Environmental Almanac.*
26 Nancy Sokol Green, *Poisoning Our Children.*
27 John Harte, *Toxics A to Z.*
28 Doris Rapp, *Is This Your Child's World?*

IMMEDIATE EFFECTS OF CHEMICAL EXPOSURE

Could this happen in your home? When Peter Schwabb of Seattle, Washington, was a year old, he crawled over to the dishwasher to watch his mother unloading it. Suddenly, he put a finger into the detergent dispensing cup and ate a fingerful of wet but undissolved Electrasol. In minutes his face was red and blistered, and the inside of his mouth and his tongue were burned white. Because of a series of lucky circumstances, Peter was in the hospital within minutes and he recovered in a few days.

While Peter was in the hospital, there was a little girl across the hall who (according to Peter's mother) ate some dishwashing detergent and required seven operations to reopen her scarred esophagus.[29]

Another 18-month-old boy had to eat through tubes for five months and at last count has had thirty operations. Detergent is what destroyed his throat, too.[30]

Three-year-old Jason Whitely, of Tulsa, Oklahoma, died a lingering and horrible death two weeks after swallowing three ounces of a hair rinse containing ammonia.

Seven-month-old Adrian Gonzalez, Jr., of Belen, New Mexico, crawled through a puddle of spilled bleach, which gave him third-degree burns on 50% of his tiny body and burned his lungs from the fumes as well. It took him four days to die.[31]

The real tragedy here is that all of these accidents could have been prevented. A simple decision to use safer products could have meant that these children would not have had to suffer and die. Unfortunately, most parents don't realize that they have a choice.

MORE DANGEROUS THAN GUNS

It may shock you to learn that according to the National Safety Council, more children under the age of four die of accidental poisonings at home than are accidentally killed with guns at home.[32] Among children age five and under, the most common poison is a cleaner or personal care product.[33]

Ninety percent of all poisonings occur at home between the hours of 4 and 10 PM, when children are home from school and playing in the house.[34] Young children are especially vulnerable. They learn by putting things in their mouths. This is even more frightening when you consider the number of products that look like something else. Window cleaner looks like blueberry drink. Ammonia looks like apple juice. Many poisons come in bright, colorful containers with small, obscure warning labels that young children can't read. Remember the skull and crossbones

29 Shirley Camper Soman, *Let's Stop Destroying Our Children* (Hawthorn Books, 1974).
30 Shirley Camper Soman, *Let's Stop Destroying Our Children*.
31 Shirley Camper Soman, *Let's Stop Destroying Our Children*.
32 *Accident Facts* (National Safety Council, 1993).
33 The National Safe Kids Campaign, *Poisoning*.
34 The National Safe Kids Campaign, *Poisoning*.

symbol? It's a symbol that children can identify easily, but manufacturers are no longer required to display it on most household products.

Lennon Miller, 18 months, of Memphis, Tennessee, drank lemon-scented furniture polish, enticed no doubt by the attractive smell. He lived during a day of suffering, and died in John Gaston Hospital of chemically-induced pneumonia.[35]

ACCIDENTS HAPPEN TO ADULTS, TOO

Young children are not the only ones at risk for chemical injury. Poisoning is the number one accidental killer in the home, accounting for over 3,000 deaths in 1985 and over 4,000 deaths in 1990. These chemicals are also responsible for thousands of injuries each year.[36]

A 34-year-old man received burns on his arm after using a caustic drain-cleaner in his bathroom sink. Fifteen minutes after applying the chemical, he ran water into the sink, but the remaining residue splashed on his arm.[37]

A woman poured boiling water into a can of oven cleaner, according to the directions on the can. As she carried the can from the table to the oven, it spilled, burning her hand and producing large quantities of ammonia gas, which gave her a choking cough.[38]

But most of the health problems related to chemicals in the home are not because of accidents like these. Most chemical-related health problems are the result of exposure to toxics day after day, year after year.

LONG-TERM EFFECTS OF CHEMICAL EXPOSURE

Before I begin discussing the long-term effects of exposure to toxic chemicals in cleaning and personal care products, I want to make two points that I think are very important. First, the different diseases and conditions linked to chemical exposure are usually the result of long-term exposure. Just as one cigarette is not likely to give you cancer, one non-acute exposure to chemicals in cleaners probably won't harm you either. But we're talking about cumulative exposure to many different products: your mouthwash, conditioner, cologne or perfume, laundry detergent, window cleaner, and so on. When you consider all the products and all the chemicals you come across each day, you can begin to understand the potential for long-term harm.

Remember, the long-term effects of exposure to most chemicals in household products are not known. And nothing is known about what happens when they mix within our bodies. Drinking alcohol while using certain drugs can be a deadly combination. Could other chemicals mix in our bodies in a similarly fatal way?

---

35 Shirley Camper Soman, *Let's Stop Destroying Our Children.*
36 Home Safety, *USA Today* (February 13, 1997).
37 Dr. Ted Ferry, *Home Safety Desk Reference.*
38 Dr. Ted Ferry, *Home Safety Desk Reference.*

My second point concerns your body. What most doctors and scientists who investigate and treat chemical-related illness contend is that the *amount* of chemical a person is exposed to is not as important as *how sensitive* a person might be.[39] Some people can drink three beers and not be intoxicated. Others can feel groggy after drinking less than one beer. It all depends on a person's size and weight and the strength of their detox system. The same concept applies to chemical exposure.

YOUR DETOX SYSTEM

Your body has a system that destroys and eliminates toxins. After all, many things that appear naturally in the environment are toxic, and we need to have a strong defense system against them. Organs like the kidneys and liver filter out and remove toxins. Our blood contains T-cells that attack foreign agents. However, many people have overloaded or very weak detox systems. High levels of toxins and a poor nutritional state leave many people more susceptible to the effects of chronic chemical exposure.

Even healthy people can be affected. When exposed to a certain toxin, the body will respond by producing more of the enzymes needed to destroy the poison. In a sense, the body has "masked" the poisoning.[40] It has prevented the effects of the poisoning from being felt, even if the effects would have been mild. But, this has stressed the immune system, possibly leaving a person vulnerable to infection.

By switching to cleaners and personal care products that are not full of toxins, you can reduce the stress on your detox system, possibly leading to a healthier life. I have not missed a day of work due to illness in over two years. I have not seen a doctor for illness in three years. My children have been to the doctor for illness only twice in three years. I believe this is, in part, the result of my wife and me deciding to switch to safer and more natural products. I encourage you to do the same. It's one decision your family can live with.

BIRTH DEFECTS

Birth defects are the leading cause of death among children ages one to four. According to the March of Dimes, one in twelve children is born with a congenital defect. Environmental factors, including exposure to toxic chemicals, cause 7% to 11% of these defects. Sixty percent of birth defects have unknown causes. Toxic chemicals are suspected in these cases as well.[41]

In fact, the Council on Environmental Quality's report on chemical hazards to human reproduction concluded that, "the relationship between exposure to chemicals and human reproductive impairment

---

39 Dr. Doris Rapp, *Is This Your Child's World?*
40 Nancy Sokol Green, *Poisoning Our Children.*
41 Paula DiPerna, *Environmental Hazards to Children.*

may be an important area of public health concern that deserves more scientific investigation."[42]

Birth defects have been found in a number of animal species where high levels of toxic chemicals are present. A 1996 University of Minnesota study found higher rates of birth defects in children who lived in areas of the state where agricultural chemicals were used the most.[43]

Dr. Marion Moses of the Environmental Sciences Laboratory at Mount Sinai Medical Center in New York strongly recommends that, as far as toxins and carcinogens are concerned, the unborn child should have NO exposure; and where there is doubt about any chemical, err on the side of the child and prevent as much exposure as possible. "If we wait until we have absolute proof for all agents, it may be too late for the child," Dr. Moses stresses.[44]

Thalidomide is a tragic example of a substance that was touted as safe by its manufacturer but was later proven to cause horrible birth defects. Children whose mothers took the drug were born with deformed limbs or no limbs at all. This tragedy destroyed the belief that the placenta was a complete barrier between the baby and the environment. It also served as a wake-up call to how chemicals within the body can disrupt normal fetal development.

The NIOSH study I mentioned earlier stated 314 chemicals that appear in personal care products can cause biological mutations.[45] Many of these chemicals, including known carcinogens, can reach the unborn child.

Chemicals can also cause defects by damaging the egg cells in women. All the eggs a woman will ever have are produced while she is still a baby in the womb. By the fifth month of fetal life, the 3 to 4 million eggs a woman is born with have localized in her ovaries. Chemical exposure at any point can destroy or damage these cells, leaving her infertile or prone to birth defects or miscarriage.[46] Once damage has occurred, repair is almost impossible.

In men, exposure to chemicals can affect sperm development profoundly. A study of male Vietnam veterans found they were 70% more likely to have a child with a birth defect due to chemical exposure.[47] Many of the same chemicals are now found in products used every day around the home.

The presence of solvents in drinking water has been linked to leukemia and birth defects in California, Massachusetts, and New Jersey.[48] You may be exposed to a number of potentially harmful solvents every day, including ethanol, styrene, trichloroethylene, vinyl chloride,

42 Paula DiPerna, *Environmental Hazards to Children.*
43 *Dioxins* (National Wildlife Federation Office of Conservation Programs, 1997).
44 Paula DiPerna, *Environmental Hazards to Children.*
45 Judith Burns, "The Cosmetic Cover-up".
46 H. Needleman & P. Landrigan, *Raising Children Toxic Free.*
47 Dr. Doris Rapp, *Is This Your Child's World?*
48 Ruth Winter, *A Consumer's Dictionary of Household, Yard and Office Chemicals.*

diethylene glycol, and toluene. All of these appear in common household products.

INFERTILITY AND MISCARRIAGE

More than 2 million American couples who want to have children are unable to do so. Perhaps you or someone close to you is living with this heartache. It may surprise you to learn that between 1938 and 1991 the sperm count of males in industrialized countries has decreased 50% in quantity and quality. A cross-sectional study of college men found that 25% were sterile. Projected figures place the male sterility rate at over 50% early in the next century.[49]

Women's fertility has also been negatively affected by the increased use of chemicals. In 1934, only twenty-one cases of endometriosis existed in the entire world. Now there are over 5 million women with this condition, which causes infertility, in the United States alone.[50] High levels of toxins have been found in German women with endometriosis. Female monkeys exposed to dioxins had an increased rate of this condition also.[51] Combine the decreased sperm count with the prevalence of endometriosis and you can see just how the infertility rate could grow so large and affect so many.

Even women who can conceive are experiencing extremely high rates of miscarriage. In 1988, more than 600,000 women experienced a miscarriage, and in most cases the cause was unclear.[52] In many cases a woman's body will reject an unborn baby if it detects a profound defect of some kind. We may begin wondering if we are living in a time when more babies have defects. Or perhaps the chemicals that enter the body somehow send mixed or wrong messages.

Many chemicals, including alkylphenol, found in many industrial and household detergents, are known hormone disrupters. This means they act like hormones and can actually change behavior, mood, development and any other bodily functions regulated by hormones. It concerns me that the delicate balance of chemicals our bodies naturally produce and need to function properly can be skewed by synthetic, toxic chemicals.

CANCER

No word strikes more fear into people's hearts than "cancer." Although the death rate from cancer has declined, the incidence rate has not. Cancer rates continue to grow in almost every segment of the American public. Breast cancer and prostate cancers have doubled in the past fifty years. Testicular cancer has tripled during the same period. Over 550,000 people will die of cancer during this year.[53]

---

49 Dr. Doris Rapp, *Is This Your Child's World?*
50 Dr. Doris Rapp, *Is This Your Child's World?*
51 Dr. Doris Rapp, *Is This Your Child's World?*
52 H. Needleman & P. Landrigan, *Raising Children Toxic Free.*
53 *National Cancer Statistics Review* 1973-1994 (National Cancer Institute, 1997).

The majority of cancer cases are due to environmental factors.[54] Most experts agree that as many as 80 to 90% of all cancers can be avoided by making certain lifestyle changes. Please understand that "environmental factors" include everything in the environment, including diet, sleep patterns, etc. Some experts argue that 30% of all cancers are caused by exposure to toxic chemicals.[55]

The National Cancer Institute has a list of twenty known carcinogens and over 2,200 chemicals that are probable carcinogens.[56] Many of these chemicals are in the cleaners and personal care products you buy at your local grocery store. The National Toxicology Program is urging that fifteen more chemicals be added to the list of known carcinogens, including an organic solvent used in grease-cutting cleaners.[57]

Cancer tumors start from the mutated growth of one cell. Even minimal exposure over a long period of time can put you at risk of developing cancer. The risk may not be that great, but for me there is no acceptable level of risk when it comes to cancer. I know I can't completely eliminate all potential hazards from my life, but I no longer put myself at risk for cancer by exposing myself to the unregulated, dangerous chemicals that appear in products like laundry detergent, bathroom cleaner, hair conditioner, and cologne.

CANCER IN CHILDREN

I know my children are safer, too. Each year 6,500 children in the United States are diagnosed with cancer. Cancer remains the leading cause of death from disease for children over the age of five, accounting for over 2,100 deaths a year.[58]

The tragedy is that only 20% of cases of childhood cancer are due to genetic factors. Remember, we now know that carcinogens can cross the placental barrier. Exposure to carcinogens in the womb may cause childhood cancer by causing tumor development or by altering the baby's genes, leaving them with a predisposition to cancer. Dr. Robert Miller of the National Cancer Institute states that many carcinogens have a short enough latent period that exposure in the womb could lead to the diagnosis of tumors in the pediatric age period.[59]

Finally, I think it is important to remember that current cancer rates reflect past toxic exposure. Only time will tell what the legacy of our increased use of household products full of toxic chemicals will be.

ASTHMA

The American Lung Association now estimates that 3.7 million American children and 20 million adults presently have asthma. That is

54 John Harte, *Toxics A to Z.*
55 John Harte, *Toxics A to Z.*
56 World Resources Institute, *The 1994 Information Please Environmental Almanac.*
57 *Press Release* (National Institute of Health, May 2, 1997).
58 H. Needleman & P. Landrigan, *Raising Children Toxic Free.*
59 Paula DiPerna, *Environmental Hazards to Children.*

three times more victims than just twenty years ago.[60] Once again, environmental factors are under strong suspicion. I have already told you that most Americans spend 80 to 90% of their time in air-tight buildings, most with less than adequate ventilation. One study concluded that the majority of the 400,000 annual emergency room visits for severe asthma attacks are brought on by poor indoor air quality. Each year, asthma claims the lives of over 4,000 people and costs Americans over 6 billion dollars in medical costs and lost time from work and school.[61]

Doctors know that irritation of the lungs by chemicals can trigger asthma attacks. Long-term exposure to chemicals can contribute to the development of asthma. This is especially true with children. A child's immune system is not fully developed until she is twelve years old. A one-year-old has practically no detox system at all.[62]

Out of germ-phobia, some parents constantly spray disinfectant into the air and on all surfaces in their baby's nursery. What they may not realize is they are exposing their children to formaldehyde, cresol, phenol, ammonia, ethanol, and chlorine. It takes much less of these chemicals to harm a baby than an adult. Babies' bodies are much smaller and they breathe at ten times the rate of adults. The average child visits the doctor twenty-three times in the first four years of life, with the most common complaint being respiratory ailment.[63] When babies get sick, the last thing they need is to have irritating chemicals filling their lungs.

CNS DISORDERS

Central Nervous System (CNS) disorders can range from headaches and dizziness to Multiple Sclerosis, Parkinson's Disease, and Alzheimer's Disease. We know that many chemicals that appear in our household products are neurotoxins. Some act as depressants, some as stimulants, and some cause mood swings. Others act similar to alcohol, leaving a person lethargic, unable to concentrate, and with a loss of balance.

It's important, once again, to remind you that only 10% of the chemicals that appear in household products have been tested for negative effects on the nervous system.[64] And we know nothing about the long-term effects of exposure to these chemicals.

We do know that young people are destroying their brains by abusing aerosol products and inhaling their deadly fumes. In fact, aerosols are the drug of choice for many of these people. This is very frightening.

Doctors have also identified a condition known as toxic encephalopathy, brought on by repeated exposure to solvents over several years. Symptoms include memory loss, behavioral changes, emotional instability, confusion, inability to concentrate, neurological

---

60 Dr. Doris Rapp, *Is This Your Child's World?*
61 Mary Ellen Fise, *Indoor Air Quality.*
62 Paula DiPerna, *Environmental Hazards to Children.*
63 National Center For Health Statistics, 1997.
64 Dr. Doris Rapp, *Is This Your Child's World?*

and personality changes, and problems with manual dexterity.[65] Chemicals that cause this condition are in household products. They include chlorinated hydrocarbons, aromatic hydrocarbons and aliphatic hydrocarbons. You need to remember that the amount of chemicals a person is exposed to is not as important as the strength of a person's detox system. Extremely small amounts of chemicals can have severe effects on certain individuals.

Alzheimer's Disease receives so much attention because it is so prevalent and yet remains such a mystery. Around 4 million people currently suffer with Alzheimer's.[66] Although we have known about this disease for some time, recently the number of cases has grown dramatically. Approximately 14 million people will have the disease by early in the next century, and it may surpass cancer and stroke numbers as a cause of death.[67]

Although there seems to be a genetic link to the cause of Alzheimer's, scientists admit it is too weak to explain the prevalence of the disease. Most research points to environmental factors. Aluminum, a known neurotoxin, is the number one suspect. However, researchers are looking at other toxins and their possible link to this horrible disease. Hopefully, science will find the answers.

Not every CNS problem is as dramatic as Alzheimer's, but some can be almost as debilitating. Betty J., of Albuquerque, New Mexico, suffered from severe migraine headaches for years with major attacks occurring every six to eight weeks. Unfortunately, the medication she was taking was as disabling as the headaches. She would spend a week to ten days in bed until the migraines finally passed and the medication wore off. As you can imagine, this caused great hardship for her, especially with regard to her work.

After doing a little investigation, Betty decided to rid her home of toxic chemicals. She threw out everything she had purchased at the grocery store and used only natural, environmentally sensitive products. Her life changed dramatically. She no longer needed to take painkillers to get out of bed and the recurring migraine attacks stopped.

Disbelieving her own success, Betty purchased a bottle of bleach to see if chemicals were indeed the cause of her problem. Within minutes of opening the bottle, she had another migraine headache. Betty became a true believer in the need to rid your home of toxic, chemical-laden cleaners.

---

65 N. Ashford & C. Miller, *Chemical Exposures, Low Levels and High Stakes* (Van Nostrand Reinhold, 1991).
66 Dr. Doris Rapp, *Is This Your Child's World?*
67 Dr. Doris Rapp, *Is This Your Child's World?*

ATTENTION DEFICIT DISORDER AND OTHER LEARNING DISORDERS

By the year 2000, 8 million children in America will be taking Ritalin so they can sit still long enough to learn to read and write.[68] Ritalin is a "Class-2" narcotic. What could be wrong? Why do we need such a powerful drug to help control our children's behavior? Most veteran teachers will tell you that the increased use of Ritalin is not the result of an increased awareness in ADD, as some would argue, but an increase in the actual number of cases. Think back to when you were in school. Was half of your class out of control? Were most of your friends taking medication for hyperactivity? Again, we must find out just what is wrong!

The problem is that many young people are being misdiagnosed. According to Doris Rapp, M.D., an expert on the treatment of environmental illness, as many as two-thirds of the millions of children on Ritalin are actually suffering from acute allergic reactions to environmental agents. Removal of certain chemicals or a profound change in diet could solve the problem.[69] These children do not need powerful drugs.

Young people are exposed to so many chemicals that many of them develop sensitivities. This happens because their detox system burns out even before it fully develops. Then they become susceptible to the effects of even traces of chemicals. I want to state one more time that when it comes to toxins, the amount of exposure is not as important as how sensitive a person is. Children need much less exposure than adults do to develop negative symptoms.

CHEMICAL VAPORS IN SCHOOLS

Take the case of Ryan. When he was four, he began going to school. He would leave feeling fine, but come home feeling weak and tired, clinging tightly to his mother. While in the gym at his school, he became so weak that he had to be carried out. Ryan's mother noticed that they sprayed the table tops and rest area of his classroom with a popular aerosol disinfectant.

Ryan's doctor, an environmental specialist, tested Ryan. She sprayed a four inch area of a paper towel with the same disinfectant and placed it a few feet away from Ryan. Within thirty minutes, Ryan was obviously different. He could no longer hold his pencil and his writing skills completely collapsed. Several tests confirmed his reaction.[70] William, another eight-year-old boy, had a similar reaction when exposed to chlorine fumes.[71]

Ryan's reaction might be considered severe, but it represents a growing number of young people who are reacting to chemicals in the

---

68 Dr. Doris Rapp, Is This Your Child's World?
69 Dr. Doris Rapp, Is This Your Child's World?
70 Dr. Doris Rapp, Is This Your Child's World?
71 Dr. Doris Rapp, Is This Your Child's World?

air in their homes and school. I wonder how many children experience learning problems because of chemicals in the environment. Even if the number is only slight, it is unacceptable. We should try to remove any possible impediment from our children's future, and that begins with providing the healthiest home possible.

Eight-year-old Peter's first class in the morning was taught by a teacher who smoked heavily and smelled strongly of perfume. In this class, arithmetic, Peter typically had difficulty remembering, thinking, and completing his work. His teacher noticed on some days he could not even add two and two.

Peter improved over the course of the morning when he had another teacher who did not smell of either tobacco or perfume. However, the smell of perfume from lunchroom aides and the odor of cleaners from the dish room caused his ability to learn and concentrate to deteriorate again.

Peter's doctor confirmed his sensitivities to many chemicals. Perfumes, colognes, and fragrances can contain harmful chemicals such as formaldehyde, toluene, ethanol, acetone, methyl chloride and benzene derivatives. All can damage the nervous system. Peter now goes to school with an oxygen tank in case he has a severe reaction.[72]

Eleven-year-old Warren always did well in school. His grades were in the 90th percentile. Exposure to phenol caused him to develop multiple ear infections and led to a progressive decline in his grades. After several tests, Warren's doctor confirmed his sensitivity to phenol. Warren eventually transferred schools to escape exposure during the day. Fortunately, his grades returned to normal.[73]

According to Sherry Rogers, M.D., also an environmental specialist, the symptoms produced by chemical sensitivity are as varied as the people affected.[74] While children like Peter and Warren might react with a breakdown of learning ability, children like Chuck become hyperactive. When Chuck was six years old, he would make very loud noises, become uncontrollably bouncy, and hit other children when exposed to certain chemicals. Fumes from furniture polish affected him so strongly that he told his mother he wanted to jump off the roof![75]

These stories hardly reflect the array of reactions that children who are chemically sensitive exhibit. Reaction is unpredictable and can change in time. The bottom line is, you can protect your children. You can limit, if not eliminate, their exposure to neurotoxins. By switching to brands that do not use chemicals like phenol and formaldehyde, you can help them reach their full potential.

MULTIPLE CHEMICAL SENSITIVITY

Multiple Chemical Sensitivity (MCS), or Environmental Illness (EI), are the names for an assortment of problems that can affect any part of

---

72 Dr. Doris Rapp, *Is This Your Child's World?*
73 Dr. Doris Rapp, *Is This Your Child's World?*
74 Sherry Rogers, *Chemical Sensitivity* (Keats Publishing, Inc., 1995).
75 Dr. Doris Rapp, *Is This Your Child's World?*

the human body. Chemicals found in cleaners, personal care products, food, plastics, and even water, can cause this condition. Persons suffering with MCS lack the ability to adequately detoxify their bodies. Symptoms include: headaches, severe fatigue, hyperactivity, muscle pain, joint pain, stomach and bowel problems, constant congestion, muscle twitches, and asthma-type symptoms. Other symptoms include emotional and behavioral problems, depression, loss of memory, and inability to learn or concentrate. More and more people are coming forth, reporting these symptoms, and having their sensitivities confirmed.[76, 77]

I have read the accounts of many victims, and personally spoken with dozens more. Most were very sensitive to chemicals in cleaning and personal care products. They had debilitating body aches, headaches, depression and other nervous disorders. Thankfully, the majority I have talked to received nearly complete relief by switching to people-friendly household products.

Dr. William Rea, a world-known environmental doctor in Dallas, Texas, reports that of all the patients he has seen with MCS, only 13% report developing the condition after a one-time acute poisoning. Sixty percent report developing the condition as the result of long-term slow poisonings involving minimal amounts of toxins. Only 28% of the cases he has documented are work-related. A staggering 72% of the cases are people who have been exposed to chemicals at home or at other places.[78]

Dr. Rea sites the following factors as influencing the onset of MCS:

• Total Toxic Body Burden – This is the sum of all toxins in the body. When the accumulation overloads a person's detox system, MCS can occur.

• Nutritional State – The more nutrient-depleted a person's body is, the more likely they are to develop MCS.

• Synergisms – This means the combination of the different chemicals in the body will have a stronger effect than individual toxins.

• Bioaccumulation of Toxins – This refers to how less dense tissues, like fat cells, can actually absorb and accumulate chemicals. Without the time and nutrition for the body to cleanse itself, the accumulation level can be dangerous.[79]

According to Doris Rapp, M.D., Multiple Chemical Sensitivity is common. Most physicians who practice environmental medicine, including herself, estimate that 25% to 50% of today's population is sensitive to one degree or another.[80]

Nancy, a young, vibrant, well-trained teacher, developed MCS over a period of eight years. She became fatigued, experienced muscle aches, constant ear ringing, difficulty concentrating, blackouts, and severe

76 William J. Rea, *Chemical Sensitivities* (1997).
77 Sherry Rogers, *Chemical Sensitivity.*
78 William J. Rea, *Chemical Sensitivities.*
79 William J. Rea, *Chemical Sensitivities*
80 Dr. Doris Rapp, *Is This Your Child's World?*

depression. She became so sensitive that even the nuance of chemical odor made her ill. Scents in her body lotions, make-up and hair spray made her so confused that she could not tell time or recall the names of her students. A whiff of perfume caused her to laugh uncontrollably and twitch.

During a leave of absence, she was too tired to get out of bed, take a shower, or prepare a snack. Her condition was traced to, among many things, phenol in the disinfectants used in the bathroom near her classroom. After two years of therapy, she began to feel better, but she still carries a charcoal filter mask everywhere she goes and fears a total relapse.[81]

Sister Martha, a dedicated teacher, was assigned by her school to tutor students who needed extra help. Unfortunately, the only available room was a converted custodial closet located between two bathrooms. The vapors from cleaners, disinfectants and deodorizers from the bathrooms constantly filtered into this room through vents in the walls.

After tutoring for a while in this room, Sister Martha developed a persistent, nagging cough, joint stiffness and swelling, facial spasms, excessive mucus, and vision problems. She was able to find a doctor who began to treat her sensitivities. Even after extensive treatment, she still lives with many limitations. Although she has eliminated toxins in her home, she cannot remain in a public place like a mall for more than a few minutes. She still needs to take an anti-allergy extract and can drink only purified water.[82]

Both of these stories represent extreme cases of MCS. Most people who suffer with MCS do not have such profound symptoms, but rather experience symptoms like recurring headaches, muscle aches, depression, and chronic fatigue.

Hopefully, more will be learned about MCS and treatments will improve. However, I think the focus should be on prevention. By reducing the amount of toxins in your home, you can help to reduce the risk for MCS in a loved one.

SOME FINAL THOUGHTS

As I am finishing this article, I have just learned that the FDA has proposed a ban on phenolphthalein, a phenol derivative found in laxatives that has been linked to cancer in laboratory animals.[83] I believe that many more chemicals will be banned as we learn about the long-term effects of exposure. Other phenol derivatives still appear in many personal care and cleaning products. I strongly urge you not to expose yourself to any chemical that could possibly cause cancer.

At the same time, another company is pulling their tire cleaning product off the shelves because even a tiny amount of the product can

---

81 Dr. Doris Rapp, *Is This Your Child's World?*
82 Dr. Doris Rapp, *Is This Your Child's World?*
83 HHS News (U.S. Department of Health and Human Services, August 29, 1997).

kill a child. This product was marketed in a spray bottle! I don't have to tell you parents how children love those spray bottles.

I understand that life is full of risk. When you drive on the highway, there is risk. Going outside in a thunderstorm is risky. It is important to distinguish between what are avoidable risks and what are unavoidable risks. Many Americans have quit smoking, changed their diet, and started exercising because they want to reduce their risk for heart disease, cancer, and a host of other possible conditions. They avoid placing themselves at risk.

In the same way, I encourage you to make your home a healthy home by eliminating toxic chemicals. By removing the dangerous cleaners and personal care products, you remove the potential harms they cause. You eliminate the unnecessary risk for cancer, ADD, nervous disorders, asthma, birth defects, MCS, infertility, and a host of other problems.

I said at the beginning of this article that there is a happy ending — a solution to this problem. Conscientious manufacturers offer people-friendly products at great prices that are just as, if not more effective than hazardous store brands. Talk to the person who cared enough to share this article with you. I am sure they will know where you can get these products.

I am glad you took the time to read this article. I pray that it has opened your eyes to a menace you may not have been aware of before. I hope you now are able to make an informed choice about what you bring into your home.

And may your home be a healthy home.

This chapter is the full text from the booklet entitled "Is Your Home a Healthy Home?" Sharing this booklet is an inexpensive way for you to help your loved ones understand the health risks associated with toxic chemicals in household products. It is available from RM Barry Publications. Call 1 (888) 209-0510 or visit us at our web site www.rmbarry.com.

CHAPTER FOUR

GRAPE SEED EXTRACT

"The most potent preventive medicine you can take!"

ABOUT THE AUTHOR, DR. CLARK HANSEN

Clark Hansen, N.M.D., is a Doctor of Naturopathic Medicine with a very busy private practice in Scottsdale, Arizona. He graduated from the John Bastyr College of Naturopathic Medicine in Seattle, Washington, in 1986. Since 1988, Dr. Hansen has served as the President and Medical Director of The Arizona Institute of Natural Medicine, a medical clinic that attracts patients from all over the U.S.

Dr. Hansen is one of the founders of the Southwest College of Naturopathic Medicine and Health Sciences in Scottsdale, Arizona, where he serves as a member of the Board of Advisors and as an Associate Professor of Clinical Medicine. Dr. Hansen is a member of the American Association of Naturopathic Physicians, the Arizona Naturopathic Medical Association, the American Holistic Medical Association, and the Physicians Committee for Responsible Medicine.

THE DISCOVERY OF A LIFETIME

Proanthocyanidin (PCO) is a natural plant bioflavonoid extracted from the seeds of grapes. Also known as Pycnogenol, this potent bioflavonoid is so essential to our existence that it should be considered a vitamin, because our bodies cannot make it and we cannot survive without it. Its healing and preventive benefits are simply phenomenal. It has been used in France for more than 40 years but has only recently been discovered by Americans. PCO has been found to be the most potent antioxidant ever discovered. It is 20 times more potent than Vitamin C and 50 times more potent than Vitamin E. It is also anti-inflammatory, anti-allergic, and anti-mutagenic. PCO bioflavonoids are found in the peels, skins, and seeds of fruits and vegetables, and the barks of certain trees, including the lemon tree, the French maritime pine tree, and the leaves of the hazelnut tree. Grape Seed Extract yields a 95% concentration of PCO, the highest of any source. Pine bark is second, with an 85% concentration.

DISCOVERY OF PCO

In 1948, Jacques Masquelier, a young Ph.D. candidate from the University of Bordeaux, France, isolated PCO from peanuts. In his doctoral thesis, Masquelier demonstrated the ability of PCO to double the strength of blood vessels within a few hours after administration to laboratory animals. In 1951, Professor Masquelier patented a PCO extract from pine bark. Nineteen years later, in 1970, he patented a second PCO extract from grape seeds which he found to yield a 10% higher concentration. In 1986, Dr. Masquelier discovered that PCO from grape seeds has an intense free radical scavenging effect. These discoveries were laid down in his U.S. Patent #4,698,360 of October 6, 1987. After years of continued research he said, "The test showed that in this respect PCO from grape seeds has an advantage over PCO from pine bark. PCO from grape seeds contains the gallic esters of PCOs. These PCO-esters have been recently described as the most active substances in the battle against free radicals."

NATURE'S MOST POTENT ANTIOXIDANT

PCO bioflavonoids have a specific affinity for the connective tissue (collagen and elastin) of the body, providing stabilization and protection from premature breakdown. When you eat them they become incorporated into the connective tissues of your skin, blood vessels, joints, and cell membranes. They protect your body from free radical damage. Free radicals are produced from oxygen metabolism within the body and from exposure to certain chemicals, environmental pollutants, sunlight, radiation burns, cigarette smoke, drugs, alcohol, viruses, bacteria, parasites, dietary fats, and more.

Free radicals destroy cell membranes, damage collagen and other connective tissues, disrupt important physiologic processes, and create mutations in the DNA of cells. They are implicated in more than 60 diseases, including heart disease, hardening of the arteries, arthritis, Alzheimer's disease, cataracts, and cancer. Free radicals are oxygen molecules with a missing or unpaired electron which spin erratically throughout the body, damaging every tissue they bounce into until they are finally quenched by an antioxidant such as vitamin C or E, beta-carotene, bioflavonoids, or certain enzymes produced by the body. As we grow older, the body's inherent production of free radical deactivating enzymes decreases. As this happens, the skin becomes leathery and wrinkled, arteries lose their elasticity, joints and cartilage stiffen, vision becomes cloudy, the spine becomes stooped, and every part of the body gradually deteriorates. PCO prevents the cross-linking of body tissues that is associated with aging. It blocks connective tissue-destroying enzymes that otherwise would have a cumulative thinning and weakening effect on the body's connective tissue over time.

THE SECRET TO YOUTHFULNESS

PCO helps protect the skin from ultraviolet radiation damage that leads to wrinkles and skin cancer. Because it stabilizes collagen and elastin, PCO can help to improve the elasticity and youthfulness of the skin. Its potent antioxidant effect in the skin has even been found to reverse the process of pigment lipofuscin, causing unsightly age spots to fade and disappear. Many individuals taking PCO have seen it reduce the appearance of surgical scars and stretch marks.

The ability of PCO to stabilize and protect collagen and elastin within joints has demonstrated remarkable effects in the relief of pain and inflammation associated with arthritis. In clinical and experimental studies, PCO has been shown to inhibit inflammatory swelling including postoperative swelling. Many arthritis sufferers say that PCO completely eliminates stiffness and restores their mobility. It also inhibits excessive production of histamine that causes allergic disorders and the inflammatory swelling related to allergies. In fact many cases of arthritis are due to allergies.

PCO has been shown to: improve blood vessel elasticity; increase red blood cell pliability; inhibit platelet stickiness and clumping; normalize blood flow; improve oxygenation of ischemic areas; decrease bruising, bleeding and edema; prevent blood clots; and reduce elevated blood pressure. People taking Grape Seed Extract have found that it can lower their cholesterol levels remarkably, and researchers have found that PCO reduces the size of cholesterol plaque in the blood vessel walls of animals.

Patients with Multiple Sclerosis (MS), a syndrome of progressive destruction of the myelin sheath that surrounds the nerves, have reported significant improvement while taking PCO. Many studies have demonstrated that patients with MS have reduced activity of the antioxidant enzyme Glutathione peroxidase. The ability of PCO to reduce the progressive symptoms of MS may be the result of the fact that it is one of the few antioxidants that can cross the blood-brain barrier.

PCO has also been shown to protect cell membranes and thereby prevent mutations caused by damage to DNA. This may help prevent the onset of cancer. One study has shown that the risk of developing cancer is 11.4 times higher in those with low levels of the antioxidants vitamin E and Selenium. Since PCO is 50 times more potent than Vitamin E as an antioxidant, it is expected to have an even greater individual cancer-preventing effect. Additionally, PCO may work with Vitamin E to enhance the body's ability to fight and prevent cancer by protecting the cancer-fighting cells known as *natural killer cells*. PCO is also known to work synergistically with Vitamin C to increase the longevity of natural killer cells.

Due to its protective effects on connective tissue within the eye, PCO is effective in stopping the progression of cataracts and reversing glaucoma and age-related macular degeneration, the leading cause of blindness.

Grape Seed Extract is the most potent preventive nutrient you can buy. It can prevent the cross-linking of your connective tissue, promote new collagen and elastin production, and slow down or reverse the biological process of aging to help prevent heart disease, cancer, strokes, diabetes, cataracts, glaucoma, arthritis, allergies, wrinkles, cellulite, and more.

Bioavailability: PCO is water soluble, readily absorbed within 60 minutes, and actively circulates in the body for three days. Unlike most antioxidants, PCO can even cross the blood-brain barrier.

Safety: PCO is nontoxic, noncarcinogenic, non-teratogenic. It has been thoroughly tested in France for more than 40 years and used by more than 10 million people. Because grape seeds are so bitter, occasional nausea or stomach upset has been reported.

Dosage: Take 50 mg to 300 mg per day depending on intensity of condition. As a general guideline a recent European Symposium on PCO recommended a starting dose of 25 mg for every 25 pounds of body weight for the first 3 days, enough to saturate the body tissues, then the amount can be reduced to ½ that amount.

CASE HISTORIES

Beverly J., Dallas, Texas

I have been taking Grape Seed Extract for 2 months now. The brown spots on my skin are clearing up, the arthritic lumps on my fingers have gone down, and my gums are more firm. The dentist was concerned about the pockets around my back teeth and was amazed when this condition had disappeared. I feel wonderful. I'll never stop taking it.

Tim B., Scottsdale, Arizona

Grape Seed Extract is awesome! I suffer from seasonal allergies and in the past have tried over-the-counter antihistamines which caused me to feel mentally dull and drowsy all the time. After taking the Grape Seed Extract for three days, my allergies cleared up completely without causing any drowsiness. Now I have a clear head and a clear mind. Thanks!

Christine P., Los Angeles, California

I used to be embarrassed to wear a two-piece bathing suit because of a surgical scar on my abdomen. But since I have been taking Grape Seed Extract over the last two months, the scar has shrunk and now is only faintly visible. Thanks! This means more to me than you can imagine.

Bill G., Franklin, Texas

Grape Seed Extract basically gave my life back to me a few months ago when I was very ill with extremely high cholesterol over 400 and triglycerides over 700. I started taking 300 mg Grape Seed Extract per day and continued limiting my fat and sugar intake. Within two months my cholesterol was down to 202 and my triglycerides to 78.

Dr. Hansen has also created an audio cassette containing an excellent 60 minute presentation on Grape Seed Extract. It is available from RM Barry Publications. Call 1 (888) 209-0510 or visit us at our web site www.rmbarry.com.

CHAPTER FIVE

GLUCOSAMINE

The Arthritis Nutrient

INTRODUCTION

Jason had been the athletic type, but no longer. That was before a string of sports injuries had damaged the cartilage in his joints and left him with two bum knees and a bad elbow. The diagnosis: osteoarthritis—a crippling, painful, usually permanent condition. When several surgeries failed to fix the problem, Jason almost gave up hope that he would ever be active again. "I was doing everything that medicine said I should, and it wasn't enough," he says. After a year of taking high doses of anti-inflammatory pain medications, he decided that he had to find another solution.

In his search to learn everything he could about osteoarthritis (OA), Jason discovered that a promising treatment for OA had been used in parts of Europe and Asia for decades. The treatment involves supplementing the diet with an inexpensive nutrient called glucosamine. Glucosamine is a substance which occurs naturally in the body and is necessary for building the cartilage which cushions the joints. Anxious to become active again, Jason dug up research dating back to 1959. The largest of these studies had 1,208 participants who took glucosamine daily. Ninety-five percent of them reported that pain was reduced and mobility increased, with no significant side-effects, and with a continuing benefit 6 to 12 weeks after they stopped the supplement.[1] In another study, microscopic examination of the cartilage before and after treatment showed it had been at least partly repaired.[2] And, in yet another experiment, glucosamine was compared with a commonly prescribed anti-inflammatory pain medicine. By the end of the study, those receiving glucosamine experienced significantly greater mobility and freedom from pain than those receiving the pain medicine.[3] The results of these studies have been duplicated in other

---

1 Tapadinhas, M.J., Rivera, I.C., and Bignamini, A.A. "Oral Glucosamine Sulphate in the Management of Arthrosis: Report on a Multi-Centre Open Investigation in Portugal." *Pharmatherapeutica* 3(3): 157-168, 1982.
2 Dovanti, A., Bignamini, A.A., and Rovati, A.L. "Therapeutic Activity of Oral Glucosamine Sulphate in Osteoarthrosis: A Placebo-Controlled Double-Blind Investigation." *Clinical Therapeutics* 3(4):266-272, 1980.
3 Vaz, A.L. "Double-Blind Clinical Evaluation of the Relative Efficacy of Ibuprofen and Glucosamine Sulphate in the Management of Osteoarthrosis of the Knee in Out-Patients." *Current Medical Research and Opinion* 8(3):145-149, 1982.

significant research over the last two decades.[4,5,6,7,8]

Jason found the research compelling, as was the fact that European physicians use glucosamine to treat OA, so he began taking the supplement himself. Within two weeks of starting on glucosamine, Jason felt significantly better. Later clinical examination showed that his damaged cartilage was actually repairing itself. Now he says, "I'm back to being a real jock."

But that's not the end of the story. You see, the patient in this story is also a doctor—Jason Theodosakis, M.D. In fact, he's a respected and well-known physician and lecturer in preventive medicine who has trained extensively in exercise physiology and sports medicine. Dr. Theo, as he likes to be called, is also the director of the Preventive Medicine Training Program at the University of Arizona College of Medicine in Tucson.

After his personal success with this "new" OA treatment, Dr. Theo began giving glucosamine to his patients. "The results have been impressive," he says. "I've helped hundreds of people either eliminate the need for surgery or greatly reduce the effects of osteoarthritis." He calls the treatment "the most overlooked medical miracle in America today." His message to OA victims is "There's no reason to suffer any more."

Other respected physicians are beginning to use glucosamine as a part of their OA treatments as well. Andrew Weil, M.D., the best-selling medical author, says "Happily, this seems to be one case where a health fad may actually merit all the attention it's receiving."

Dr. Amal Das, an orthopedic surgeon, has been recommending glucosamine to his patients for three years. "If more people start taking these supplements, it's going to cut down on my business," he says. "I'm having to do less surgery."

Dr. Joseph Houpt, a rheumatologist at the University of Toronto, learned that some of his patients were taking glucosamine on their own. "Enough of them have come back feeling better that I feel it's worth doing a study," he says. He is currently conducting research on 100 patients in his practice.

The mainstream media is beginning to report on glucosamine as well. For example, Newsweek says "...unlike many arthritis fads, this one has some science behind it," and "...if half the people now lining up for the stuff respond to it, arthritis treatment will never be the same."[9]

---

4 Muller-Fasbender, H., et al. "Glucosamine Sulfate Compared to Ibuprofen in Osteoarthritis of the Knee." *Osteoarthritis and Cartilage* 2:61-69, 1994.
5 Noack, W., et al. "Glucosamine Sulfate in Osteoarthritis of the Knee." *Osteoarthritis and Cartilage* 2:51-59, 1994.
6 Pujalte, J.M., Llavore, E.P., and Ylescupidez, F.R. "Double-Blind Clinical Evaluation of Oral Glucosamine Sulphate in the Basic Treatment of Osteoarthrosis." *Current Medical Research and Opinion* 7(2):110-114, 1980.
7 Vajaradul, Y. "Double-Blind Clinical Evaluation of Intra-Articular Glucosamine in Outpatients with Gonarthrosis." *Clinical Therapeutics* 3(5):260, 1980.
8 Crolle, G., and D'Este, E. "Glucosamine Sulphate for the Management of Arthrosis: A Controlled Clinical Investigation." *Current Medical Research and Opinion* 7(2):104-109, 1980.
9 "The Arthritis Cure?" *Newsweek,* Feb. 17, 1997: 54.

OSTEOARTHRITIS FACTS

Approximately 16 million people in the U.S. have osteoarthritis, a painful condition also known as degenerative joint disease. It is the most common form of arthritis, mostly affecting middle-aged and older people. Osteoarthritis is characterized by pain and loss of movement in the hands and weight-bearing joints, such as the knees, hips, feet, and back. What's alarming about OA is the fact that most people over sixty show to have it on X-ray, but may not have actual symptoms yet, according to the Arthritis Foundation.[10]

Currently, the standard treatment for OA involves the use of anti-inflammatory pain medications which only mask the symptoms and do nothing to correct the underlying cause. In fact, regular use of pain killers may actually accelerate the degeneration of cartilage, making the problem worse.[11] When taken regularly, common pain medications have significant side effects like gastrointestinal bleeding and kidney or liver damage.

By contrast, glucosamine has no significant known side effects. It does not mask the pain, it works to help repair damaged cartilage—the root of the problem. In other words, glucosamine relieves pain by helping to restore and normalize joint function. Most people begin to notice a difference in about two to six weeks after beginning to take glucosamine. Then they are able to wean themselves off the pain medicines.

DOCTOR RECOMMENDED?

Is glucosamine the universally recommended treatment for OA here in America? Not yet, but this is quickly changing. There is an extensive body of clinical research proving that glucosamine is an effective OA treatment in both humans and animals. But most of the research has been done in other countries, and doctors here are slow to accept medical advances from abroad.

Why haven't there been American studies? It all boils down to money. Since glucosamine is a nutritional supplement, it cannot be given patent protection as with new drugs. Consequently, there is very little incentive for drug companies to fund research or promote glucosamine by flooding doctors offices with free samples.

However, some American studies are currently in progress. Results from several studies are being analyzed at the Harrington Arthritis Research Center in Phoenix, according to Dr. Louis Lippielo, the center's senior scientist and biochemist. "I think it's pretty promising," he says. "I'd call it the most promising thing in the last twenty years." But for now, you may have to search to find a doctor who is familiar with glucosamine and

---

10   The Arthritis Foundation. *Osteoarthritis Fact Sheet*, 1997.
11   Hodgkinson, R., and Woolf, D. "A Five-Year Clinical Trial of Indomethacin in Osteoarthritis of the Hip Joint." *ACTA Orthop. Scand.* 50:169, 1979.

has read the research. Or you may want to give your doctor a copy of this book and ask him to read the research articles which are listed here.

WHICH GLUCOSAMINE IS BEST?

There are several different types of glucosamine. The two most common are glucosamine HCL and glucosamine sulfate. After they are metabolized, both supply the body with the same active ingredient—glucosamine. However, glucosamine HCL is purer, more stabile, and delivers more of the beneficial glucosamine than the sulfate version. And glucosamine HCL has the added benefit of being less expensive, especially when you account for concentration.

Quality is a big issue as well. A University of Maryland analysis found that some brands contained significantly less glucosamine than was stated on the label. So, for best results, buy from a source you know and trust.

This chapter is the full text from the pamphlet entitled "Glucosamine–the Arthritis Nutrient." Sharing this pamphlet is an inexpensive way for you to introduce glucosamine to your loved ones. It is available from RM Barry Publications. Call 1 (888) 209-0510 or visit us at our web site www.rmbarry.com.

CHAPTER SIX

PROSTATE HEALTH

"A Natural Alternative"

If you are a man over age fifty, the chances are 50/50 that you have an enlarged prostate, medically known as benign prostatic hyperplasia (BPH), and the odds escalate as you grow older. It is no picnic—a swollen prostate gland typically two to three times normal size can squeeze your urethra, interfering with normal urination. Symptoms range from having to get up frequently at night to urinate, to pain from obstruction of urinary flow and trouble with erections. It is a non-malignant condition.

You can treat it several ways. You can have surgery, which is very effective but carries the risk of incontinence or impotency. You can take prescription drugs that may or may not work, but can also depress your libido and make you impotent. You can try various therapies, such as laser or microwave, to zap or vaporize unwanted prostate tissue. You can just "watch and wait," as some physicians advise, to avoid drugs and surgery as long as possible. You may also get rid of the symptoms by taking a berry extract, a successful treatment widely used in Europe, that costs about one-third as much as conventional drugs and has virtually no risk of side effects. It has worked for millions of men.

A number of conventional drugs are used in the treatment of BPH, most notably finasteride (Proscar®). Several clinical studies have shown that it produces a moderate improvement over placebo. In Europe, up to 90 percent of BPH patients are treated with phytopharmaceuticals or herbal-derived products.

There are about 30 different plant-based compounds currently available in Europe for the treatment of BPH. The most popular (and most effective) is the extract of saw palmetto berry.

It is not clear exactly how saw palmetto works. The most common theory is that saw palmetto reduces levels of a very active form of the male hormone testosterone known as dihydrotestosterone or DHT, thought to be the primary spur to enlargement of the prostate. It is a weird situation. An enzyme switches on the DHT, fooling the cells into thinking they are in puberty again and need to get going. The DHT causes an overproduction of prostate cells, causing the gland to grow bigger. Men with an enlarged prostate have exceptionally high levels of DHT; so do men with prostate cancer. In other words, saw palmetto works as a hormone suppressor.

A major clinical study, which was published in the journal *The Prostate,* involved dozens of researchers in France, Scotland, England, Italy, Portugal, the Czech Republic, Greece, Switzerland, Slovakia and the United States. It compared the use of a commercial saw palmetto extract product available in Europe with the convention drug finasteride (Proscar®) in the treatment of 1,098 patients diagnosed with BPH.

The researchers conclude that both treatments do relieve symptoms of BPH in about two-thirds of patients. This study confirms that the saw palmetto product is equally effective as the conventional drug in relieving symptoms of BPH while producing fewer side effects.

While the drug finasteride (Proscar®) typically takes up to a year to produce significant benefit, saw palmetto extract produces better results in a much shorter period. Most patients achieve some relief of symptoms within the first 30 days of treatment.

The first American randomized clinical trial of saw palmetto shows that the plant reduces swelling in enlarged prostate tissue. The study was published in the March 1999, issue of the peer-reviewed journal *Urology,* followed by a presentation at the Annual Meeting of the American Urological Association in Dallas, Texas, from May 1-6, 1999.

Clearly, saw palmetto offers superior symptomatic relief in prostate disease, as defined by the most common clinical tests. In addition, it improves quality of life and has a "practically negligible side effect risk." This review makes a compelling case for the use of saw palmetto as treatment of choice among physicians and patients concerned with meaningful improvement and greater safety compared with conventional synthetic drugs. (While cost was not a consideration in this review, saw palmetto extract is also significantly less expensive than conventional prescription drugs.)

Like saw palmetto berry extract, pumpkin seed extract helps to ensure normal urinary and prostate function. Initially used in Germany to promote normal urination as well as a healthy urinary tract, recent European tests have shown that pumpkin seed can have a positive effect on the function of the prostate as well.

Pumpkin seed extract is also known to have marked anti-inflammatory action. In other words, like saw palmetto berry, it may help reduce the swelling of the prostate, which is helpful in relieving both BPH and certain types of prostatitis. In addition, pumpkin seed extract has been shown to reduce the symptoms of the disorder, including both the frequent urge to urinate and the amount of residual urine. An added benefit, no unwanted side effects.

Zinc, like saw palmetto berry extract and pumpkin seed extract, has been associated with enhancing prostate health. In one study, more than two-thirds of patients who took zinc supplements daily experienced a positive effect on prostate function. Though it is true that zinc is used internally for bone formation, for the digestion of protein, and for the conversion of nutrients to energy, it is also very crucial to prostate health. Indeed, the prostate gland normally contains 10 times more zinc than any other male body organ.

Unfortunately, older Americans consume less than two-thirds of their Recommended Daily Allowance for zinc. In addition, they don't absorb it as well as they did when they were younger. Consequently, just when a man really needs this nutrient to help the prostate through the changes that occur as he gets older, his diet and his body let him down. Therefore, a supplement rich in zinc can help meet his changing needs.

When considering the overall health of the prostate, it would be negligent not to mention lycopene. Responsible for making tomatoes red, lycopene is a carotenoid (a class of yellow to deep-red pigments occurring in many vegetable oils). It is also considered much more potent antioxidant than beta-carotene.

According to Harvard University researchers, led by Dr. Edward Giovannucci of the Harvard School of Public Health, foods containing tomatoes, which are rich in lycopene, are believed to provide high levels of protection against prostate cancer. In Dr. Giovannucci's detailed studies of 52,000 men over a six-year period, results showed that men with the highest intake of lycopene had a 21 percent lower risk of prostate cancer than men with the lowest intake. Only lycopene had this significant relationship to reducing prostate cancer risk.

If an individual is experiencing some of the symptoms of BPH, it is important that he sees his doctor and not automatically assumes that the problem is, indeed, BPH. After all, there are other possibilities that can cause some of these same symptoms. Examples include a normal bladder that is simply aging, an infection of the bladder, cancer, prostatitis, bladder stones, diabetes, multiple sclerosis, and Parkinson's disease.

Lifestyle changes can also make a difference in lowering the risk of prostate disorders. Consider the following:

1. Cut down on coffee, tea, and cola drinks.
2. Reduce or eliminate beer or other alcohol from your diet.
3. Eat dinner earlier.
4. Eat a diet rich in natural whole foods.
5. Go easy on salt and spices.
6. Increase water intake to stimulate urine flow and prevent urinary retention and kidney infection.
7. Reduce fluids taken after 7 P.M.
8. Stay regular.
9. Keep blood cholesterol below 220 mg per deciliter.
10. Avoid antihistamines and decongestants.
11. Limit exposure to pesticides and other environmental contaminants.
12. Use a well-designed nutritional supplement, which supplies the nutrients important to prostate health.

Working together, saw palmetto berry extract, pumpkin seed extract, zinc, and lycopene extract assist the body in maintaining proper urinary function and in sustaining a normal, healthy prostate. With the help of a nutritious diet that includes these ingredients, an individual may find himself aging while still maintaining a high level of prostate health.

Melaleuca's answer to a healthy prostate is ***ProstAvan***. A natural alternative, ***ProstAvan*** is made of the highest quality botanical extracts, including saw palmetto berry, pumpkin seed, and lycopene, as well as the nutrient, zinc. European studies have shown that these ingredients maintain normal urinary and prostate function.

For additional information, see the section on *Benign Prostatic Hyperplasia (BPH)* in the *Healthy Body* chapter of this book.

Suggested References

Balch, J., M.D., and the Urology Research Center, "Maintaining and Regaining Prostate Health," *Prostate Health*. (Alternative Medicine Updates, Publishers), 1994

Carper, Jean, "Prostate 'Remedy of Choice'", *Miracle Cures,* HarperCollins Publishers, Inc. New York, (1998) 151-158

Foster, Steven, "Men's Health and What you Need to Know about Saw Palmetto" Steven Foster Group

Giovannucci, E., et. al., "Intake of Carotenoids and Retinol in Relation to Risk of Prostate Cancer," *Journal of the National Cancer Institute,* December 6, 1995

Murray, Dr. Michael T., "Saw Palmetto Extract: Nature's Answer to Prostate Enlargement", *Dr. Murray Online*

"Phytomedicines outperform synthetics in treating enlarged prostate," Herb Research Foundation, Boulder, Co.

CHAPTER SEVEN

MENOPAUSE

"The Natural Way"

Hot flashes, night sweats, mood changes, loss of libido and vaginal dryness are some of the most common symptoms of menopause. A single event, menopause is a woman's last period of menstruation. This usually occurs between the ages of 40 and 55 and even though the term "menopause" refers to that single event, the time of change can last for several years. This time is marked by a drastic loss in estrogen, or what is commonly referred to as the "female hormone" and can affect at least 300 of the body's systems. That is why it is beneficial to maintain a normal level of hormones.

But does it have to be done chemically? No. There are natural alternatives. Doctors have turned to hormone replacement therapy (HRT) to combat the symptoms associated with falling estrogen levels. HRT is the administration of the female hormones estrogen and progesterone. Estrogen replacement therapy (ERT) refers to administration of estrogen alone.

ERT is thought to help prevent the devastating effects of heart disease and osteoporosis. However, hormone treatment for menopause is quite controversial. The long-term safety and efficacy remain matters of great concern. There is simply not enough existing data for physicians to suggest that HRT is the right choice for all women.

A study published in the March 21, 2001, issue of the *Journal of the American Medical Association* found that women who used ERT for more than 10 years had twice the risk of dying of ovarian cancer as those who did not use such therapy.

According to an article in the *Journal of the American Medical Association*, the bottom line of a seven-year study of 2,763 women (Heart and Estrogen/Progestin Replacement Study—HERS) is "in these women ... the net effect is harm."

An article in the Washington Post on July 3, 2002, stated that other synthetic hormone studies have shown "an increased risk of serious blood clots in the legs and lungs, as well as in increased risk of gall bladder disease ... some studies have also noted an increased risk of breast cancer in women who took hormones for longer than about five years."

Is there an alternative? Yes. Herbal medicines have long been used in traditional healing systems to treat conditions of particular interest to women, such as premenstrual syndrome (PMS) and menopausal symptoms. For relief of menopausal symptoms, black cohosh root extract, dong quai, and soy have all proved to provide beneficial effects during menopause.

Dong quai is used for almost every gynecological complaint from regulating the menstrual cycle to treating menopausal symptoms caused by hormonal changes. Dong quai contains vitamins A, E, and B12 and research has shown that it produces a balancing effect on estrogen activity.

Black cohosh has a history of usage for women's gynecological problems dating back to the Algonquian natives living in the Ohio Valley. The eclectic doctors of the 1800s often recommended black cohosh for what they called "hysterical" disease, i.e. female reproductive disease. Today, black cohosh is still used for gynecological problems from menstruation to menopause, with multiple studies over the past 40 years backing this up.

Several studies have shown soy's natural health benefits for menopausal women. In 1998 a study published in the *American Journal of Clinical Nutrition*, found that postmenopausal women who ate 40 grams of soy protein per day significantly increased the bone density in their spines.

If an alternative to HRT is of interest to you, Melaleuca's *EstrAval* is excellent at helping bodies maintain a normal, healthy function both before and after the actual menopause occurs. It is composed of soy extract, black cohosh extract, and dong quai extract. And, best of all, these natural extracts have a minimum potential for side effects. Their natural origins help them to work easily with the body's own system. After all, as Melaleuca says, "*EstrAval*: because you have a lot of living to do."

For more information, see the section on *Menopause* in the *Healthy Body* chapter of this book.

Suggested References:

Crawford, Sharon, "Black cohosh," *Gale Encyclopedia of Alternative Medicine.*
Hardy, M. L., "Herbs of special interest to women," *J Am Pharm Assoc* (Wash) 2000 Mar-Apr, 40 (2) 234-42: quiz 327-9.
Headline Watch, Mayo Clinic.com, October 27, 2001.
"Managing Menopause," MDchoice.com, October 27, 2001.
"Soy intake related to menopausal symptoms, serum lipids, and bone mineral density in postmenopausal Japanese women," *Obstet Gynecol* 2001 (January, 1997) 109-15.

CHAPTER EIGHT

PROTECT YOUR VISION

"Nutrition for Your Eyes"

What handicap do people fear the most? If you guessed blindness, you are right, according to the National Eye Health Education Program of the National Institutes of Health. Our eyes bring in more than 90% of the information that enters our brain. And yet, according to the Louis Harris survey, only 41% of all Americans have an annual eye exam and only 46% have a regular eye doctor.

Vision loss is a catastrophic issue and one particularly facing the aging population. However, proper nutrition can help prevent, and possibly reverse, the most common visual disorders, namely cataracts and macular degeneration. "The traditional thinking is that as age increases, visual sensitivity decreases," says D. Max Snodderly, Ph.D., head of the laboratory at The Schepens Eye Research Institute. "But what we are saying is, maybe that's not inevitable. Improved nutrition could help to retard the loss of visual sensitivity with age."

Cataracts are the leading cause of impaired vision and blindness overall, and age related macular degeneration (AMD) is the leading cause of blindness in people over age 65. Cataracts are opacities or white cloudy spots on the normally transparent lens of the eye. Vision for cataract sufferers is somewhat like trying to see through eyeglasses smeared with salad oil. Macular degeneration is a deterioration or breakdown of the macula. For macular degeneration sufferers, vision is like having a penny taped to the center of your glasses—poor central vision but better peripheral vision.

The consensus is that AMD is a nutritional deficiency disease. The carotenoids lutein and zeaxanthin are most strongly associated with a reduced risk for AMD. "Increasing the consumption of foods rich in certain carotenoids, in particular dark green, leafy vegetables may decrease the risk of developing macular degeneration." Reported Johanna M. Seddon, M.D., of the Department of Ophthalmology, Harvard Medical School.

Although current research does not provide strong conclusive evidence to support the potential role of antioxidants in preventing macular degeneration, many physicians and ophthalmologists do recommend supplementing with these nutrients if it is not contraindicated by other health conditions. In addition, the elimination of the most common risk factors should be carefully considered. Smoking, and cardiovascular disease (atherosclerosis, arteriosclerosis, hypertension) are high among the list of risks for AMD, as is a low dietary intake of pigmented antioxidants found in green, orange, and red vegetables and fruits.

Blueberries are recommended for good eye health because they contain high levels of antioxidants, compounds that neutralize free radicals. Free radicals can attack the lens membrane, causing it to harden and relay a fuzzy image. That is why many people who turn 40 joke that "their arms aren't long enough to read." To get the antioxidants that researchers recommend for eye health, you would have to eat a half-cup of blueberries every day. This isn't practical for most people, so Melaleuca combined 100 milligrams of vitamin C, and 20 milligrams of bilberry extracts in each *NutraView* capsule.

"Lutein in the lens acts as nature's own sunglasses," says Steven Pratt, M. D., senior staff member at Scripps Memorial Hospital in La Jolla, Ca. Due to the ongoing research of lutein's benefits to eye health, Centrum recently added ¼ milligram to each dose, even though the research on lutein suggests that you must consume six milligrams per day to get the eye care benefits of this nutrient. In other words, to get the research-based recommended dose of lutein by taking Centrum, you would need to take 24 tablets per day. In contrast, one capsule of *NutraView* provides 120 milligrams of lutein. That's 20 times the minimum amount recommended by research, all for less than fifty cents a day.

Paul Harvey advertises a popular product called "Ocular Nutrition." The price for this product is $159.79 for a three month supply (you receive a discount of $40 if you mention hearing about it from Paul Harvey), so that is $53.26 per month or, with the discount $39.93 per month. The recommended dosage is four capsules a day to get 30 milligrams of lutein and 20 milligrams of bilberry each day.

With Melaleuca's *NutraView*, in one capsule, you receive 120 milligrams of lutein (which protects the eye, especially the macular, from free radical damage), 20 milligrams of bilberry (which helps maintain normal circulation to the eye and helps support night vision), plus 100 milligrams of blueberry powder (a super-powerful antioxidant called the "vision fruit" in Japan), and 100 milligrams of vitamin C (which has been proven to maintain the health of the lens). All of this for only $13.99 for a one month supply or $41.97 for a three-month supply. So basically is costs almost the same for three months of *NutraView* as it does for one month of Ocular Nutrition (with the discount). But with *NutraView*, you get four times as much lutein and other additional beneficial ingredients.

Whatever brand you choose, it is exciting to know that certain nutrients may help us to enjoy the miracle of vision far longer than ever before.

Suggested Research

Aesoph, Lauri M., N.D., "Eat Right for Sharp Eyesight."

"Consumer's Guide to Macular Degeneration" www.eyecare.org

Macular Degeneration International 6700 N. Oracle Road, Tucson, AZ 85704.

Quillin, Patrick, Ph.D., R. D., C.N.S., Director of nutrition at the Cancer Treatment Centers of America, Inc., Tulsa, OK, "Sight For Sore Eyes."

CHAPTER NINE

DEPRESSION

The Natural Way to Emotional Health

Every day it seems our lives are moving faster, giving us less time to adjust to, cope with, and enjoy the world around us. We have the same difficult events to deal with, like deaths in the family, divorces, lost jobs, financial difficulties, health problems, and just the trying task of keeping up with things. Though the world would like us to just "deal with it" and move on, our emotions don't work this way. At times we feel overwhelmed, tired out, unmotivated, and unable to handle everything life throws our way.

Depression is a common illness that strikes perhaps 1 in 15 Americans each year. A person's mood, thoughts, physical health, and behavior all may be affected. Symptoms can include a persistent sad, anxious, or "empty" feeling, loss of energy, appetite, or sexual drive, and lack of interest in socializing, work or hobbies.

Researchers have found that certain chemical messengers in the brain affect our mood and our ability to cope with the stresses of life. Fortunately, they have also found nutritional compounds that help maintain the health and levels of these brain messengers, thus supporting our efforts to deal with our fast-paced lives and with the many events that can throw us off balance.

Can chemicals really affect the way I feel? Though some may be skeptical that brain chemicals can actually affect mood, when one considers the effects of alcohol, nicotine, caffeine, prescription drugs, and other compounds on disposition and emotional outlook, it is easy to see that many of our emotional reactions are affected by factors other than our thoughts. The good thing is that, similar to the way we can support the body's physical health through good diet and exercise; we can do the same for our emotional health. In addition, researchers have discovered natural plant extracts and specific vitamins that can help support a strong sense of well being.

The fastest rising star in herbal medicine in Germany and now the United States is the St. John's Wort extract. Why? The simple answer is that St. John's Wort produces equal or better results than prescription drugs in relieving depression, but has far fewer side effects.

Three trials examining treatment of depression compared St. John's Wort with prescription antidepressants. Two studies compared extracts of St. John's Wort with the selective serotonin reuptake inhibitors Prozac and Zoloft. In all three studies, St. John's Wort matched the effectiveness of the prescription antidepressants. Patients taking St. John's Wort experienced fewer and milder side effects than patients receiving prescription antidepressants. St. John's Wort also costs far less than prescription antidepressant medication.

Another herbal extract that researchers have found that may possess abilities to maintain healthy neurotransmitters in the brain is 5 HTP, which is extracted from the seed of a plant that grows in Africa—called Griffonia simplicifolia. It is an amino acid that is the intermediate step between L-tryptophan and the important brain chemical serotonin. There is a massive amount of evidence that suggests that low serotonin levels are a common consequence of modern living. As a result, many people are overweight, crave sugar and other carbohydrates, experience bouts of depression, get frequent headaches, and have vague muscle aches and pain. All of these maladies are correctable by raising brain serotonin levels.

Studies of patients with major depressive disorder have also found that the lower the level of folic acid, the longer and more severe the episode. Another study found that individuals with low folic acid levels were not only more likely to experience depression, they were less likely to respond to antidepressant treatment with a pharmaceutical drug.

In addition, deficiencies of various B complex vitamins have been strongly implicated in depression. Researchers have found a connection between levels of B-12 and the age at which depression symptoms may begin to appear. B-12 deficiencies are linked with poorer cognitive perform-ance in individuals with depression.

Luminex is a dietary supplement specifically formulated to help maintain good emotional health. A unique combination of St. John's Wort, Griffonia seed, folic acid and vitamin B-12, *Luminex* works with the brain's own natural systems to help sustain a strong sense of well-being.

But remember, lifestyle changes can provide a pathway for getting beyond prolonged therapy. Maintaining a well balanced diet, with good nutritional supplements, getting regular exercise and cutting back on sugar and caffeine are a good start. Other things that could help would be to spend more time with positive people, become better at a sport or a craft or start a new project with a goal. Be good to yourself. Treat yourself to something you enjoy and always make plans for the future.

Suggested References

Birdsall, Timothy C., N.D., "5-Hydroxytryptophan: A Clinically-Effective Serotonin Precursor"

Levitt, A. J., Joffe, R. T., "Folate, B12, and life courses of depressive illness", *Biol Psychiatr* 1989 25(7):867-872

"St John's Wort", *National Institutes of Health,* Gaithersburg, MD (July 25, 2001)

CHAPTER TEN

YOU CAN ACTIVATE YOUR IMMUNE SYSTEM

As the world gets smaller, contact from person to person becomes more frequent and germs grow more prevalent, what are we to do to protect our health? The answer is often much closer than we may think, for operating inside each one of us is a very powerful and effective defense called the "immune system."

Much like any other biological system, the immune system is a reflection of our overall health. Eat too much fat, smoke cigarettes, get little sleep, and experience a lot of stress, and your immune system will become weak and less able to protect you. Some studies have found that even negative emotions can detrimentally affect a strong immune system.

For over 4,000 years, the Chinese have used herbs to prevent common diseases. They knew nothing of bacteria or viruses, yet some of these herbs were said to "strengthen the exterior," or the "shield." Modern scientific research is confirming that they were right. We are coming to realize that it is possible to boost the immune system, which can then fight naturally against infectious agents, without the drawbacks of antibiotic therapy.

One of the known immune stimulants is the purple coneflower. Echinacea has appeared in over 300 scientific journals with relation to its immune boosting effects. Clinical studies have shown that astragalus, a Chinese plant, has the ability to stimulate the immune system, and pure arabinogalactan (a specific compound found in Western larch trees) has also been found to have a significantly positive effect on the body's natural defenses.

Echinacea (pronounced ek-in-NAY-sha) is one of America's most popular herbal products, used to prevent and treat the common cold, influenza, and infections. If you feel a cold or the flu coming on, you may want to take Echinacea every day for about two weeks or until symptoms disappear. It may also help fight off other viral and bacterial infections such as strep throat, staph infections, recurring vaginal yeast infections, urinary tract infections, herpes, bronchitis, and ear infections. Thirty million Americans take it each year. It is the best known and one of the most researched of immunostimulants.

Astragalus stimulates virtually every phase of immune system activity and has been used as an immunity booster in China for nearly 4,000 years. It is suggested for people who have chronic recurrent infections, especially respiratory infections. It is also recommended for many cancer patients, both those undergoing conventional treatment and those who have completed treatment. It doesn't interfere with chemotherapy or radiation and can be used concurrently.

Though all vitamins and minerals are necessary to maintain a strong immune system, certain nutrients have demonstrated a unique power effect. The first of these is vitamin C, which enhances white blood cell response and function. A common partner with vitamin C, vitamin E has also shown strong immune-enhancing properties, and supplementation with vitamin E has been found to positively affect the immune system.

In addition, studies have found that folic acid, a B vitamin, is necessary for proper immune function. Minerals like zinc and selenium, as well, are crucial to the development of white blood cells.

Echinacea, astragalus, and a good vitamin program are an excellent start for a good immune stimulant program. When you add arabinogalactan, you find a combination that is hard to beat.

Arabinogalactan is a pure, renewable resource that has been discovered to help strengthen the immune system. In fact, it has demonstrated many talents, one of the most prominent being its effect on the body's defense.

Whether at the office, around the kids, at school, or traveling on the airplane, there are many microscopic organisms lurking in our everyday world. To stay healthy enough to enjoy our lives to the fullest, we need a strong immune system. It's important to start with a healthy lifestyle. Trying to get 7-8 hours of sleep every night, eat a healthy diet, exercise regularly, manage your stress and thinking positively can only improve your chances for good health. Taking advantage of dietary supplements such as those offered by Melaleuca can boost those chances. *Activate Immune Complex* contains echinacea, astragalus, arabinogalactan, vitamin C, vitamin E, folic acid, selenium, and zinc. It is formulated specifically to help strengthen the immune system and is effective and safe for both adults and children.

As Melaleuca says, "When you are feeling like you need a little boost, take *Activate Immune Complex*, and activate your body's natural defenses."

Suggested References

"Astragalus Asserts Immunity" *Nutrition Science News* (October, 2000)"

Carper, Jean, "Unique Infection Fighter (Echinacea)," *Miracle Cures*, HarperCollins Publishers, Inc. New York, (1998): 108-119

Leigh, Evelyn, Editorial Director, HRF Greenpapers, Boulder, Co., (2001) *"Echinacea"*

Kelleher, J., "Vitamin E and the Immune Response," *Proceedings Nutr. Soc.* 50 (1991): 245-9

CHAPTER ELEVEN

HEAD LICE

"Don't Poison Your Child With Pesticide Treatments!"

Few things can strike such fear in the hearts of parents as head lice! While the bloodsuckers rarely, if ever, cause direct harm or transmit disease, they cause parents to engage in everything from blaming to explaining. They wonder where their child got the lice, worry that it reflects on their parenting abilities, and even offer explanations about their housekeeping and cleanliness.

Head lice, according to Harvard researcher Richard J. Pollack, "do not respect socio-economic distinctions. They don't care who you are, and have nothing to do with your level of hygiene. We're just as likely to find them on children who live in million dollar estates as in children who live in far lesser conditions," he adds. "Virtually anyone at some level is at risk."

Every year, an estimated 6 million to 12 million people—mostly children—and their families get head lice and they are becoming resistant to the leading chemical treatment used to combat them.

The treatments can often be worse than the lice. Parents turn to prescription medications with high concentrations of permethrin when over-the-counter versions fail. Some parents resort to everything from kerosene to chemicals intended to put on dogs to kill fleas.

Recommended alternatives to permethrin include pediculicides or anti-louse medications containing lindane and malathion, both available by prescription. But neither is without risk. Dr. Paul Auwaerter, assistant professor of medicine at Johns Hopkins University says that lindane can have unpleasant side effects like stinging sensations. However, others feel much stronger about the negative effects of lindane and pediculicides.

Steve Tvedten's book, *Best Control*, says: "Lindane, has been banned in 18 countries and severely restricted in 10 others. It has not been produced in the U.S. since 1977, but it is still imported here. You may still find lindane as the active poison ingredient in flea collars, moth, and other household sprays. As a scabicide poison (against lice) on children it may be present in lotions, creams, and shampoos.

Lindane (gamma-HCH) is one of the few organochlorine pesticides left on the market. It is the active ingredient in products best known by the brand name KWELL, now available only in generic form. Lindane is frequently used on young children, pregnant women, nursing mothers, and the elderly. These groups are most at risk from lindane's adverse effects."

Chemical treatments for head lice contain potent pesticides and insecticides known as pediculicides. These pediculicides have been known to cause immuno suppression, seizures, vomiting, diarrhea, convulsions, circulatory collapse, behavioral change, neuromuscular damage, chronic skin eruptions, liver damage, asthma, respiratory failure, stillbirths, birth defects, cancer and even death.

Also, consider these facts:

• The FDA issued an alert as far back as June 1975 in its bulletin to the medical community regarding the potential harmful effects of lindane.

• The National Pediculosis Association (NPA) testified before the FDA in 1983, 1984, 1985, and 1992 documenting the misinformation, misuse, and abuse of products containing lindane, and the NPA President testified in legal suits on behalf of children permanently disabled after use of lindane in 1990 and 1993.

• On September 5, 2000, California Governor Gray Davis signed Bill AB 2318, banning the sale and use of lindane to treat people for lice and scabies.

Is there an alternative? Many people think so. Check out this notice posted on one school bulletin board:

"Dear Parents, did you now that the leading lice shampoo contains a potent pesticide called LINDANE, which has been known to cause vomiting diarrhea, convulsions, liver damage and many other health issues with our kids. LINDANE has been banned in 18 countries and severely restricted in 10 others. Why are we using it on our kid's heads? The health of our kids is at stake, don't let them be exposed to this sometimes deadly treatment when there is a natural, safe, non-toxic, chemical free, and effective way to prevent and treat lice infestations. Let's get rid of these pests once and for all in or community! LETS DO IT FOR OUR KIDS!!"

What is the safe alternative? Melaleuca products. How do you use them? See the section on *Head Lice* in the "Healthy Body" chapter of this book.

SUGGESTED REFERENCES
http://www.lindane.org
http://www.kidsource.com
http://www.safe2use.com
http://onhealth.webmd.com

CHAPTER TWELVE

HEALTHY BODY

Every effort has been made to ensure that the information contained in this book is complete and accurate. However, neither the publisher nor the author is engaged in rendering professional advice or services to the individual reader. The ideas, procedures and suggestions contained in this book are not intended as a substitute for consulting with your physician. All matters regarding health require medical supervision. Each person's health needs are unique. To obtain recommendations appropriate to your particular situation, please consult a qualified health care provider. Neither the author nor the publisher shall be liable for any loss, injury, or damage allegedly arising from any information or suggestion in this book.

The five most essential elements of good health are nutrition, exercise, water, rest, and a positive attitude. Fifty years ago we ate fruits and vegetables from our nutritious gardens, and got our exercise from weeding, pushing a lawn mower, and walking to school. In modern society, we have almost none of that available. Our gardens and farms are no longer the nutrition providers they once were because of the nutritional depletion of the soil. It is essential to good health to supple-ment our diets. The ***Melaleuca Daily for Life Pack***, which includes ***The Vitality Pak (Mel-Vita*** and ***Mela-Cal)***, ***Cell-Wise***, and ***ProVexCV***, is an excellent place to start. This quartet of nutritional products is designed to give you basic nutrition, powerful antioxidant protection, and superior heart maintenance at a special low price. Add to that the superior antioxidant power of ***ProVex*** and ***ProVex-Plus*** and you will be ready to wage war against the free radicals that wreak havoc on your circulatory and immune systems and hasten the aging process. A good night of rest, plenty of water, a few minutes of daily exercise and a good laugh or two and your day is off to a wonderful start! If you are dealing with any of the conditions listed below and these support products are not mentioned, it should be assumed that they are a part of your overall good health program. Here's to good health and happy living!

ABDOMINAL DISTRESS

The area between the pelvis and the rib cage contains more organs and more sites for discomfort than any other area of the body. Colic or upset stomach in infants, indigestion, reactions to foods and constipation are common problems that can occur. The bowel, liver, pancreas, kidneys, spleen, stomach and gallbladder are all possible sites of distress.

Of all abdominal distress, gas and indigestion account for 80% of complaints. Abdominal distress is often caused by unhealthy eating habits. While we should all drink at least eight glasses of pure water a day, this water should be consumed between meals rather than at mealtime. When we drink too many liquids with our meal, digestive enzymes are diluted. This, in turn, can be manifested as indigestion or abdominal pain caused by bloating and gas.

Upon feeling discomfort in the abdomen, try to remember if food was ingested which was of questionable freshness. The so-called "summer flu" is actually due to bacterial toxicity from improperly handled food.

Overeating in the evening hours, or eating in a hurry, packs food in the stomach before nerve and hormone stimulation can properly begin the digestive process. Eating rich, fatty meals stresses the stomach, gallbladder, and pancreas, which slows down digestion and allows bacterium to begin fermentation and putrefaction in the bowel.

Constipation is at epidemic levels in our country. Eating high roughage food helps hold moisture in the bowel, giving the muscles of the bowel physical material to propel along its approximately 26 feet in length. The roughage rapidly carries ingested toxins, proliferating bacteria and metabolic byproducts out of the body. Experts agree that 20 to 30 grams of fiber per day is advisable for adults. The average American eats approximately 7.3 grams of fiber each day.

* Celebrate eating. Give thanks. Eat as many meals as possible with soft music and candlelight, in the presence of people you love. Drink adequate amounts of liquid each day including 2 or 3 cups of *G'Day Melaleuca Tea* between meals. Slow Down! Use *FiberWise* drink or bars to supplement your daily intake of fiber. Each serving supplies 5 grams of the much-needed fiber. Get 20 to 40 minutes of moderate daily exercise to promote circulation within the abdomen and stimulate bowel peristalsis. Multiple small meals are generally preferable to one or two large meals each day. Take *The Vitality Pak* and *Cell-Wise* daily to encourage proper metabolism and waste excretion from cells. If indigestion occurs, use *Calmicid Antacid Plus* as directed. *Calmicid* provides fast relief of acid indigestion, heartburn and gas. It aids digestion with ginger root and helps relieve cramping with chamomile and fennel seed.

To correct colic in infants, give several teaspoons of warm *G'Day Melaleuca Tea* during the day and before bedtime. Many infants have

---

*Please consult your health care provider before starting any course of supplementation or treatment, particularly if you are pregnant or currently under medical care. Make sure you carefully read and understand all product packaging prior to use.

also found relief when given *ProVex* once or twice daily. Simply open a capsule and dissolve the *ProVex* in distilled water, juice, or expressed breast milk.

See the section on *Indigestion* in this book.

ABRASIONS

These injuries occur when your skin slides across coarse materials, such as concrete, gravel, or asphalt. The top layers of skin are damaged, causing nerves, blood vessels, and lymph vessels to be exposed to the air. This causes immediate pain and creates an opportunity for germs to enter the body. After the bleeding and oozing stops, a dry protective scab will usually form within a few hours and is nature's protection against infection.

* Washing the area gently, yet thoroughly, with *Antibacterial Liquid Soap* and cool water quickly reduces the pain. (Warm or hot water increases nerve stimulation and pain in most people.) Allow the stream of water to wash off all visible particulates. Pick out any embedded material. Apply *Triple Antibiotic Ointment* or *Mela-Gel* and allow to remain open to the air if possible. Otherwise, use a loose bandage saturated with *Triple Antibiotic Ointment* or *Mela-Gel* to prevent sticking. Repeat administration of *Triple Antibiotic Ointment* or *Mela-Gel* as frequently as needed for several days until the wound is adequately covered with a scab.

ABSCESSES

These painful, pus-filled sacks of infection can occur in or on any surface of the body. Abscesses may start from a cut, scratch, pimple, ingrown hair, ingrown fingernail or ingrown toenail, hemorrhoid, or any piercing of the body. Improper treatment of an infection can produce a characteristic swollen, red, painful lump. The typical bacterium which causes abscesses is Staph epidermis, which is found on healthy skin. While antibiotics are often necessary, the overuse of antibiotics, both by prescription and in the meat we eat, has led to the development of many antibiotic-resistant strains of bacteria.

* Begin drinking *G'Day Melaleuca Tea* in place of other liquids 3 to 4 times each day. Apply *T36-C5* to the abscess. This can help to lessen the pain of the abscess, due to the penetrating effects of the oil.

To encourage drainage and drive the *T36-C5* into the wound, apply hot moist packs over the area. If the abscess can be lanced and drained, soak afterwards in a solution of 1 oz of *Sol-U-Mel* and 2 Tbs. of Epsom salts mixed with 1 quart of warm water. Saturate a hand towel in the solution, wring it out, then apply to the affected area for 10 minutes. Repeat every hour to speed the draining. Apply *Triple Antibiotic Ointment* or *Mela-Gel*. If needed, cover with gauze to absorb any seeping fluid and keep the area clean.

---

*Please consult your health care provider before starting any course of supplementation or treatment, particularly if you are pregnant or currently under medical care. Make sure you carefully read and understand all product packaging prior to use.

ACHES

See Aches and Pains, Massage

ACHES AND PAINS

A strained muscle does not necessarily cause aches and pains. It may simply be the fatigue of a muscle or set of muscles because of prolonged inactivity, such as sitting in a car or concentrating on a particular task. Psychological stress may also be the perpetrator. Generally the aches and pains occur in the lower back or neck and shoulder area, although any muscle could be involved, including the feet.

* When involved in a prolonged activity, be sure that you get up and move around at least once every hour, preferably every half hour. This can prevent a lot of unnecessary aches and pains. When they do occur, **Pain-A-Trate** can give dramatic relief. When time allows, a long soak in a hot bath with **Renew Bath Oil** is very relaxing. If your feet are feeling a little numb from sitting too long, try the **Sole to Soul Revitalizing Foot Lotion**. It is very soothing.

ACID INDIGESTION

See Abdominal Distress

ACNE

The products of overactive oil glands in the skin can dry and harden, forming blackheads. This may produce a local bacterial infection and pimples. This condition primarily affects adolescents and can occur on almost any part of the body. Outbreaks generally appear on the face, chest and upper back.

Acne is common to those working in hostile chemical environments, people suffering from hormonal imbalances, or those under physical or emotional stress. Additional factors can include the use of oil-based cosmetics, the use of some prescription drugs, heredity (the condition seems to "run" in some families), and changes in the human body at the onset of puberty. Skin blemishes in individuals of all ages arise from improper nutrition, toxicity, and rapidly changing needs for hormonal regulation. Blemishes frequently occur in women during pregnancy. While proper hygiene, including at least twice daily washing of areas most prone to becoming affected, will not in itself prevent acne, it may help to reduce or limit the spreading nature inherent in most acne outbreaks.

* Be aware of food allergies and experiment with elimination diets or get tested by your health care provider. Minimize your sugar intake. Drink 3-4 cups of **G'Day Melaleuca Tea**, hot or iced, each day, in addition to the eight glasses of pure water you should normally drink. Reduce fats to less than 20% of total calories. Perspire for twenty minutes each day, preferably from exercise, but sauna or steam baths work also.

---

*Please consult your health care provider before starting any course of supplementation or treatment, particularly if you are pregnant or currently under medical care. Make sure you carefully read and understand all product packaging prior to use.

Shower with *Antibacterial Liquid Soap* or *The Gold* or *Platinum Bar*. For those who prefer bathing, always put 1 oz of *Sol-U-Mel* in the tub. Avoid eating cooked oils such as are in margarine and potato chips. Get 20 grams of fiber daily including *FiberWise* drink or bar. Take *The Vitality Pak* and *Cell-Wise* daily for the added nutritional benefits of vitamin A, zinc, the B vitamins, and vitamin C. It is also been suggested that *ProVex Plus* be taken at the rate of 1 capsule for every 25 lbs of body weight each day.

The *Zap-It Acne Treatment System* was specifically developed for the prevention of acne. Consistent use of this system usually delivers clear skin. Clean skin with the *Zap-It Facial Wash*; apply *Zap-It Astringent*, and then *Zap-It Pore Clarifying Cream*. Carry *Zap-It Quick Stick* for a convenient treatment away from home.

In addition, you can apply *T36-C5* to any developing pustule. Use the *T36-C5* to clear the plugged oil ducts. The *Renew Intensive Skin Therapy* should be used afterward to keep moisture in the skin and resist oil accumulation. Avoid dry brush or friction rubs with alcohol as this naturally stimulates oil production. Get enough rest.

ADD AND ADHD

Attention Deficit Disorder and Attention Deficit Hyperactive Disorder are found in children and adults who have a reduced attention span and a variable pattern of behavioral challenges. Clinical studies indicate that there is a link to dietary and environmental factors. Simple sugar cravings and intolerance to sugar appear to be indicated. Several studies show a link to essential fatty acid deficiencies within the brain.

* Identify any and all food, food additives, household cleaners, and synthetic substances shown to be reactive, and remove them from the environment. Convert your home to the environmentally friendly Melaleuca cleaning and personal care products. Reduce fried foods, cooked and rancid oils (potato chips, French fries, etc.), sugar (including artificial sweeteners), and food colorings. Have a metabolic and nutritional physical exam by a certified clinician.

The following supplements, along with appropriate dietary changes, may be useful to help improve symptoms: *The Vitality Pak*— 2 each per day—should be used to help maintain proper nutrition. (Children should be taking the *Vita-Bears*.) *Luminex* will help to maximize cerebral circulation. *Provex* will reduce free-radical activity and help to reduce sensitivities to allergens. *Cell-Wise with Natural E*— 2 per day—is used to help maintain cell structure in the brain, and *Sustain* will help maintain proper blood sugar balance and reduce sugar cravings.

When people with ADD took grape seed extract (*ProVex*) for other purposes, such as allergies, they began to notice an improvement in concentration and mental focus. These are classic symptoms of attention deficit. It has been observed that those who took grape seed extract (***ProVex***) on a regular basis showed just as much improvement as those who took stimulant drugs. Generally, children fared better on a lower dose (25 milligrams of grape seed extract (***ProVex***) per 25 pounds of body weight daily), and adults did better with a higher dose of 50 milligrams per 25 pounds of body weight daily. Other positive effects such as decreased heartbeat, disappearance of tennis elbow, relief of acne and improvement in sleep and moods were also noted.

Valerian Root found in ***Rest-EZ*** has been useful for this disorder with exceptional results and no side effects. The capsule can be opened and mixed with applesauce or juice. One capsule (or ½ capsule if under 80 pounds) two or three times a day can work wonders.

Avoid carbonated drinks. The phosphate additives may be the cause of hyperkinesias (exaggerated muscle activity). The phosphorus found in soft drinks may also leech calcium and magnesium from the body creating a deficiency, which creates further potential for increased hyperactivity and even seizures. Meat and fat are also high in phosphorus. The fructose-compounded calcium and magnesium found in ***The Vitality Pak*** and ***Vita-Bears*** will provide a calming effect, as well as replenish the body.

AGE SPOTS

Sunspots, liver spots and age spots are all names for skin imperfections. They usually appear when people reach their mid-50s. People who become sun worshippers may find that they have them much earlier.

While most age spots result from an overexposure to the sun, it is important to remember that if the size or color of any spot changes, immediately consult your health care provider. This could be an early warning sign of skin cancer!

* ***T36-C5*** has been known to fade sunspots in some cases. It certainly won't hurt the skin. Also, ***ProVex*** and/or ***ProVex Plus*** may help to reduce age spots over time. However, to prevent the imperfections as much as possible, use the ***Nicole Miller Skin Care*** program. The ***Day Cover Perfecting Liquid Foundation*** has an SPF of 10 and the ***Day Cover Creme To Powder Foundation*** has an SPF of 15. Other exposed parts of the body should always be covered with a minimum of ***Sun-Shades SPF 15*** when out of doors. (If you have very fair skin, you may want to use ***Sun-Shades SPF 30***.) These products will protect you against UVA, UVB and infrared rays.

AIR PURIFICATION

The quality of air you breathe in your home may be robbing you of good health. Modern energy-efficient homes, by virtue of their airtight

---

design, often trap chemical vapors from furniture, carpets, and building cements. Condensation from air ducts, houseplant soil, and sink areas can produce harmful mold, fungus, yeast and bacteria. Many respiratory, eye, ear, nose and throat complaints appear in doctors' waiting rooms because of overexposure to foul household air. Changes of seasons often shift populations of these microbial species as growing conditions fluctuate.

* Convert your home to Melaleuca products, replacing toxic cleaning and personal care products with safer Melaleuca products. The outgassing of toxic vapors from both personal care and home hygiene products significantly increases air quality challenges.

Remove browning leaves from houseplants immediately. Provide good drainage for houseplants, and do not overwater.

Change air return filters monthly during extreme weather usage. Frequently spray all filters and vents with diluted *Sol-U-Mel*. To do a Melaleuca oil purge of your house two to twelve times a year, attach an inverted open bottle of *T36-C5* on the furnace intake filter. The high air volume will diffuse the entire contents of the bottle throughout your house over the next 12 to 36 hours (depending upon temperature and relative humidity). This treated air flows throughout all the rooms and stops the growth of bacteria, molds, fungus and viruses.

Take *ProVex* and/or *ProVex-Plus* when exposed to toxic substances.

ALLERGIC REACTIONS

Skin rashes, itching skin, sore throat, runny nose, sinus congestion, eye irritation, headaches and fatigue are common symptoms of allergy sufferers. While individuals vary in their degree of sensitivity to allergic substances, it is important to minimize discomfort and prevent complications such as infections. Many of the aromatic oils from Melaleuca alternifolia have local-acting, anti-inflammatory and desensitization effects.

* Always try to avoid the allergen when possible. Your health care provider can help you determine the substances you are reacting to and begin a program to gain permanent desensitization. Applying *T36-C5* directly to exposed skin reaction sites (hands, arms, legs, feet, scalp, neck and abdomen) usually neutralizes the local histamine reaction and reduces symptoms. A word of caution—do not apply any Melaleuca products near or in the eyes. Avoid rubbing the affected skin to prevent further irritation. *Renew Intensive Skin Therapy* or *Mela-Gel* can be applied afterwards to give long-lasting protection. Soaking in a bath containing 1 oz of *Renew Bath Oil* (and 1 oz of *Sol-U-Mel* if infections are present) offers an added soothing effect.

Remember, allergies are the result of an unhealthy immune system so maximizing your nutrition is essential. Besides, eating wholesome food, *The Vitality Pak*, *Cell-Wise*, *ProVex* and/or *ProVex-Plus*, give extra protection against allergies by providing antioxidants in the form of beta-carotene, vitamin C, vitamin E, citrus bioflavanoids, and proantho-cyanidins. Antioxidants reduce histamine levels, which cause the itching, rashes, and burning. The calcium in **Mela-Cal** often gives immediate relief from sneezing and general body aches during a reaction.

For both chronic and acute allergies/hay fever, many people find relief from **ProVex** and/or **ProVex-Plus**. These may need to be taken at the rate of 1 capsule for every 25 pounds of body weight in order to provide the most relief and prevention of allergies.

When your nose and throat are affected by hay fever, dust, pollen or food reactions, try this: breathe hot steam from either a vaporizer or bowl of steaming water with 10 drops of **T36-C5** and 2 capfuls of **Sol-U-Mel** for a minimum of 15 to 20 minutes twice a day (all night is even better). This gives welcome relief.

ALLERGIES
See Hay Fever

ALOPECIA
See Hair Loss

AMPUTATION
This is a surgical removal of a portion or all of a limb. The word amputation may also be used to describe the removal of fingers and toes. It is estimated that 70% of all of the non-traumatic amputations are performed annually on diabetics. Diabetes inhibits the free flow of blood to areas farthest from the heart. This means that fingers and particularly toes are susceptible to the development of gangrene.

* Once an extremity has reached the point of gangrene, it must be taken care of by your health care provider. In order to prevent that condition, diabetics in particular need to be very aware of circulation in their extremities. Several things might be tried. Soak the feet or hands in a mixture of **Sol-U-Mel**, mixed with Epsom salts and hot water for up to a half hour at a time. After drying the area, apply either **T36-C5** or **T40-C3**. **Pain-A-Trate** is also good for stimulating the flow of blood and enhancing circulation. See also *Diabetic Gangrene.*

ANAL FISSURES
The anus is a muscle at the end of the digestive path. Many conditions can cause pain in this area, such as hemorrhoids and fissures. If blood is detected in your stool, check with your health care provider immediately. Don't play games with your health. This can be an indication of problems much too serious for self-diagnosis.

* Be aware of whether or not your diet contains enough fiber. Two servings of **FiberWise** can supply nearly half the fiber an average adult needs on a daily basis. In addition to the eight glasses of water that each

person should consume daily, drinking multiple cups of *G'Day Melaleuca Herbal Tea* would be very helpful. It can be drunk either cold or hot and is quite tasty.

In a warm (not hot) bath, add ½ oz each of *Nature's Cleanse* and *Sol-U-Mel*. After enjoying a healing bath, apply *Mela-Gel* to the sore anal area.

Be very aware of your nutritional supplements. The *Vitality for Life* program will provide the balance of vitamins and minerals that are needed for a healthy lifestyle.

Remember to wear loose-fitting clothing during your healing process. There is no point in further aggravating your condition. Also, consistently use white toilet paper in your bathroom. Many colored or printed toilet papers contain formaldehyde since this chemical tends to hold both the color and the pattern. Formaldehyde is a poison and should be avoided at all costs.

ANEMIA

Insufficient red blood cells and/or hemoglobin cause fatigue and lack of motivation. Blood loss due to hemorrhage somewhere within the body or decreased production of red blood cells are the two causes. There are several conditions that result in anemia. Iron deficiency due to poor nutrition is most common in teenage girls and the elderly. Those with anorexia, starvation or bulimia-style eating disorders also suffer from anemia since they fail to get the irons and vitamins into their system that can begin to assure some semblance of good health. Heavy menstrual flow is often associated with anemia. Drugs such as aspirin thin the blood and can cause micro-hemorrhage in the gastrointestinal tract. This could cause anemia, especially in women who use this medication for menstrual pain and cramps. Copper, zinc, protein and B vitamins are essential for a healthy supply of red blood cells. Deficiencies of any of these can lead to various types of anemia, which are often difficult to diagnose. A sudden drop in red blood cells (hemolytic anemia) or hemoglobin (hypochromic anemia) is one of the early warning signs of cancer. Infestation of bowel parasites from outdoor pets can also lead to anemia and malnutrition. Often, anemia can only be clearly identified by a complete blood chemistry and blood cell study.

*Avoid over-the-counter drugs. Ask your doctor about the side effects of any prescription medications. Eat an adequate amount of raw fruit and vegetables, whole grains, and fish. Take *The Vitality Pak*, *Cell-Wise*, *ProVex* and/or *ProVex-Plus* regularly to supplement the iron and essential nutrients that are needed to ensure adequate red blood cell building blocks. Drink two cups of *G'Day Melaleuca Tea* each day to maximize kidney detoxification. Get 20 minutes of moderate exercise five times each week to adequately oxygenate the body.

---

*Please consult your health care provider before starting any course of supplementation or treatment, particularly if you are pregnant or currently under medical care. Make sure you carefully read and understand all product packaging prior to use.

ANGINA
See Chest Pains

ANOREXIA
See Anemia

ANTISEPTIC

An ounce of prevention is worth a pound of cure when it comes to germs that cause infection. Any break in the skin is a potential site for infection. Use protective gear, clothing, boots, hats, back braces, or goggles when needed.

* Bathe or shower with *Antibacterial Liquid Soap* or *The Gold* or *Platinum Bar*, which leaves a fine layer of Melaleuca oil on the skin. For jobs where your hands will become dirty, use *Clear Defense*, *Antibacterial Liquid Soap* or *Sol-U-Mel* as a preventive hand glove. If an injury occurs, there is a barrier between you and the awaiting germs. You can simply rinse the pre-treated area with warm water and lift the germs off with the soap. Apply *Renew Intensive Skin Therapy* afterwards. This is especially good for mechanics to prevent grease and grime (often loaded with germs) from forcing their way into the skin. It is also especially effective around farm machinery and animals. Carry *Clear Defense* with you at all times when in public places so it can be used before meals and after the use of a public rest room. Even shaking hands can spread dangerous and contagious germs, so become more aware of where you are and what and whom you touch.

ANUS
See Anal Fissures, Pruritis Ani

ANXIETY

When a person gets excited there are several adrenal hormones that are released to combat the stress. When these hormones are either set off randomly or they do not return to normal after stimulation, it creates a condition known as anxiety. Menopause or PMS can induce anxiety in some women. While adequate exercise and rest are vital, nutritional supplementation can also be beneficial.

* Good nutrition should include *The Vitality Pak* and *Cell-Wise*, along with *ProVex* and/or *ProVex-Plus*. Taking *ProVexCV* may also be wise, depending on your age. *Luminex* and *Sustain* taken as directed can be very helpful as well. Hormonal fluctuations resulting in anxiety during times of PMS or menopause might improve when *EstrAval* is taken daily.

Recent studies have shown that anxiety disorders can also have a real physical basis. Experts believe that brain chemistry may malfunction so that some areas of the brain become hyperactive and release norepinephrine, which causes blood pressure to rise with rapid pulse

---

and breathing—the classic symptoms of panic attack. *The Vitality Pak* is essential, and it may help to throw in an extra *Mela-Cal* since the calcium and magnesium will do a lot to relieve anxiety, tension and nervousness and promote a sense of calm. *Rest EZ* can also be a tremendous benefit and can be taken during the day to help relieve severe anxiety.

ARMS/LEGS ASLEEP

Loss of feeling in the arms or legs (paraesthesia) can be caused by pressure on muscles, which temporarily cuts off the blood supply. It also can be progressive due to peripheral circulatory problems where the sensory nerves in the extremities do not receive enough blood. Some people who have handled toxic solvents, paints, cleaners, pesticides, or herbicides experience extremity paraesthesia soon after.

* Use *Pain-A-Trate* on any tender muscles in your neck and upper back. If you are susceptible to paraesthesia, do not try to sleep in a moving vehicle without an inflatable cushion behind your neck. Trade legs often when holding someone on your lap. Be checked by a doctor or chiropractor when you have any kind of traumatic accident to your neck or back. Always have adequate ventilation when using volatile solvents or paint. Remember—at first your nose will alert you to the danger. If unheeded, the signal will diminish until you "get used to it." Use only environmentally safe sprays.

ProVex and/or *ProVex-Plus* should be taken daily. Take *The Vitality Pak* and *Cell-Wise* as directed, to offset the destruction of nutrients by these toxic substances in your liver. Take *FiberWise* drink or bars to carry the substances out of your digestive tract quickly. Drink extra water, *G'Day Melaleuca Tea* and *Sustain* to maintaining blood sugar during environmentally stressful times. Exercise after an exposure to harsh volatile chemicals to flush the lungs. Sweat from exercise or in a sauna or steam bath to wash out as many toxins as possible. If symptoms persist longer than 24 hours, see your health care provider if you haven't already.

ARTERIES

See Atherosclerosis

ARTHRITIS

Hot, red, painful, stiff and swollen joints of the hands, wrists, elbows, neck, back, hips, and knees are common symptoms of arthritis. It can be caused by old injuries, allergies, gout, mineral deficiencies, hyperactive immune response, toxicity, poor circulation, handling of cold things, or prescription drug side effects.

It may start as a vitamin deficiency. Studies show that cartilage cannot grow without sufficient levels of the vitamin known as pantothenic acid. Without the production of new cartilage to replace damaged or worn spots in your joints, deterioration occurs. This

---

condition is known as osteoarthritis.

Osteoarthritis is probably the most common form of arthritis. It afflicts millions and is characterized by chronic inflammation occurring in usually more than one joint. According to the Arthritis Foundation, most people over sixty show to have it on X-ray but may not have actual symptoms yet. Knees, hips, feet, hands, the spine and shoulders can all be affected. Osteoarthritis is known as the joint's cartilage degeneration. Some believe it affects weight-bearing joints such as those mentioned— hips, feet and knees—and they are partially correct. However, it also brings devastatingly harmful movement impediments to the hand, wrists, and fingers. Osteoarthritis is chronic and found primarily in adults older than their mid-30s.

Rheumatoid Arthritis is caused by inflammation of a joint membrane lining. Not only are joints swollen and painful, but they are also "red" and "hot." Common areas affected are wrists, hands and feet. It is characterized by a pain that is ongoing and never seems to be adequately relieved or alleviated. Women from their 30s to their 50s have a greater likelihood for developing this form of arthritis.

* More remedies are sold to treat arthritis than any other common condition. The best long-term treatment is the one that gets at the cause. Some cases of arthritis respond to reducing white sugar, white flour, nicotine, caffeine, and alcohol. Generally avoid cold temperatures to the affected joint. For osteoarthritis, take **Replenex Joint Replenishing Complex** to help rebuild cartilage and restore normal joint function. For all forms of arthritis, take **ProVex** and/or **ProVex-Plus** to help reduce inflammation. There are those that say **ProVexCV** has made a remarkable difference for them.

Some forms of arthritis respond well to resting the joint, while other forms, such as osteoarthritis, respond to motion such as knitting. **Pain-A-Trate** and **T36-C5** can be applied to the affected area to achieve rapid relief of pain and stiffness. Taking **The Vitality Pak** and **Cell-Wise** as directed provides essential trace nutrients for reducing further injury and increasing healing. Since dehydrated joints ache, drink more liquids, including 2 to 4 cups of **G'Day Melaleuca Tea** per day.

ASTHMA

Congestion and restriction of the lungs causes labored breathing and wheezing, and affects one out of every twelve people. Many are small children. Although it is associated with airborne allergies and occasional food sensitivities, improvement can occur by following a few simple suggestions.

* Identify and restrict all sensitizing substances (see *Air Purification*). Rid your home of all toxic personal care and home care products. Convert your home to Melaleuca products, beginning with the **Ecosense Laundry System**. As you convert your home to the safer products, remember to shampoo your carpets with **MelaMagic** or one

of the other effective Melaleuca products. See the *Carpet Cleaner* section in this book.

Adults and teenagers should take *The Vitality Pak*—2 each per day and children should take the *Vita-Bears*—as directed, along with *Cell-Wise with Natural E*—2 per day. *ProVex* and/or *Provex-Plus*—1 capsule for each 25 lbs of body weight per day should be taken to increase resistance to attacks. Apply *Pain-A-Trate* to the chest of adults and children before bed. Get enough rest. If congestion exists, increase the amount of *ProVex* and/or *ProVex-Plus* until you find the level that provides relief. *ProVex* and/or *ProVex-Plus*, as well as *The Vitality Pak* or *Vita-Bears* have given many asthma sufferers much relief.

It has even been suggested that a concentration of *ProVexCV* would be helpful when dealing with Asthma. Increase the daily dosage of *ProVexCV* to six a day for two weeks and then return to the normal dosage. Continue to repeat this periodically when needed.

Further relief may come from a humidifier or vaporizer with water plus 10 drops of *T36-C5* and 2 capfuls of *Sol-U-Mel*. Use in the bedroom each night for best results.

Adults can try adding 10 to 20 drops of Tabasco sauce (capsicum) in a few ounces of water and drinking it immediately before a meal to reduce congestion and thin mucous in the lungs.

One drop of *T36-C5* on a Q-tip, gently used to clean pollen and dust from each nostril before bed, has helped many children.

ATHEROSCLEROSIS

Hardening of the arteries can lead to high blood pressure, strokes, shortness of breath and cold hands and feet, as well as senility and premature aging. Cholesterol (LDL—the bad kind) and ionic calcium make up part of the "cement" that lines arteries of the liver, bowel, lungs, brain, kidneys, legs and arms. Several common-sense suggestions can help.

* Begin taking *ProVexCV*—1 capsule for each 35 lbs of body weight per day, *The Vitality Pak*—2 each per day and *Cell-Wise with Natural E* —2 per day. Every adult should be on this regimen for prevention of atherosclerosis.

Stop smoking and avoid smokers. Avoid animal fats and cooked vegetable fats. Reduce total fat to less than 20% of your total diet. Eat a good variety of raw fruit and vegetables each day. Begin a gradual daily exercise program. Eat an *Access Bar* 15 minutes before exercising and drink a *Sustain* drink one half hour after exercising to speed up the fat-burning process. *FiberWise* bars contain 5 grams of fiber and are an excellent quick snack. Drink 3 to 4 cups of *G'Day Melaleuca Tea* daily.

ATHLETE'S FOOT

Athlete's foot is a fungus known as tinea pedis. When the fungus infects the upper body, this is known as tinea corporis, or ringworm,

---

*Please consult your health care provider before starting any course of supplementation or treatment, particularly if you are pregnant or currently under medical care. Make sure you carefully read and understand all product packaging prior to use.

causing raised and reddened rashes with clear centers. Athlete's foot is commonly found in athletic showering areas and long-term athlete's foot often involves the toenails and can totally destroy the nail plate and/or enter the bone. Blistering can occur when the immune system becomes sensitized to the fungus. It can usually be found between the toes where the skin has a greater tendency to crack, blister, or become sore and itchy. The infection will persist indefinitely until treatment is effective. The general health of the individual tends to determine the magnitude of the infection and extent of the symptoms. The good news is that athlete's foot rarely develops in young children or in those who go barefoot or wear sandals.

Products with Melaleuca oil are highly effective in the treatment of foot and toenail fungal infections. It is much more effective than griseofulvin, which has been commonly used. If the two are used together, the griseofulvin may lessen in effectiveness. It is also important to note that griseofulvin may be toxic to the liver and liver enzyme functions must be monitored during therapy with this drug.

Several years ago in a report issued by *The Physician and Sportsmedicine* it was stated that in some instances irritation was misdiagnosed as athlete's foot when it is really an allergic reaction to a chemical in sneaker insoles. This "contact dermatitis" can be differentiated from athlete's foot because the reaction occurs mainly on the ball, outer sides and top of the foot where it comes in contact with the shoe. Athlete's foot usually appears in the cracks between the toes.

If you have contact dermatitis, an entirely different method of treatment is required. With contact dermatitis, you must not use any pure Melaleuca alternifolia oil. To be safe, avoid every product that has the pure oil as an ingredient. For additional information, please read the information under *Dermatitis*.

 * As in most infections, prevention is the best treatment. Always wear shower sandals when in public showers, such as athletic locker rooms and swimming pools. Spray feet with **Melaleuca Essentials Antibacterial Foot Spray** and apply **Dermatin Antifungal Creme** between toes and to bottoms of feet immediately after showering. **Sole to Soul Revitalizing Food Scrub** and **Revitalizing Foot Lotion** can also be used to cleanse and stimulate circulation. Direct sunlight and air-drying the feet after showering or swimming is also a helpful preventive measure. Take *The Vitality Pak*, *Cell-Wise*, and a *ProVex* product daily, to optimize trace nutrients. Drink 2-3 cups of *G'Day Melaleuca Tea* daily.

To eliminate athlete's foot, clean the affected area well with **Antibacterial Liquid Soap** and water. A great foot soak for athlete's foot is to combine **Tough & Tender, Liquid Pain-A-Trate**, and **Renew Bath Oil** in a pan of hot water. An alternative would be to use just **Tough & Tender** or add a little **Sol-U-Guard** or **Renew Bath Oil** and soak your feet for about 30 minutes. For a severe case of athlete's foot, put 4 Tbs. of **Sol-U-Guard** in hot water and soak for 20-30 minutes, morning and night for one week. After soaking, apply *Dermatin Antifungal Cream* as directed. It will kill fungus and bacteria. *T36-C5*, followed by *Renew Intensive Skin Therapy* or *Mela-Gel* could also be used each morning and night. If there is no improvement after one week, discontinue use and consult your health care provider if you haven't already.

Be sure to wear clean white cotton (if possible) socks daily. These should be washed only using *EcoSense Laundry System*. Don't use store-bought laundry products because too often they contain harmful chemicals. Each time you change socks, dribble a few drops of *T36-C5* on the clean socks. Rub them together before putting them on. You might even spray the inside of your shoes with a mixture of one-half ounce of *Sol-U-Mel* with four ounces of water.

To avoid reinfection, always wear bathing slippers in public swimming pools, saunas, and showers, as well as in dorms and hotels. Dry your feet carefully after washing. Avoid wearing polyester socks and shoes not made of leather. Don't wear rubber boots or tennis shoes the entire day and change your socks and shoes every day.

ATHLETIC INJURIES

The human body is designed for motion. Actually, everyone is an athlete—you are either actively practicing or you are not. More middle-aged and elderly people are enjoying the benefits of regular exercise than ever before. Typical athletic injuries in all ages include pulled muscles, strained ligaments and tendons, bruises and muscle cramps. Common sense tells us that a proper warm up and cool down before and after exercise is essential.

* Take T*be Vitality Pak*—2 per day, as well as *ProVex*, and/or *ProVex-Plus*, to optimize tissue-strengthening nutrients. The *Cell Wise* should also be taken at the dosage of 2 per day. Of course, all adults should be taking the *ProVexCV* as well to support a healthy cardiovascular system. Take more *Mela-Cal* if you have muscle cramps after a workout. Eat an *Access Bar* 15 minutes before exercise to inhibit adenosine and open fat stores in the body for energy. *Sustain* drink can be mixed in your water bottle for continual replenishment of waning blood sugar.

Joints are repeatedly stressed as we go about our daily activities, and the body must constantly work to repair them. With age, the body becomes less efficient. *Replenex*, with 500 mg of the purest glucosamine available, plus ginger, bromelain and green tea extracts to reduce inflammation and discomfort, helps preserve the health of joints, thereby promoting ease of movement. It has been suggested that you take 3 per day.

Pain-A-Trate should be in the equipment bag of every athlete. Immediate application of *Pain-A-Trate* to any closed injury will start the healing process. Regular application of *T36-C5* stimulates circulation to injured tissues as well. Ice is good for injured joints, muscles, tendons

---

*Please consult your health care provider before starting any course of supplementation or treatment, particularly if you are pregnant or currently under medical care. Make sure you carefully read and understand all product packaging prior to use.

and ligaments. Apply ice for no more than 5 to 10 minutes at a time. Longer treatment periods can actually cause frostbite or reverse the anti-inflammatory effect. Heat can cause problems so it should be avoided, in most cases, for the first 24 to 48 hours after an injury to bruised or pulled muscles. A health care provider, trained to treat sports injuries, should see chronic or untreated injuries.

ATTENTION DEFICIT DISORDER
See ADD and ADHD

ATTENTION DEFICIT HYPERACTIVE DISORDER
See ADD and ADHD

BABY TEETH
All 20 baby teeth are usually present by the age of 3. Children will lose these teeth between the ages of 5 and 12, as the size of the growing head and mouth require larger teeth. Care and protection of these teeth is important to ensure a healthy environment for the permanent teeth, which may need to last 75 to 100 years.

* Do not put a child to bed with a nursing bottle of fruit juice or formula. This is the most common cause of dissolved baby teeth and the need for capping. As soon as the baby teeth appear, brush with *Koala Pals Sparkling Tooth Gel* or *Classic Tooth Polish*, after every meal. Give your child *Vita-Bears* to insure strong healthy teeth. Children should start seeing their dentist regularly by the age of four unless there are obvious cavities prior to that age. See the section on *Teething* in this book.

BACK PAIN
More than one half of the adult American population suffers with back pain. Our sedentary lifestyles, motorized transportation, and poor diets cause a large portion of our discomfort. Stretching and strengthening exercises, eating a healthy diet, maintaining a healthy weight, supplementing calcium, magnesium, and micro-nutrients, and correcting spinal injuries before they become chronic can go a long way toward reducing back pain.

* Apply *Pain-A-Trate* to over-worked muscles. Apply moderate heat (use cold immediately after injury or acute pain 5 to 10 minutes each hour for the first 6 to 24 hours before using heat). Use *T36-C5* on skin over spasming back muscles to promote the relaxation reflex. Take *Replenex*—3 per day. Drink 2 to 4 cups of *G'Day Melaleuca Tea* each day.

Take *ProVex* and/or *ProVex-Plus*, in addition to *The Vitality Pak*— 2 each per day—and *Cell-Wise with Natural E*—2 per day, to help heal collagen structures in your back.

BACTEREMIA
See Boils

BAD BREATH
Bacteria that live inside the mouth create most bad breath. Sometimes it is caused by foods such as onions and garlic. Some find a coffee drinker's breath offensive, especially after several cups have been swallowed and digested. Alcohol and especially beer breath can be very offensive. Smokers generally have bad breath. The residues of digestion caused by sulfur compounds such as certain cheeses, cabbage, beans, some other milk products, and sausages may create bad breath. Another culprit can be medications such as tranquilizers, cough and congestion medicines, and other pharmaceuticals used to control angina and hypertension.

* *Breath-Away Mouthwash* is an excellent start in improving one's bad breath regardless of the reason. Another way to improve is to change to Melaleuca's *Denti-Care* system. This will include adopting the regular use of products such as the *Denti-Clean* line of tooth cleaners, the *Exceed Dental Flosses*, *Insta-Fresh Dental Gums*, and *Hot/Cool Shot Mouth Spray*. In addition, Melaleuca's *Denti-Care* system cleans and stimulates taste buds, thus improving your ability to taste food.

Drinking a sufficient amount of water each day can help improve our breath, too. When you do this, include several cups of *G'Day Melaleuca Herbal Tea*.

Keep your toothbrush germ-free by soaking it in a solution of 5-10 drops of *T36-C5* and ½ cup of water for ten minutes and then rinsing. Using *Breath-Away Mouthwash* is also very effective, as is the simple process of applying a couple of drops of *T36-C5* directly to your toothbrush once or twice each week. (It is not advisable to use peroxide, as it will disturb the oral flora. *T36-C5* will not do this.) Replace your toothbrush at least once each month and immediately after any illness.

Breath-Away Mouthwash Concentrate is an excellent choice in that you can determine the strength and flavor of your gargling or rinse solution. Be sure to follow the directions on the bottle or you will understand why it is called *Breath-Away!* Gargle daily after meals and before bedtime. Bacteria in your mouth are the principal causes of mouth odor. To help kill serious odors caused by bacteria, add 2 or 3 drops of *T36-C5* to the *Breath-Away Mouthwash* before gargling. This aids in relieving odors, which arise from the intestinal tract.

Most commercial mouthwashes use alcohol as their antiseptic, which is found in concentrations as high as 30%. Studies suggest that this alcohol content is toxic to the mucous membranes, particularly those of the oral mucosa and that regular use of alcohol-based mouthwashes significantly increases cancer risks. This is another great reason to use *Breath-Away Mouthwash*.

---

*Please consult your health care provider before starting any course of supplementation or treatment, particularly if you are pregnant or currently under medical care. Make sure you carefully read and understand all product packaging prior to use.

BALDNESS
See Hair Loss

BARBER'S ITCH
This is caused by a fungus from an improperly cleaned razor, shaving cream brush, or electric shaver. Fortunately, the use of disposable razors and canned shaving foam and gel has made this fungus much less common. The rash leaves the skin slightly flaky and (looking) sore. See the sections on *Athlete's Foot* and *Acne* in this book.

* Two things that you might try: the new *Zap-It* products and the **Dermatin Antifungal Creme**. Follow the directions on each of these products. Also periodically, add a drop of *T36-C5* to your razor before using it.

BATHING
One of the most self-pampering events of life is taking a hot bath. Getting the most out of your time and effort is essential. Showers expose people with respiratory or skin sensitivities to 8 to 10 times the amount of chlorine as bathing. Chlorine-sensitive people should run hot bath water and allow it to de-gas for about 5 minutes with the window open or the vent fan running before plunging in. Never take long baths (30 minutes or more) with a breeze in the room, as the lungs are susceptible to infection from cool air when the body is heated above 100 degrees.

* Put *Sol-U-Mel* (1 oz per tub) in the water to thoroughly sanitize and disinfect the skin. The **Renew Bath Oil** is real therapy for the pores of the skin. It is also very relaxing to simply soak for ten minutes or so in a warm bath to which 8-10 drops of *T36-C5* have been added.

For alternate bathing suggestions, see the section on *Sitz Bath* in this book.

BED SORES
Also known as decubitus ulcers, bedsores occur when people are bedfast or confined to a wheelchair. A lamb's wool or "egg carton" foam pad can be placed under the person to prevent the deep crater sores from forming. Daily inspection is important to identify the blanched skin heralding the onset of a bedsore. Once started, bedsores can lead to infections and delayed healing. Prevention is the best treatment.

* Healing begins at the outer edges and works inward when pressure is removed from the area. Apply *T36-C5* to any blanched skin areas before the sore begins. It can often be halted at this stage. If a sore is present, gently wash the area with *Antibacterial Liquid Soap* enriched with one capful of *Sol-U-Mel* in 1 quart of warm water. Apply *Triple Antibiotic Ointment* or *Mela-Gel*. Cover with loose gauze. Use a minimum amount of tape. Repeat washing and *Triple Antibiotic Ointment* every 8 hours until the wound heals. This can take from one day to several weeks depending upon the overall health of the individual. Some health care facilities will not allow the **T36-C5** to be brought in without a physician's orders. In such cases, **Renew Intensive Skin Therapy** or **Moisturizing Hand Creme** has been used very effectively. They can also be used as covering lotion after the bedsore has been treated.

It is important to couple treatment with preventive actions that will help prevent future bedsores from forming. Minimizing pressure on areas prone to develop sores is crucial. Placing pillows, cushions and ripple types of pressurized mattresses under the patient will help decrease the chances of the patient developing future sores. Sheepskin wraps for the heels and buttocks may also be helpful. A growing list of long-term care-staffs are now using Melaleuca alternifolia oil and products containing the oil, having discovered the oil's effectiveness in accelerating healing and alleviating patient discomfort.

WARNING: Bedsores should be taken very seriously in diabetics, persons on immune-suppressive drugs, and those with leg ulcers due to poor circulation.

BEE AND WASP STINGS

Bees are territorial creatures. They defend their territory by injecting a powerful chemical, formic acid, into the intruder. This injection also contains traces of immune reactive agents that can provoke violent reactions in humans.

* Carefully remove the stinger by scraping it out. Wash the area with **Antibacterial Liquid Soap** and cold water. Immediately apply **T36-C5** or **Mela-Gel** to stop pain and prevent secondary infection. Do not use any other home remedies, such as baking soda, with the Melaleuca products for this. Reapply every 15 minutes until all signs and symptoms are gone. Four to six applications may be necessary. Take **ProVex** or **ProVex-Plus** immediately and continue for 24 hours.

WARNING: When a person is allergic to bee or wasp stings, this can be life threatening. The allergic person should carry an antidote kit containing adrenaline and benadryl. Administer this according to the directions before any other therapy. Shortness of breath or difficulty breathing, puffy or swollen throat or eyes, rapid heart rate, dizziness, or profuse sweating are signs of an allergic reaction and can appear within 10 to 30 minutes after being stung. **DO NOT DELAY! GET EMERGENCY HELP!**

BENIGN PROSTATIC HYPERPLASIA (BPH)
(Prostate Health)

As men age, and especially after "male menopause," testosterone is inefficiently utilized in the prostate gland. Physical trauma (sitting), stress, excessive animal fat intake, and nutrient deficiencies transform testosterone into dihydrotestosterone. This causes the prostate gland to

---

*Please consult your health care provider before starting any course of supplementation or treatment, particularly if you are pregnant or currently under medical care. Make sure you carefully read and understand all product packaging prior to use.

enlarge and become less functional. Flow or dribbling urination, difficulty starting urination, incomplete emptying of the bladder, getting up multiple times at night, and reduced sexual function accompany this condition. After the age of 50, approximately one half of all men experience symptoms of BPH. BPH does not indicate cancer and should be differentiated from this more severe condition.

* Get an annual prostate exam after the age of 50 including the sensitive blood tumor marker for prostate cancer called PSA. Prevention is the best treatment. Regular hot baths seem to reduce the incidence of BPH. Native Japanese men have a lower incidence of BPH and other prostate challenges due to their custom of very hot baths. Americans tend to shower and have a statistically higher incidence of prostate challenges. The ingredients in *ProstAvan* have a proven effect in helping prevent BPH and should be taken every day by men over the age of 40. One extra tablet for every decade past 40 is advised. *Luminex* is advised to maximize cerebral circulation and hormone regulation. *The Vitality Pak*—2 each per day, and *Cell-Wise with Natural E*—3 each per day are vital. Men with higher levels of vitamin E in their systems have been found to have a 41% less incidence of fatal prostate cancer.

ProVex and/or *ProVex-Plus* should also be included in your daily routine. Of course, *ProVexCV* should always be taken for cardiovascular protection. The recommended dosage is 1 capsule per each 35 lbs of body weight taken daily. Drinking 3-4 cups of *G'Day Melaleuca Tea* each day is also very helpful.

BI-POLAR DISORDER
See Depression

BITE
See Cat Bites and Scratches, Dog Bite, Insect Bite, Mosquito Bite

BLACK EYE
Bruising almost anywhere on the head resulting from an automobile accident, sports accident, bump, fall, or even dental work, can cause a black eye.

* Apply an ice pack as soon as possible to the affected area, to slow down facial swelling. Do not use any Melaleuca products near the eye, as its aromatic vapor is drying to the eye and may cause pain. Take *The Vitality Pak* as well as *ProVex* and/or *ProVex-Plus* to speed healing and prevent easy bruising.

BLACKHEADS
See Acne

BLADDER INFECTIONS

Bladder infections, most often in women, can be bothersome at least, and a potential full-blown illness at worst. Underwear made of synthetic fabric causes excessive perspiration, which leads to bacterial growth at the opening of the urethra. Some even think that getting too cool can aid in the development of a bladder infection, which can possibly be traced back to reasons related to fashion. Not drinking enough water encourages bacteria to grow within the urethra and bladder. Repeated infections are a cause for alarm.

WARNING: Recurrent infections treated with antibiotics can lead to highly resistant strains of bacteria and yeast infections.

* Drink 2 to 6 cups of *G'Day Melaleuca Tea* along with 2-4 quarts of pure water each day. Wear cotton underwear. Douche with *Nature's Cleanse* weekly to reduce bacteria in the area. Add 1 oz of *Sol-U-Mel* in the rinse water of washing cycles when laundering undergarments. Use the *Ecosense Laundry System* to avoid harsh chemicals.

Use white toilet paper, as many colored or printed toilet papers contain formaldehyde, which should be avoided if at all possible. Wiping from the front to the back prevents the possibility of introducing bacteria into the urethra. When treating a bladder infection, add 10 drops of *T36-C5* to a quart of distilled water and dab the external urinal tract after each urination with a cotton ball soaked in this mixture. Keeping the abdominal area warm is very comforting, as is massaging the lower back with *Pain-A-Trate*.

There is some indication that baths can contribute to bladder infections, probably due to the harsh chemicals in most bath soaps. If you prefer to bathe rather than shower, bathe with *The Gold Bar* or *Platinum Bar* and/or add 3 to 10 drops of *T36-C5* to your bath water.

BLEEDING GUMS

Plaque or periodontal infections can cause bleeding gums, swollen gums or dental pain. Brushing too hard is a common cause. Chronic vitamin C deficiency, alveolar (jaw) bone loss, or chemical poisoning are other possible causes. The mouth is the literal window to overall health of the body.

Diabetics and pregnant women both tend to suffer from bleeding gums as they experience changes in hormone levels. When noted in youngsters, it is oftentimes seen in a milder form.

Bleeding without cause such as from injury or infection should be investigated. It is not normal to have bleeding gums.

* Switching to the Melaleuca dental care products often gives relief from bleeding gums. Regular brushing with *Classic Tooth Polish* and rinsing with *Breath-Away Mouthwash* is a good way to control the buildup of bacteria-causing plaque. Daily flossing with *Exceed Waxed Dental Floss* and chewing *Insta-Fresh Gum* can clean between teeth where a brush cannot reach. Just before bedtime, dip a pixel brush into

the *T36-C5* and "brush" in between your teeth at the gum line. It will provide a "deep cleaning" to help alleviate pockets and sore gums.

Drinking 2 to 4 cups of *G'Day Melaleuca Tea* per day helps promote a healthy environment in the mouth. Take *The Vitality Pak*, *Cell-Wise*, *ProVex* and/or *ProVex-Plus* while eating a healthy diet.

Using a Q-tip or your fingertip, apply *T36-C5* to affected gums. Most people do not enjoy the taste of pure Melaleuca alternifolia oil, however, a product does not have to taste good or sweet to accomplish healing. A Melaleuca mouth is far better than one harboring sore or bleeding gums. Get professional dental care if bleeding, pain or swelling of gums persists. Regular checkups can prevent dental problems.

BLISTERS

They are frequently caused by friction or by chemical or burn injuries, such as sunburns. Blisters can also be caused by skin conditions such as eczema, impetigo and dermatitis. Sometimes they occur when an area is scratched repeatedly. They appear as oval-shaped, raised areas of skin holding collections of fluid beneath the outer layer. They should not be punctured. Blisters can lead to blood poisoning, if not properly treated.

* Blisters diminish rapidly after gingerly applying *T36-C5*. Dab the oil on the blistered area, and then leave it alone until the next application. The blisters will heal over quickly without itching or burning.

If the blister is small and closed, leave it alone. It already has its own natural covering bandage. If it needs protection from further damage, fit some sort of loose bandage about it. If the blister is in a weight-bearing area (big toe, little toe or heel), consider some sort of donut-shaped moleskin pad to help assure the blister will not break and become worse.

When blisters break, all sorts of potential problems occur. Avoid these if possible. Protect the broken blister from further rubbing with a loose bandage, and avoid the activity that originally caused it. *Triple Antibiotic Ointment* may help, when used as directed. It is the strongest antibiotic ointment you can buy. It kills staph, strep and pseudomonas bacteria, which helps prevent infection in minor burns, cuts and scrapes.

For other types of blisters, see the section on *Cold Sores* in this book.

BLOCKED SINUS PASSAGES
See Sinus Congestion, Sinusitis

BLOOD PRESSURE
See Cardiovascular Disease, High Blood Pressure

BODY LICE
See Lice

---

*Please consult your health care provider before starting any course of supplementation or treatment, particularly if you are pregnant or currently under medical care. Make sure you carefully read and understand all product packaging prior to use.

BODY MASSAGE
See Massage

BODY ODOR

Bacteria, yeast, bowel putrefaction, dental disease, vaginitis, chronic tonsillitis, kidney or liver failure, as well as a number of chronic degenerative disorders and chemical exposures, can lead to a foul body odor. Perfume was invented in Europe during the Dark Ages when the prevailing theory was that bathing and exposing the body to the air was the cause of infectious disease. WRONG! However, body odor may prevent people from getting close enough to you to give you a disease. Foul-smelling sweat (bromhyperhidrosis) is observed in some diabetics, nervous individuals, chronic smokers and people on certain prescription medications. People who have a bad odor become desensitized to it and need to be told by someone who cares. Read the sections on *Bathing* and *Yeast Infections* in this book.

 * Drink 2 to 4 cups of *G'Day Melaleuca Tea* each day for detoxification. Take *The Vitality Pak* as directed. Brush regularly with *Denti-Clean Classic Tooth Polish*, floss with *Exceed Waxed Dental Floss*, and use *Breath-Away Mouthwash* after meals. Use *Hot/Cool Shot Mouth Spray* before going out in public, and chew *Insta-Fresh Gum* frequently. If you are a smoker, STOP! Bathe instead of showering. Use *Antibacterial Liquid Soap* and *The Gold* or *Platinum Bar* lavishly. *Naturals Invisible Solid Deodorant* should be used after bathing and frequently during warm weather. Women can use *Nature's Cleanse* douche weekly if needed. Often body odor comes from the groin or feet and is caused by a fungus. That's why Melaleuca's extraordinary *Dermatin Antifungal Creme* works so well. It is soothing and healing and contains *T36-C5* as well as clotrimazole. Take *ProVex* and/or *ProVex-Plus* daily.

Pass the "odor test" from someone in your family before you use perfumes and colognes. When serious health concerns are causing the body odor, consult your health care provider.

BOILS

Staphylococcus organisms can cause raised, red, hard, hot and extremely painful pus-filled skin abscesses. They may appear anywhere on the body. Ears, nose, fingers and scalp are the most painful sites due to thin skin and constant pressure. The boil may start very small and then become red as it grows into a painful, pus-filled lump. The staphylococcus organism may be contracted from farm animals and it can remain dormant in the body for years before erupting, usually when the person is run-down, tired and overlystressed. Those with depressed immune systems and those with diabetes are more likely to develop boils.

---

*Please consult your health care provider before starting any course of supplementation or treatment, particularly if you are pregnant or currently under medical care. Make sure you carefully read and understand all product packaging prior to use.

WARNING: Staphylococcus is very infectious, and many strains are becoming resistant to prescription antibiotics. If fever is present, consult your health care provider immediately.

* Apply *T36-C5* every hour to a developing boil. Some boils can be stopped at this stage. Leave exposed to the air if possible. When a focal head begins to appear, usually after a couple of days, use a sterilized needle to lance the boil and allow drainage. The release of pressure usually provides immediate relief of pain. Continue applying *T36-C5* as long as drainage lasts. Soaking the site in a solution of 1 oz *Sol-U-Mel* and 1 Tbs. Epsom salts in a quart of hot water can speed drainage. Apply *Triple Antibiotic Ointment* to a soft gauze bandage and cover. Drink 2 to 6 cups of *G'Day Melaleuca Tea* each day. Take *The Vitality Pak* as directed. If redness and swelling does not disappear after 7 days, see your health care provider if you haven't already. Take *ProVex* and/or *ProVex-Plus* daily.

BREAST CANCER
See Cancer Prevention

BREASTFEEDING
See Sore Nipples

BROMHIDROIS (Foot Odor)
Excessively sweaty feet can occur in people of all ages. While it is often attributed to nervousness, it can be caused by other factors.

* Use *The Gold* or *Platinum Bar* or *Antibacterial Liquid Soap* to wash the feet, including the areas between the toes. Rinse and pat day. Apply *T36-C5* to the soles of the feet and between the toes. Repeat this process at least twice daily. Change socks after each application to help eliminate odor. Place several drops of Melaleuca oil on your clean socks and rub them together. A few drops inside your shoes may be helpful as well.

An alternative treatment is to use the *Sole to Soul Revitalizing Foot Scrub*. Be sure to dry the area between your toes carefully before you follow up with the *Sole to Soul Revitalizing Foot Lotion*. It is amazing how wonderful your feet can feel.

BRONCHITIS
Irritated bronchial membranes in the lung can swell and restrict airflow, resulting in a condition known as bronchitis. Chronic cases can lead to asthma. Possible irritants include: low-grade bacterial, yeast, or viral infections, allergies, household cleaning chemicals and irritation from cigarette smoke. See the sections on *Asthma*, *Sinus Congestion* and *Coughs* in this book.

* Treat the cause. Protect your air quality by converting your home

---

*Please consult your health care provider before starting any course of supplementation or treatment, particularly if you are pregnant or currently under medical care. Make sure you carefully read and understand all product packaging prior to use.

to Melaleuca home care and personal care products. Drink at least 7 to 10 glasses of water daily. Avoid forced air heat and over-the-counter medicines that dry coughs, suppressing the beneficial coughing action that brings up phlegm. Take *The Vitality Pak*, *Cell-Wise*, *ProVex* and/or *ProVex-Plus* daily. Drink 2 to 6 cups of *G'Day Melaleuca Tea* each day.

Breathe the enriched steam from a vaporizer or bowl of steaming water each morning and night before bed. To do this, add 5 drops of *T36-C5* directly to the water. Form a tent over your head and vaporizer or bowl, breathing the aromatic vapors through your nose and mouth gently into your lungs. Keep your eyes closed. Add 1 or 2 drops of *T36-C5* every 5 minutes for 15 to 20 minutes. (*NOTE:* Do not use *Sol-U-Mel* for this breathing treatment as it can cause irritation to the lungs.) Many people find additional relief when sleeping in a room with a vaporizer or cool mist humidifier. Add two capfuls of *Sol-U-Mel* and 10 drops of *T36-C5* to the tank's water. For acute attacks, put 1 or 2 drops of *T36-C5* on a Q-tip and swab the inside of each nostril. It will also help to steam your chest by placing 5 drops of *T36-C5* on a warm, wet cloth and applying to the chest area.

Try these simple dietary tips: eliminate milk and milk products, substituting other sources of calcium; eat garlic regularly for its antibiotic effects; and eat fresh horseradish and hot mustard regularly to liquefy bronchial secretions.

WARNING: Consult your health care provider, especially if any of these conditions are present: fever, intensified attacks or coughing up blood. A health care provider should always be consulted if the person suffering from bronchitis has other underlying medical or lung problems.

BRUISES

Ruptured blood vessels near the surface of the skin or in muscles can occur from injury, infection or blood disorders. Discoloration is at first red, then black and blue, and finally green as healing takes place. Bruises can accompany other injuries such as sprains and strains, fractures or a more serious injury. The elderly and those with more sensitive bodies seem to experience bruises more frequently than does the typically healthy young adult.

* The immediate application of ice to a traumatized area helps reduce bruising. *Pain-A-Trate* has a deep penetrating effect and reduces swelling, increases circulation, and speeds healing. Apply as often as needed until pain, discoloration and swelling disappear. In place of the *Pain-A-Trate*, *T36-C5* can be used on the bruise. It will start the healing from the inside out. This should be repeated at least twice a day. If the bruised injury is near the eye, use caution to not get the oil in or too near the eye.

To prevent easy bruising and speed healing, take *ProVex* and/or *ProVex-Plus* on a daily basis. These improve the strength and elasticity of blood vessels and thus help to prevent bruising.

---

*Please consult your health care provider before starting any course of supplementation or treatment, particularly if you are pregnant or currently under medical care. Make sure you carefully read and understand all product packaging prior to use.

BULIMIA

See Anemia

BUNIONS

Bunions are caused by the swelling of the second synovial joint bursa producing enlargement and displacement of the big toe, which eventually laps over the second toe. They are sometimes caused by misalignment in the spine, causing improper biomechanics in the foot. Some cases have been linked to improperly fitted shoes during childhood development. See the section on *Bursitis* in this book.

* Apply *T36-C5* or *Pain-A-Trate* generously to the affected joint as often as discomfort exists. Soak in a solution of 1 oz of *Sol-U-Mel* and 1 Tbs. of Epsom salts per quart of hot water each night. Wear only well-fitting shoes, and see your local chiropractor for a walking gait analysis.

Don't forget to pamper your feet with the *Sole to Soul Revitalizing Foot Scrub* and the *Sole to Soul Revitalizing Foot Lotion*. It feels so good!

BURNS

No burn is simple to treat! This is true for a first-degree burn that is red and swollen, a second-degree burn that produces a blister, or a third-degree burn that penetrates into muscle and deep tissue and occasionally chars the flesh. Infections, scars, and even shock can result if burns are improperly treated. Too much sun tanning damages skin cells. Ozone depletion in our atmosphere is increasing the amount of harmful ultraviolet rays from sunlight we are exposed to. There is an increase in melanoma skin cancer in those who are exposed to excessive ultraviolet radiation. Always protect your skin from sun exposure by using *Sun-Shades Waterproof Sunblock SPF 15* if you have dark skin or *SPF 30* if you have a fair complexion.

* Immediately flush a fresh burn with cold water and apply ice and continue until the area is cold. Pat dry and apply *T36-C5*. Then cover with a thin coat of *Renew Intensive Skin Therapy*. Take *ProVex* and/or *ProVex-Plus* daily to speed recovery and reduce scarring. Most first-degree burns will subside very soon. Repeat the *T36-C5* and *Renew Intensive Skin Therapy* application every hour until pain is gone. For second-degree burns, apply *T36-C5* and *Pain-A-Trate* each hour until pain and swelling are gone. If the burn does not show signs of healing, seek medical care if you haven't already. Third-degree burns require professional care immediately, since deep blood vessels, nerves and lymphatic vessels in the skin are damaged. After cold applications, apply *T36-C5* and *Renew Intensive Skin Therapy* or *Triple Antibiotic Ointment*. Cover with a sterile covering. Contact your health care

provider immediately!

It is always wise to keep a bottle of *T36-C5* in the kitchen for treating grill and fryer burns. Melaleuca alternifolia oil provides an anesthetic-like action. It soothes and alleviates most pain on contact. It also will help prevent blistering and even scarring. Since infections nearly always develop in severe burns, frequent applications of *T36-C5* will help stop itching and accelerate healing.

For other types of burns, see the sections on *Radiation Burns* and *Razor Burns* in this book.

BURSITIS

Small, fluid-filled, shock-absorbing sacs are present in some joints such as the elbow, knee, shoulder, hip, ankle or big toe. Inflammation of these sacs, called bursa, causes swelling and painful movement of the joint. Trauma, infections, allergies, or toxic accumulation are the usual causes. Gradual development from repetitive motion occupations can lead to chronic bursitis. Reducing coffee drinking curiously reduces bursitis of the shoulder. Acute bursitis can result from prescription drug reactions or sudden injury to the area. See the sections on *Bunions* and *Gout* in this book.

* Take *ProVex* and/or *ProVex-Plus* to help reduce inflammation. Apply *Pain-A-Trate* generously to the affected area every 2 to 4 hours. Moist heat and limiting joint motion may be helpful during the healing phase. Do not exercise the joint until pain and swelling are reduced. If the pain does not subside in a few days, see your health care provider if you haven't already.

Of course, for overall better health, *The Vitality Pak* should be taken at the dosage of 2 each per day, as well as *Cell Wise with Natural E*—2 per day. *Replenex* may also be very helpful with bursitis. It should be taken at a dosage of 3 per day.

CALLUSES

Thickening of normal skin caused by friction, usually on the hands or feet, is seen in people whose work causes repeated pressure on a particular area. Brick layers, musicians, runners, and surfers develop typical calluses. See the sections on *Corns* and *Warts* in this book.

* Eliminate undue pressure to the affected site. Wear softer and better-fitting shoes. A moleskin or foam rubber protective bandage or arch inserts often help. *Mela-Gel* and *Renew Intensive Skin Therapy* applied regularly help to prevent friction at the active site. Use *Sole to Soul Revitalizing Foot Scrub* as directed, then apply *Sole to Soul Revitalizing Foot Lotion*. Massage this in until the lotion is fully absorbed. You will be amazed at how wonderful your feet feel.

---

*Please consult your health care provider before starting any course of supplementation or treatment, particularly if you are pregnant or currently under medical care. Make sure you carefully read and understand all product packaging prior to use.

CANCER - CHEMOTHERAPY
See Chemotherapy

CANCER PREVENTION

Cancer is the second most common life-threatening condition in North America next to heart disease. One of every two citizens will develop it. Most will die despite the best care available. Prevention is still the wisest strategy. While no clear cause for cancer is known, there appears to be a combination of circumstances that greatly increases the risk.

$$\text{Cancer Risk} = \frac{\text{Hereditary Tendency} + \text{Carcinogen Exposure}}{\text{Immune Weakness} + \text{Time}}$$

Each one of us is responsible for our own health. Applying a few simple facts can give us the advantage we need. Many scientists agree that this is a reasonable formula for preventing cancer as well as most chronic degenerative illnesses.

$$\text{Cancer Prevention} = \frac{\text{Optimum Diet} + \text{Exercise \& Rest}}{\text{Positive Attitude} + \text{Lifetime Practice}}$$

*Whether you have had cancer or not, these recommendations can give you a greater measure of future cancer prevention. Many cancer researchers now believe that a combination of approaches will prove to be the best treatment. Study your family tree for patterns of specific cancer types. Breast, colorectal, skin, prostate, uterine, and lung cancers seem to be more hereditarily linked. Tobacco (cigarettes, pipe, smokeless tobacco), fatty diet (animal or cooked vegetable oils), toxic chemical exposure (household cleaners and personal care products, food additives, pesticides, herbicides, etc.), electromagnetic radiation (x-rays, TV, ultraviolet, etc.), and putrefying food in our digestive tract are the greatest known risks.

Get an annual wellness checkup from a preventive health care provider. New blood tests (PSA for prostate, etc.) are being developed to detect antigens (immune sensitive chemicals) given off by early forms of cancer. Follow your doctor's recommendations.

Remove all sources of chemical exposure from your environment (especially household chemicals), and reduce your exposure to electromagnetic radiation as much as possible. Eat as if your life depended on it, because it does! Take **ProVex**, and/or **ProVex-Plus**, and **ProVexCV** to ensure adequate antioxidants, B vitamins and essential trace minerals, all of which are associated with cancer prevention. Research findings announced at the American Association of Cancer Research conference in 1998, stated that "a potent grape seed extract, currently available as a dietary supplement, has been shown to significantly inhibit and even kill cancer cells while increasing the growth and viability of normal healthy cells."

Take **The Vitality Pak** and **Cell-Wise**. Researchers at the Arizona Cancer Center found that people who had high amounts of the trace mineral selenium had significantly less cancers. Increase your fiber intake by eating a **FiberWise** bar for a quick snack or drinking the excellent **FiberWise** drink.

Men should take **ProstAvan**, which contains lycopene. This has been found to reduce the risk of prostate cancer. Drink plenty of water and **G'Day Melaleuca Tea** to continually detoxify.

Apply **T36-C5** or **Triple Antibiotic Ointment** immediately to any suspicious skin lesion, mole, wart, skin tag, or discoloration. Continue application 2 to 4 times each day until it disappears (probably 2 to 3 weeks) or until seen by your health care provider. Laugh, sing, and play at least 30 minutes each day.

CANCER – RADIATION BURNS
See Radiation Burns

CANDIDA ALBICANS
See Thrush, Jock Itch and Yeast Infections

CANKER SORES
Mouth ulcers, known as canker sores, form on the gums and on the inside of the cheeks. They are a localized bacterial infection characterized by a white scab appearance with a bright red border. The sores may form from pinhead size to lesions the size of a dime, and are very painful. They can originate from a number of causes such as damage from brushing your teeth, biting your cheek, wearing dentures, or eating hard foods. Food allergies are often linked to repeated outbreaks. See the section on *Cold Sores* in this book.

* Brushing with **Denti-Clean Classic Tooth Polish** or **Denti-Clean Fluoride Tooth Gel** and then rinsing with **Breath-Away Mouthwash** reduces the bacterial count in the mouth. At the first sign of a canker sore, apply **T36-C5** to the injured site. Repeat every four hours.

CARBUNCLES
Carbuncles are similar to boils. This painful condition is also caused by the staphylococcus organism. Sometimes a fever will accompany a carbuncle outbreak. Healing takes longer than when treating boils and may be more difficult as well. This is especially true when the person suffering is diabetic, older or has other contributing factors that may impede a more rapid healing.

WARNING: Staphylococcus is very infectious and many strains are becoming resistant to prescription antibiotics. If fever is present, consult your health care provider immediately.

* See the section on *Boils* in this book.

---

*Please consult your health care provider before starting any course of supplementation or treatment, particularly if you are pregnant or currently under medical care. Make sure you carefully read and understand all product packaging prior to use.

CARDIOVASCULAR DISEASE

In 1912, the first case of atherosclerosis was documented in an elderly man. It was called a disease of old age, and was a novelty that took up only one paragraph of a medical textbook. By 1960, cardiovascular diseases were the number one cause of adult death in North America. The wars in Southeast Asia identified 19-year-old American soldiers killed in action who showed moderate to advanced plugging of the arteries in their hearts. In 1992, 485,000 Americans died from this disease. Researchers now suspect that dietary excesses and a sedentary existence may be the greatest contributors. Conditions such as diabetes, high LDL cholesterol, and those brought on by smoking and eating a diet low in roughage and containing over 30 percent fat, seem to be the pattern of most of those affected. Hardening of the arteries can lead to high blood pressure, shortness of breath, strokes, and cold hands and feet, as well as senility and premature aging. Oxidized cholesterol (LDL, the bad kind) and ionic calcium make up part of the "cement" that lines arteries of the liver, bowel, lungs, brain, kidneys, legs and arms. Some new research indicates that heart attacks are caused not by high levels of cholesterol, but by low levels of a B vitamin known as folic acid. There is also a study of men over 50, which found that those who had the highest blood levels of bioflavonoids (a form of vitamin C) had the smallest risk of heart disease. Every one needs a personal plan for prevention. See the sections on *Exercise* and *Cholesterol* in this book.

ProVexCV is looking better all the time. It is difficult to understand why anyone who knows about this incredible, well researched, patent pending product, is not using it. It could be because doctors are not recommending it as readily as other products. Surely, that is not because most doctors do not consider prevention cost effective.

ProVexCV does not cause gastrointestinal bleeding or strokes. It will help to prevent those problems. Some seem to think that the answer is to simply take an aspirin a day. **Do not** take aspirin unless your health care provider has recommended it for an existing heart condition. Taking it could be a serious mistake.

* Take *ProVexCV*—1 capsule per 35 lbs of body weight per day to inhibit LDL cholesterol oxidation and regulate blood platelet activity. If you are on Coumadin or other blood thinners, get your doctor's approval to take one *ProVexCV* every other day. Get tested regularly for bleeding time. If the health care provider reduces your prescription, then take one *ProVexCV* every day. *ProVexCV* is taking the place of aspirin. In a recent study done on humans, *ProVexCV* was shown to reverse coronary heart disease. *ProVexCV* is most effective if you can take half of your dosage in the morning to prevent creation of sludge and the other half of your dosage in the evening as that is when you are most likely to throw a clot.

Stop smoking and avoid smokers. Have a thorough physical examination performed to determine your risks. Follow the doctor's recommendations, and chart your progress. Avoid animal fats and cooked vegetable fats. Reduce total fat to less than 20% of your total diet. Eat two green, yellow, and orange-colored vegetables each day. Begin a gradual exercise program. A half hour of minimal exercise can give people with hardening of the arteries in their legs or arms a boost in protection from a heart attack or stroke. Eat an **Access Bar** 15 minutes before exercising in order to speed up the fat-burning process. Take **The Vitality Pak**—2 each per day and **Cell-Wise with Natural E**—2 per day.

Twenty to thirty-five grams of fiber is recommended daily for good health. **FiberWise** contains 5 grams of fiber and the bars can easily be carried for a quick snack. **ProFlex 20** is an excellent high-protein meal replacement and can be used alone or mixed with **Attain** for a delicious shake.

Periodontal disease is linked to the development of heart disease and stroke, so practice good oral hygiene. The Melaleuca **Denti-Care** program is an excellent place to start. See the *Dental – Gum Disease* section in this book.

CARPAL TUNNEL SYNDROME

Those who use their hands with a continual repetitive motion, such as computer operators, may experience a thickening of the nerve sheath in their wrists, causing numbness, coldness, and often pain. Prevention is the best line of defense. B vitamins and trace minerals are needed.

* First, eliminate the repetitive motion that caused the problem until healing is completed (often 4 to 12 weeks). Take **The Vitality Pack** as directed and saturate with **ProVex** and/or **ProVex-Plus** by taking 1 capsule for every 25 pounds of body weight for two weeks. Then gradually reduce the dose until a maintenance level is reached. In addition, take **Replenex Joint Replenishing Complex** as directed. It has also been found to be helpful to saturate with **Replenex**, at least for a short time. Apply **Pain-A-Trate** to the inside of the wrist and outside of the elbow every 4 hours to reduce inflammation and control pain. Avoid cold water. Hot water gives temporary relief.

CATARACTS

Damage from ultraviolet (UV) light, pollution, or steroid drugs can lead to cataracts. Free radical damage causes clouding of the lens of the eye, slowly producing fuzzy vision and a halo appearance to lights at night. Surgical treatment is more successful in the young and healthy. Nutrition and alternative therapy provide hope for many who are not able to have the surgery. A ten-year study showed that women with higher-than-average levels of vitamin C in their blood had almost no signs of cataracts or other vision loss. Prevention is the best treatment. See the *Eye* section in this book.

* Approved UV protection lenses should be worn by everyone who is exposed to sunlight or computer monitors. Avoid animal fats, antacids,

---

*Please consult your health care provider before starting any course of supplementation or treatment, particularly if you are pregnant or currently under medical care. Make sure you carefully read and understand all product packaging prior to use.

and excessive sugar. Take Melaleuca's *NutraView* as directed. Also take the *The Vitality Pak* and *Cell-Wise* as directed. *ProVex-Plus* will give additional protection for both the treatment and prevention of cataracts.

CAT BITES AND SCRATCHES

Bites and scratches from all animals, and man, promote infection. Cat bites and scratches are among the worst. Because of the high population of bacteria growing on the claws, scratches can be particularly bad. See the section on *Disinfectants* in this book.

* Immediately wash the area with *Antibacterial Liquid Soap* or *The Gold* or *Platinum Bar.* Apply a few drops of *Sol-U-Mel* to the wet washcloth for additional disinfecting. Apply straight *T36-C5* to deep and bleeding wounds to speed drying and to slow bleeding. Apply *Triple Antibiotic Ointment* to a sterile bandage and cover. Take *ProVex* and/or *ProVex-Plus* daily.

CERUMEN

See Earaches

CHAPPED HANDS

Chapped hands are often caused by excessive exposure to cleaners, solvents, detergents and soapy water. This condition is characterized by small cuts or cracks in the skin.

People in the northern half of the United States and those who live higher in the mountains where there's snow and cold, as well as most people throughout Canada, experience chapped hands in the winter months. It is caused by the skin becoming excessively dry due to the lack of natural oils. In cold weather, the body's oil-secreting glands produce less oil, and what's left is often removed with hand washing.

* Wash hands with *Antibacterial Liquid Soap*. Apply *Renew Intensive Skin Therapy* or *Moisturizing Hand Creme*. Massage into the skin until the oil penetrates. If skin cracks still appear, repeat washing and apply *T36-C5* to all cracked areas. As the oil is drying, reapply the lotion or creme. Repeat this procedure as often as necessary.

By regularly using Melaleuca's *Moisturizing Hand Creme* throughout the day, you can frequently alleviate chapped hands and dry skin. In some cases, particularly where the hands are washed frequently or latex gloves are being worn, *Renew Intensive Skin Therapy* would be more effective.

See the section on *Dry Skin* in this book.

CHAPPED LIPS

Wind, cold and sun take its toll on mucous membranes of the lips. Fevers, medications and certain health conditions that lead to dehydration often cause chapped lips.

---

*Please consult your health care provider before starting any course of supplementation or treatment, particularly if you are pregnant or currently under medical care. Make sure you carefully read and understand all product packaging prior to use.

* Usually cracking and pain can be prevented and restored to normal within 1 to 2 hours by applying *Sun Shades Lip Balm* every 15 to 30 minutes. *Mela-Gel* can also be used to speed recovery. In extreme cases, apply the *T36-C5* directly to the lips with the fingertip, cotton ball or a Q-tip. It does not taste great, but it is very effective.

CHEMOTHERAPY

Chemotherapy is the use of chemical agents in the treatment or control of disease or mental illness.

* Chemotherapy and the accompanying treatments can frequently leave you with little or no energy. It has been suggested that cancer patients may find that after only a few weeks of *The Vitality Pak*, *Cell Wise with Natural E*, and *ProVex-Plus*, their energy will "zoom through the roof." Nutrition is important, so *The Vitality Pak* and *Cell Wise* are excellent. *ProVex-Plus* and *ProVexCV* both contain gingko biloba, which is a mild blood thinner, and they should not be used during chemo due to lowering of platelet count and the potential for bleeding. After chemo, once the platelet count is back to normal, *ProVexCV* and *ProVex-Plus* are helpful. If you get to the point where swallowing pills becomes a challenge, you might consider crushing them in your juice or *Attain* in order to continue the level of nutrition.

When eating becomes challenging, try *Attain*. Some find it easier to tolerate when enduring chemo, and it has an excellent flavor. You might try freezing it, as sometimes it is easier to take things by mouth if they are frozen. *Sustain* will also help with energy during periods of nausea.

During chemo, mouth sores are common, and there is a potential for gum infection. Try the *Classic Tooth Polish* because it has Melaleuca oil. The *Breath-Away Mouth Wash* is also very helpful, but it must be much diluted. Use *Sun-Shades Lip Balm* for the cold sores in the corner of the mouth. It even works under lipstick. See the section on *Cold Sores* in this book. *T36-C5* used on the incision area following surgery seems to help with the deep aching.

Taking *Luminex* would be a good idea, as some depression during this sort of treatment is very common. If the cancer is breast cancer, especially estrogen-dependent breast cancer, estrogen cannot be used, but *EstrAval* is excellent. Depending on the age of the patient (if it is a woman), menopausal symptoms come on immediately, because the chemo knocks out the estrogen production, resulting in instant menopause with severe symptoms. *EstrAval* is excellent in this case.

Use *Renew Intensive Skin Therapy* and the *Moisturizing Hand Creme* on your hands regularly when taking chemo. It may help with fingernail loss.

Be sure to convert your home to the safer Melaleuca products. Having an environment without harmful products can help to prevent recurrent bouts of pneumonia and asthma, which can follow radiation damage to the lungs.

CHEST PAINS

Chest pains can be quite harmless or quite dangerous depending upon the cause. Emotional stress can cause chest tightness and localized pain. Air pollution can cause lung irritation and related chest pains. Persons who eat late in the evening, overeat, or eat in a hurry tend to have frequent indigestion and experience chest pains due to a hiatal hernia. This condition occurs when the stomach pushes up through the diaphragm due to gas in the bowel. On the other hand, when chest pain is from an occluded blood vessel, a reflex pain is usually felt extending from the chest into the left shoulder and neck area. A thorough checkup including a resting electrocardiogram is recommended for active persons over 40 in an annual physical exam. Don't procrastinate! In over half of the cases of heart disease, there are no warnings signs. A massive heart attack and death may be the only sign a doctor sees.

* See your health care provider if you have any chest pains! Listen to your body! Slow down when eating, and eat smaller portions. Decrease your dietary fat to 20% of your total calories. Begin a progressive exercise program to maximize circulation and oxygen to the diaphragm and heart. Minimize your sugar intake, since it is directly converted into fat within your body if you do not exercise enough. Maximize your lean body mass through weight training. Make sure you eat 2 fruit servings and 5 vegetable servings every day. Take *The Vitality Pak*, *Cell-Wise*, and *ProVexCV* daily to ensure adequate nutrient levels. See the sections on *Exercise*, *Hiatal Hernia*, and *Nutrition* in this book.

CHICKEN POX

This is a highly contagious disease caused by the herpes zoster virus. While chicken pox generally affects children, when it appears in adults and teenagers if can be far more serious. The incubation period is usually 14 to 21 days. The symptoms start with a skin rash. Often a fever, headache, and aching muscles are experienced. The rash changes into pimples and then blisters that enlarge and become filled with pus. The skin can become very itchy. Do not scratch the affected areas, as it could cause scarring. The blisters dry up in a few days and are covered with scales. After all the blisters have scabbed, the disease is no longer contagious.

* To help relieve symptoms, wash the affected area with *Antibacterial Liquid Soap*. Pat dry and liberally apply *T36-C5*. Allow the oil sufficient time to soak into the skin. After the rash has fully developed, usually within 2 or 3 days, soak in 1 oz. Of *Sol-U-Mel* and 1 oz. of *Renew Bath Oil* in a tub of warm water for 15 minutes to help with the itching. After soaking, pat dry and reapply the *T36-C5*. When the oil has started to be absorbed into the skin or is dry, apply either

Mela-Gel or *Renew Intensive Skin Therapy*. Repeat the process several times a day. Drinking one to four cups of *G'Day Melaleuca Tea* each day may also be helpful.

CHIGGERS

These are described as tiny red larva having a bite that causes extreme itching. Walking through the grass in the summer in the southern, southeastern and southwestern areas of the U.S. occasionally results in painful, itching eruptions on the feet, legs, and thighs. The female mite digs into the flesh and lays eggs that cause a sore. The larvae hatch and then bore under the skin, causing an intense dermatitis. Read the section on *Scabies* in this book.

* Wash the bite areas with *Antibacterial Liquid Soap*. Rub *T36-C5* on the area of the bites each morning and evening. Follow by applying *Triple Antibiotic Ointment* to prevent a secondary infection. Large areas can be treated by soaking in a bath of warm water conditioned with 1 oz. of *Sol-U-Mel* and 1 oz. of *Renew Bath Oil*.

For prevention, apply *T36-C5* to the bottom of pant cuffs, or spray pants and socks with 1 ounce of *Sol-U-Mel* diluted with 7 ounces of water.

CHILBLAIN

Chilblain is a painful swelling or sore, especially on the fingers or toes, caused by exposure to cold or poor circulation. It resembles a mild case of frostbite or trench foot, but is characterized by an itching or burning dermatitis and probably a sensitization to recurring exposure to cold. The main contributing factors may be contact with wetness or metal and inadequate clothing. Alcoholism or an underlying vascular or systemic disease can also cause it. The young and the old are especially vulnerable. Vitamin and mineral deficiencies can also contribute to chilblain.

* A good nutrition program such as the *Daily for Life Pack* can make a difference in almost any physical challenge, as can exercise and, in this case, warm clothing.

Keep your feet warm. Massage them daily with *Renew Bath Oil* or *Sole to Soul Revitalizing Foot Lotion* to stimulate circulation. Carefully apply *T36-C5* directly on the chilblain. See the section on *Frostbite* in this book.

CHOLESTEROL

Cholesterol is our body's own antioxidant protecting us against naturally occurring free radicals. It is needed for life. There is good cholesterol (made from balanced nutrition during exercise and play) and bad cholesterol (made during stress or from over-cooked animal fats). We need a certain amount of cholesterol to handle stress. We make about four times as much cholesterol in a day as we eat in our diet. Excess dietary fat (including margarine) tends to increase blood cholesterol. People who have high blood cholesterol and high stress cannot lower blood cholesterol by avoiding it in their diet. Adequate fiber and roughage in the diet carries fat and toxic substances quickly out of the body. Heat converts normal cholesterol found in animal products into oxycholesterol, which is unhealthy and toxic. The original heart disease scientists in the 1970s told us about the dangers of too much cholesterol in our blood. Today the researchers are telling us about the dangers of it being too low!

*Take *ProVexCV* and *The Vitality Pak* daily, as directed. Begin a regular exercise program, and eat an *Access Bar* 15 minutes before your workout. Put *Sustain* drink in your water (1 Tbs. per quart) while working out to maintain needed energy and electrolytes. Drink 2 to 4 cups of *G'Day Melaleuca Tea* each day.

CHRONIC FATIGUE SYNDROME (CFS)

Diagnosis of chronic fatigue and immune dysfunction syndrome (CFIDS—also known as chronic fatigue syndrome, or CFS) has only been possible in recent times. Previously the aches, pains, and tiredness that people with this condition suffered wasn't classified into a specific diagnoses, so treatment (if any) was often less than fully effective.

The outstanding symptom of CFIDS is extreme, even disabling fatigue lasting at least six months. Muscular pains, flu-like symptoms, and mood changes are also common and overlap with symptoms of fibromyalgia. The signs and symptoms of CFIDS vary from person to person and in severity.

The cause of CFIDS is unknown and therefore it is also not known whether or not it is contagious. Fortunately it is not progressive and does not lead to other serious diseases or destruction of body tissues. There is no known cure, and symptoms may come and go.

* Not much is known as to a definitive treatment for this condition; however, a healthy diet, rest, limited amount of exercise and good nutritional supplements seem to be the most effective. Stress seems to aggravate the condition appreciably.

It has been suggested that someone with chronic fatigue syndrome take 2 each per day of *The Vitality Pak,* as magnesium supplementation has produced good results. This may be due to its importance in the serotonin function of the body. In addition, take 2 per day of *Cell-Wise with Natural E*, and 3 per day of *Replenex*. *Pain-A-Trate* is an excellent topical pain relieving cream. Taking a saturation dose of the *ProVex* and/or *ProVex-Plus* should also help the arthritic-type pain. (Take 1 capsule for each 25 pounds of body weight daily for approximately two weeks. Then begin to decrease the number of daily capsules until a maintenance dose is determined.) *Luminex* may help the potential depression associated with CFIDS. See the *Immune System* section in this book.

---

*Please consult your health care provider before starting any course of supplementation or treatment, particularly if you are pregnant or currently under medical care. Make sure you carefully read and understand all product packaging prior to use.

Try the **Sustain** as a "fatigue buster." It will not make you feel wired like caffeine or sugar. The **Access Bar** can also be a tremendous help with energy.

Get a Value Pack to change your entire household to an environmentally safe atmosphere. Expect 12 to 16 weeks on the above regimen before any change is noted.

CIGARETTE SMOKING

Imagine a 747 jumbo jet filled with passengers crashing every hour of every day within the United States borders. How long would this tragedy be allowed to continue? Of all the plagues of man, cigarette smoking has probably caused more deaths and resulted in more disease than all other non-infectious causes combined. Over 50 toxic or banned substances have been identified resulting from smoking; these include carbon monoxide, carbon dioxide, dioxane, arsenic oxide, biphenyls, and cadmium salts, just to name a few. Nicotine, after the Latin name of the plant meaning nightshade, is a powerful insect repellent, aphid killer on roses, and deadly poison, which is never eaten by animals in the wild.

Smoking one cigarette reduces the infection-fighting ability of the immune system by 50 percent for 1 hour. The March of Dimes has advised against it since 1974 for causing birth defects. Second-hand smoke has been linked to a 15 percent lower IQ among children of households where at least one parent is a smoker. Nicotine is an addictive alkaloid drug related to codeine, morphine, and cocaine. Recently, cigarette companies have been accused of actually adding nicotine to their higher-priced brands to induce greater addiction and desire for their product. Many congressmen list financial holdings in the lucrative tobacco industry, which may account for the 30-year struggle to gain governmental bans of this deadly waste of human health.

* There is no greater single health measure you can take than to quit smoking and forbid the practice in your home or around your loved ones. Like any drug addiction, it must be faced with courage and compassion. If you have the personal strength to stop smoking, DO IT RIGHT NOW! If you need help, seek a health care provider who is trained in chemical addiction treatment with diet, herb, acupuncture and hypnosis. Begin a lifestyle of wellness rather than self-destruction. Take **ProVex** and/or **ProVex-Plus**, as well as **ProVexCV** daily. Take **The Vitality Pak** and **Cell-Wise** as directed. Drink 2 to 4 cups of **G'Day Melaleuca Tea** each day.

CLAVUS
See Corns

COLD
Cold viruses attack the moist, cooler regions of the nose, throat, sinuses, vocal cords, and larynx when our systems are run down. The

---

*Please consult your health care provider before starting any course of supplementation or treatment, particularly if you are pregnant or currently under medical care. Make sure you carefully read and understand all product packaging prior to use.

virus has developed a way of avoiding destruction by the immune system and is present in a dormant state. Apparently, when we contact a cold from someone else (sneeze, handshake, kiss), the two viruses exchange fragments of genetic information to form a slightly new strain. Being a new strain, it is unrecognized by the immune system. It enters living cells undetected and begins to multiply until cell damage has taken place. The immune system drives the virus into seclusion until the next opportune time arises. Mucous membranes become swollen, red and irritated as the virus spreads from one cell to the next. Untreated colds can progress into more threatening conditions.

* The common cold usually gives a warning that it is about to develop. From the earliest signs of tiredness, sneezing, and hoarseness you are given a few hours to launch an attack. Immediately take *Activate Immune Complex*—1 three times per day during a cold or flu and take a hot bath. Take *CounterAct Night-Time Cold*, *Allergy*, *Sinus Medicine* as directed. Rub *Renew Bath Oil* over the chest and back, as it will boost the immune system. Breathe the steamy vapor of five drops of *T36-C5* and water in a steam inhaler for fifteen minutes (air temperatures above 104 degrees kill the virus). Apply one drop of *T36-C5* to each nostril of your nose every four hours. Sip vegetable broth and/or Mom's chicken soup every couple of hours. Avoid any temptation to eat heavy foods as your digestive tract, including smell and taste, are on vacation for a while. If coughing is present, use *CounterAct Cough Relief Medicine* as directed. Try a hot *Sustain* drink to fight any fever you may produce. To reduce painful muscles, bathe with *Renew Bath Oil* frequently. "Drown the cold" with *G'Day Melaleuca Tea*, by drinking one cup per hour. Take *The Vitality Pak*—2 each per day and *Cell-Wise with Natural E*—2 per day. You should also take 2 capsules of *ProVex Plus* each day. Get all the rest you can.

Some prefer to be a little more aggressive in the beginning of a cold by taking 5 *Activate* throughout the day for the first three days of symptoms and increasing *The Vitality Pak* to three each per day.

Getting rid of a cold quickly can be very challenging, but it cannot hurt to try. Maybe the wonderful Melaleuca products will dispel the childhood doctor's theory that you will get rid of a cold in 7 days if you treat it and in a week if you don't.

COLD SORES

Very painful, clear, fluid-filled eruptions on the border of the mouth form hard, oozing scabs resulting from an infection of either the herpes simplex or herpes facialis virus. Once thought to be more common in infants and children, adults are becoming more susceptible. The infection makes chewing difficult and may impede the appetite. Mild damage associated with exposure to the sun, stress, abrasions from a toothbrush, bad allergies to certain foods, the onset of menstruation, or any disease that produces a fever or increases metabolic rate may

---

*Please consult your health care provider before starting any course of supplementation or treatment, particularly if you are pregnant or currently under medical care. Make sure you carefully read and understand all product packaging prior to use.

produce a lesion. As a rule, the symptoms generally go away after 7 to 10 days. Dehydration and secondary infections give reason for concern. Those having secondary health problems where intake of food and liquid are essential (such as seniors, very young children, diabetics, or those with low blood sugar) need to be particularly careful that their cold sores don't interfere with any other medical problems they may be experiencing.

Since cold sores are a virus, they don't respond to antibiotics. Modern medicine appears sometimes to be at a loss as to how to "fix" the problem. Maybe that is one reason treatment will too often be centered on alleviating pain and preventing the spread of other infections rather than seeking the source of the problem and eliminating it. See the section on *Canker Sores* in this book.

* Since the virus feeds on an excessive intake of the amino acid arginine, diets avoiding citrus fruit and nuts should be followed. Supplementation with the amino acid L-Lysine, found in most health food stores, is advised to stop the early spread of the infection.

In 1991, a clinical study by Mayo and Shemesh, revealed the effectiveness of Melaleuca oil for the treatment of this difficult and recurring challenge. Dab *T36-C5* on the lesions immediately upon detection. Repeat every hour until the lesion either disappears or comes to a head. If it comes to a head, continue to apply *T36-C5* once every two hours followed by *Mela-Gel* or *Renew Intensive Skin Therapy*. For persistent or large surface sores, use *Triple Antibiotic Ointment* every four hours.

For sores in the mouth, gargle with 10 drops *T36-C5* blended with a half-cupful of warm water. Repeat several times daily. Dab *T36-C5* onto your finger or a Q-tip and apply to the affected area. Regularly use *Breath-Away Mouth Wash*, *Melaleuca's Denti-Clean Classic Tooth Polish* and the *Hot* or *Cold Shot Mouth & Throat Spray*.

COLIC

Chronic severe abdominal pain can be caused from a number of conditions. Some may be life-threatening. Newborns may experience colic when the digestive system has not developed enough to handle food properly. Gas or constipation is the usual cause of the abdominal pain. Heavy metal poisoning (lead, copper, zinc, cadmium, etc.), food or environmental allergies, ovarian cysts, gallstones, kidney stones, intestinal parasites, pesticide residue from produce, food poisoning, chlorine poisoning, and chronic constipation can all cause colic.

* Get a thorough examination from your health care provider to identify the cause of the abdominal pain. Chiropractic adjustments can be effective in giving relief. *ProVex* can also give relief. A hot moist pack with *Pain-A-Trate* on the affected area may be beneficial.

Soak fruits and vegetables in 2 quarts of cold water and ½ tsp. of *Sol-U-Mel* for 1 minute, then rinse in pure water. Detoxify by using only steamed and juiced vegetables at least one meal each day. Drink 1 to 2 quarts of water, plus 2 to 4 cups of *G'Day Melaleuca Tea* per day. Eat the *FiberWise* bars as a snack or try the *FiberWise* drink for a perfect nutritional boost. Exercise regularly.

For the infant suffering from colic, there are several treatments to consider. The food source is the first possible problem. Mother's milk is best for an infant, at least for the first year. If colic is present, the mother may need to be careful not to eat any rich, spicy, or gas-forming food. Also, if she is experiencing stress, her milk may be affected, so she needs to stay calm and get plenty of rest. Do not introduce any other foods for the baby until advised by your health care provider. If the baby is drinking formula, he may be having an allergic food reaction. A change in formula may be needed. Gas is a common cause for colic. Gently but firmly patting the baby on his back or bottom should help eliminate the gas. Giving the baby a pacifier may help reduce tension and colic. If constipation is a serious concern, a health care provider will suggest some possible solutions for the baby.

To correct colic in infants, give several teaspoons of warm *G'Day Melaleuca Tea* during the day and before bedtime. Many infants have also found relief when given *ProVex* once daily. Simply open a capsule and dissolve the *ProVex* in distilled water, juice, or expressed breast milk. Chiropractic adjustments are also effective for correction of colic in infants.

COLITIS

Colitis is a chronic, inflammatory, and ulcerative disease of the colon. The disease may occur at any age, but it most frequently attacks young adults aged 20-40. It usually appears as a series of bloody diarrhea attacks of varying intensity and duration.

Ulcerative colitis and Crohn's disease are similar conditions that can be extremely painful and even temporarily disabling. Both involve loss of appetite, abdominal pain, general fatigue, weight loss, diarrhea, and rectal bleeding. The main difference between the two conditions is the degree of involvement of the wall of the intestinal tract. The cause or causes of most cases of colitis and Crohn's disease are unknown, but infectious agents such as bacteria cause some cases. This type of damage is often associated with the use of antibiotics, which alter the normal bowel flora and permit microorganisms that are normally held in check to proliferate. The symptoms can range from simple diarrhea to the more severe type of symptoms associated with ulcerative colitis. Other possible contributing factors include poor eating habits, stress and food allergies.

* The most important thing you can do is keep a daily record of what you eat and what symptoms you experience. By checking your daily record, you can see what food or foods have caused flare-ups or made you feel better.

Good nutrition is always a first choice for any challenging illness. Start with a high-fiber, low-fat diet. Keeping the colon healthy is critical. Lots of fiber cleanses the body, removes toxins, and helps to dilute, bind, and deactivate many carcinogens. Twenty to thirty-five grams of fiber each day will change your life. *FiberWise* drink and bars are excellent and taste great. Metamucil orange flavor requires two servings to be equivalent in fiber content to one serving of *FiberWise*. The ingredients in *FiberWise* are three times more healthful, and the cost is just 20% more. In addition, Metamucil orange uses aspartame.

FiberWise contains all fiber sources including natural psyllium seed husks, rice bran, apples, beets, and whole grains. It contains vitamins A, C, and E, which are necessary to protect the mucous membranes of the digestive tract and aid in healing. Also included are prebiotics and probiotics such as fructooliogosaccharides and acidophilus which combat symptoms of colitis and Crohn's disease and returns intestinal flora to a healthier balance. In addition, most herbs recommended for treatment are included in *FiberWise*.

In addition to the fiber supplements, make sure your diet contains these high fiber foods: whole-grain cereals and flour, brown rice, all kinds of bran, most fresh fruit, dried prunes, nuts, flaxseeds, beans, lentils, peas, and fresh raw vegetables. Leave the skin on apples and potatoes. Coat chicken in corn bran or oats before baking. Add extra bran to cereals and breads. Melaleuca's *FiberWise* bar is an excellent, delicious substitute for a candy bar, and is packed with 5 grams of dietary fiber.

Eat a low-carbohydrate, high-vegetable, high-protein diet. Keep fats and oils out of your diet, and stay away from high-fat milk and cheeses. Fats and oils worsen the diarrhea that comes with colitis. Eat cooked foods broiled or baked. Avoid fried or sautéed foods. Avoid sauces made with butter. Avoid all carbonated soft drinks, spicy foods, and anything containing caffeine. These substances irritate the colon, aggravate symptoms, and deplete the body of important vitamins and minerals. Avoid red meat, refined sugar, and all processed foods. Try soy-based cheese instead of dairy cheese. Try soymilk or rice milk instead of cow's milk. Try soy burger instead of ground beef. (Boca Burger is available at grocery stores and makes a delicious, healthful meat substitute.)

Drink plenty of liquids—at least eight 8-ounce glasses of water daily to make up for the fluid lost with diarrhea. Carrot and cabbage juices are also good. Do not eat fruit on an empty stomach. Fruit juices should be diluted with water and taken during or after meals.

Take a high-quality organic multi-mineral/vitamin complex. Make sure it contains a di-basic calcium phosphate (not carbonate), chromium, magnesium, and zinc. Malabsorption of these minerals is a problem with colitis and Crohn's disease. Calcium is also needed for easing spasms and prevention of cancer, which may occur due to constant irritation. (*The Vitality Pak* from Melaleuca has been proven to

*Please consult your health care provider before starting any course of supplementation or treatment, particularly if you are pregnant or currently under medical care. Make sure you carefully read and understand all product packaging prior to use.

be the most bio-available supplement to date due to a unique patented fructose compounding process. It also includes important enzymes and amino acids.)

Glucosamine HCL is an important component in the protective mucous secretions of the digestive tract. **Replenex** offers the most potent glucosamine HCL to date, with the benefits of green tea leaf extract, ginger root exact, and bromelain, which is a protcolytic enzyme that aids in digestion and helps reduce inflammation.

Avoid antibiotics and drug therapy as much as possible. These prescriptions drugs will not create health, and they are not designed for long-term use. In the end, they often cause more harm. It is usually best to try health-promoting alternatives first. If they don't work, then go for the traditional drug therapy.

ProVex-Plus should also be added to your daily routine, as it is effective for any "itis" or inflammation. Take it as directed.

COMPRESS

Compresses are made from sterile, folded pieces of bandage, cotton, or linen that can be put on wounds that are draining. They may be hot or cold. They are a proven remedy for infections, varicose veins, and many other ailments because they work slowly and deeply. The compress produces a unique healing component with **T36-C5**.

* Put 3 to 6 drops of **T36-C5** onto a wet cotton ball or a washcloth, depending on the size of the affected area, and leave it in place for at least one hour. See the section on *Poultice* in this book.

CONGESTION

See Sinus Congestion

CONJUNCTIVITIS

An irritation of the pink skin flap of the eyelid can be caused by a bacterial infection (often contagious), allergy (itching and burning), or chemical contact (red and painful). Children often get contagious "pink eye" from playmates. Consult your health care provider.

* Great relief can come simply from rinsing the eye in warm distilled water several times a day. Often this one treatment will allow the eyelid to heal. Some have had good success treating mild conjunctivitis in the early stage by putting 5 drops of **T36-C5** in a warm air vaporizer and slowing blinking the eyes carefully in the direct path of the vapor. Repeat every 5 minutes for three consecutive doses before bed. Repeat morning and night for 3 days. If the irritation persists, see your health care provider. Take **ProVex** and/or **ProVex-Plus** daily.

It has also been suggested that it would be helpful to place a moistened **G'Day Melaleuca Herbal Tea** bag over the closed eye.

NOTE: Do not put any Melaleuca products directly on the eye. Use only products that are certified ophthalmologic grade.

CONSTIPATION

It is healthy and normal to have a bowel movement within one to two hours after eating. Wastes, including undigested fiber, pass out of the healthy body within 12 hours after eating the meal. Poor diet, lack of exercise, not drinking enough water, stress, and many drugs can cause constipation. We are a constipated society. Colorectal diseases are at an epidemic level. See the section on *Hemorrhoids* in this book.

* The following four things help most sufferers of constipation: eat enough fiber, drink enough liquids, get enough exercise to maintain bowel mobility, and don't worry so much. Specifically, get 20 to 30 grams of fiber each day. (*Note:* 1 medium apple + ½ cup of old-fashioned oatmeal + ¼ cup raisins + 2 carrots + 1 cup of broccoli + ½ cup of cooked beans = 10 grams of fiber). Eat *FiberWise* bars—2 per day to maximize fiber. *FiberWise* drink is also an excellent way to increase dietary fiber. *FiberWise* drink and bars contain 5 grams of fiber per serving and healthy biotics to help maintain digestive balance and keep you regular. Drink 1 to 3 quarts of water including *G'Day Melaleuca Tea* each day. *The Vitality Pak* should be taken—2 each per day as well as *Cell-Wise with Natural E*—2 per day. Take *ProVex-Plus* at the rate of 1 capsule for each 25 lbs of body weight each day. Run, walk, jog, bike, or swim, etc. for 30 minutes each day. Replace thought of fear or worry with happy, optimistic thoughts. This releases hormones in the bowel, which aids digestive juices and propels food along through the bowel and out of the body.

CORAL CUTS

Coral cuts are often jagged and irregular, and they harbor bacteria. This necessitates thorough cleansing and disinfecting. Some form of aggressive treatment should always be initiated whenever any coral cuts have been incurred. See the section on *Disinfectants* in this book.

* Thoroughly cleanse with pure water and *Antibacterial Liquid Soap* enriched with *Sol-U-Mel*. Remove particles of sand and coral. Apply *T36-C5* or *T40-C3* for maximum disinfecting. Suturing wounds that cut through the skin and into muscle speeds healing and reduces secondary infection. Apply *Triple Antibiotic Ointment* over the stitches, if applicable, and cover with a gauze bandage. Daily inspect the wound for redness or swelling, which gives indication of the spread of infection. When sutures are not needed, soak affected areas in a solution of 1 ounce of *Sol-U-Mel*, 1 ounce of *Renew Bath Oil,* plus ¼ cup of Epsom salt in 1 quart of hot water. Rinse open wounds daily with 1 ounce of *Sol-U-Mel* in 1 pint of water. Change the dressing daily and reapply *Triple Antibiotic Ointment* or *Mela-Gel.*

CORNS

Corns are raised areas of hyperkeratosis or thick, callused skin that are caused by friction or pressure over a bony extension of the foot, such as the ball or the toe joints. Hard corns occur over the toes, and soft corns occur between the toes. Corns may ache spontaneously or become very tender upon pressure. Properly fitting shoes will help prevent corns. See the section on *Calluses* in this book.

* Soak your feet in a solution of 1 ounce of *Sol-U-Mel* and 1 ounce of *Renew Bath Oil* in 1 quart of hot water for 15 minutes. Dry them thoroughly and apply *T36-C5* followed by *Mela-Gel* or *Renew Intensive Skin Therapy*. Repeat twice daily until the corn softens enough to painlessly remove with tweezers. Apply *Triple Antibiotic Ointment* or *Mela-Gel* and cover the area with a small bandage. **Sole to Soul Revitalizing Foot Scrub** and **Sole to Soul Revitalizing Foot Lotion** can also be used to cleanse and stimulate circulation. Wear only shoes that fit properly.

A 1972 study by Dr. M. Walker indicted a significant degree of success using tea tree oil to treat corns and other problems related to health conditions of the feet.

WARNING: Long-term diabetics often suffer from poor circulation to areas furthest from the heart. Because of the delicacy of their condition, diabetics especially should consult a health care provider before initiating any idea—including any of the ones mentioned in this book.

CORYZA

See Cold

COUGHS

Our bodies produce phlegm and mucous in the throat and lungs when exposed to severe temperature changes, chemical irritation, or allergens. We instinctively cough to remove this phlegm and foreign substances. Smoking is the most common cause of chronic coughs.

Severe coughs can cause bleeding in the throat or even an inner ear infection. They can also be one of the body's early warning signs. Persistent coughs may indicate a potentially serious medical problem. Contact your health care provider, particularly if there are other medical problems present. If coughing is caused by a common irritant, or by the flu or a cold, the following may help alleviate symptoms.

* Treat the cause and eliminate your exposure to the irritating substances.

In mild cases, breathe the vapor of 5 drops of *T36-C5* in a bowl of steaming water for 15 minutes while holding your head over the bowl. Make a tent over your head and the bowl with a bath towel. Repeat morning and evening. Drink the *G'Day Melaleuca Tea* throughout the day. Use *CounterAct Cough Relief Medicine* as directed. If congestion

---

exists, use *CounterAct Night-Time Cold*, *Allergy*, *Sinus Medicine* as directed.

For a more serious cough, apply *T36-C5* followed by *Moisturizing Hand Creme* on your upper chest and around your throat. Dab *T36-C5* under each nostril, as this will help you breathe easier.

Placing a cool mist humidifier by your bed each night with 10 drops of *T36-C5 Melaleuca Oil* and 2 capfuls of *Sol-U-Mel*, added to the water will help with your breathing and thus your cough. Also, try placing a few drops of *T36-C5* on your pillow at night.

Try these simple dietary tips: eliminate milk and milk products, substituting other sources of calcium; eat garlic regularly for its antibiotic effects; and eat fresh horseradish and hot mustard to help liquefy bronchial secretions.

CRABS
See Scabies

CRACKED SKIN
See Dry Skin

CRADLE CAP
Cradle cap is a yellowish scaling and crusted area on the top of the scalp of an infant during the first month of life. The scales may pile up because the mother is afraid to wash the baby's scalp thoroughly. The face may also be affected. Cradle cap is more extensive in chubby infants. Susceptibility to bacterial infection and candidiasis is increased.

* Make a very diluted mixture of *T36-C5* blended with olive oil. Combine thoroughly and apply to the affected area. Leave it on for several minutes before shampooing with the *Koala Kids No Tears Shampoo*.

CRAMPS
Sudden decreases in tissue oxygen, decreases in muscle or nerve calcium levels, or hormonal changes before menstrual flow can trigger muscle cramps. Side aches during or after strenuous exercise are due to diaphragm spasms caused from low oxygen and low calcium levels in that muscle.

* After eating a meal, wait 45 minutes before exercising. Properly stretch and warm muscles before exercise. *Mela-Cal* taken 4 times per day and at bedtime can prevent sub-optimum levels of calcium in the blood and prevent cramps. Eat an *Access Bar* 15 minutes before exercise. Drink *Sustain* drink during and immediately after exercise. A warm bath and a good massage can help reduce pain greatly. Massage *Pain-A-Trate* into muscles that cramp easily. The therapeutic dose of *ProVex* (1 capsule for every 25 pounds of body weight per day) can also give good relief, as can *CounterAct Extra-Strength Acetaminophen* or *CounterAct Ibuprofen*. See the section on *Leg Cramps* in this book.

CROHN'S DISEASE

Crohn's is a disease that is passed on through genetics. A person with Crohn's can expect to have it the rest of their life, but how it affects them depends on whether or not they get it under control and whether or not they keep it under control.

With Crohn's, if your intestines stay ulcerated, it can lead to cancer, so many times the irritated section of the intestine is removed. It can also cause a low immune system, irregular absorption of nutrients and can lead to blindness.

* The *Daily for Life Pack* has been very effective for some people with Crohn's. It has helped avoid additional surgery and has restored energy levels. The *Mela-Gel* has also been suggested for the fistulas. See the *Immune System* section in this book. Crohn's disease is similar in many ways to colitis. Reviewing the section on *Colitis* in this book will be very helpful.

CUTICLES

The rolled skin at the edge of the fingernails and toenails can give evidence of your general health. Dry cuticles, which split and become infected, are often due to exposure to harsh soaps or solvents such as gasoline or paint thinner. See the section on *Dry Skin* in this book.

* After washing your hands with *Antibacterial Liquid Soap* or *The Gold* or *Platinum Bar*, apply *Moisturizing Hand Creme* and work it into the cuticles to prevent dryness. Apply *Triple Antibiotic Ointment* or *Mela-Gel* to the infected cuticles. See your health care provider for further advice.

CUTS

Cuts are narrow slices or slashes that break the skin's surface. When skin is cut the immediate area becomes red and inflamed. White blood cells, which fight infection, rush to the site. As cuts heal, scabs form natural bandages that protect the injured site.

If the object that caused the injury was dirty or exposed to disease-causing organisms, extra care must be taken in thorough cleaning. Cuts should be treated soon after injury. Serious cuts can lead to further complications and should be treated by a health care provider immediately.

* Clean the affected area with a washcloth, warm water, and *Antibacterial Liquid Soap* and/or *Sol-U-Mel*. Pat dry and apply *T36-C5*, followed by *Renew Intensive Skin Therapy*, *Mela-Gel* or *Triple Antibiotic Ointment*. Cuts heal faster and have less opportunity to develop infection if this suggestion is used as soon as an injury occurs. Keep the cut clean with a bandage and check the healing progress daily.

---

*Please consult your health care provider before starting any course of supplementation or treatment, particularly if you are pregnant or currently under medical care. Make sure you carefully read and understand all product packaging prior to use.

Reclean and apply new bandages as often as needed. Deep or wide cuts may require a visit to your health care provider for suturing.

WARNING: Tetanus can occur when cuts are deep or contaminated. If it has been more than five years since your last tetanus shot, immediately contact your health care provider. The majority of victims dying from tetanus are older adults who have not kept current on their booster shots.

CYSTITIS
See Bladder Infection

DANDRUFF
This dry flaking of the scalp is one of the most common conditions affecting nearly one half of Americans. White, scaly skin sloughs off of the head in a "snow storm" fashion to disgrace the victim. At one time, it was believed that dandruff was caused by poor personal hygiene. Occasionally it is an indication of extremely dry skin. Home remedies usually consist of trying to increase the scalp's oil, which just creates more dandruff.

Many dermatologists believe that dandruff is another form (albeit a mild one) of seborrheic dermatitis, which can be caused by a yeast-like fungus. Seborrheic dermatitis is an inflammation of the skin that can appear on the scalp and eyebrows. It is characterized by flaky, white, scaly skin that sloughs off, leaving a dry or greasy scalp that produces the itching so common with dandruff.

There are others who believe dandruff is caused by using harsh detergents, soaps, and chemical-laden shampoos that challenge normal skin bacteria. Other factors may include Candida albicans, stress, inadequate blood circulation to hair sites, and even inadequate diets.

* Avoid harsh soaps, shampoos, and chemical-laden hair care products. Shampoo with *Naturals Melaleuca Oil Shampoo* once or twice a day while dandruff is present. Leave the *Naturals Melaleuca Oil Shampoo* on the scalp for at least three minutes before rinsing. It contains an abundance of healing *T36-C5 Melaleuca Oil* and works particularly well in the treatment of common scalp conditions such as dandruff. Since this shampoo contains conditioner, do not use an extra conditioner, as it could be a scalp irritant.

Also, check your diet and make sure that you are getting an adequate supply of balanced nutrition. *The Vitality Pak*, along with Melaleuca's other nutritional supplements, are worth a closer look.

DECAY
See Dental – Decay

DECIDUOUS TEETH
See Baby Teeth

---

*Please consult your health care provider before starting any course of supplementation or treatment, particularly if you are pregnant or currently under medical care. Make sure you carefully read and understand all product packaging prior to use.

DENTAL – DECAY

Dentists have done an admirable job in helping prevent tooth decay. Brushing, flossing and washing after eating have become a way of life for most of us. Nonetheless, some decay still takes place. Some dentists and scientists argue that the use of fluoride, while definitely reducing tooth decay, may pose a greater risk in the long run to the general health of the body.

Refined foods (mainly sugar in its many forms) promote rapid yeast, bacterial, and other microorganism growth in the many cracks and crevices in and around the teeth. These microbes secrete acids, which erode the calcium-rich enamel of the teeth. Proper brushing and flossing habits are essential to reduce the microbial population.

* Gently brush the teeth and tongue after every meal with *Denti-Clean Classic Tooth Polish*. Swish your mouth with *Breath-Away Mouthwash* to reduce mouth microbes as well as to control jungle breath. Floss frequently with *Exceed Waxed Dental Floss* and chew *Insta-Fresh Gum*. Take *ProVex* and/or *ProVex-Plus* to help prevent plaque buildup. Have regular checkups with your dentist to maintain healthy teeth.

For a painful tooth, apply a small amount of *T36-C5* to the gum surrounding the tooth. It will help with the pain until a dentist can be contacted. See the section on *Toothache* in this book.

DENTAL – GUM DISEASE

Also known as periodontal disease, gum disease is the plague of modern times. Over 90% of Americans have it, and some reports indicate that every one of us suffers with it to some degree. It should be of concern to everyone.

Conditions range from a mild inflammation to severe gum recession and bone loss. Inflammation of the gums, or gingivitis, is the most common gum disease and is due primarily to infection within the tissues. See the section on *Gingivitis* in this book.

We should be very aware of periodontal disease, as it is linked to the development of adult onset diabetes, heart disease, and stroke. In addition, pregnant women with gum disease have seven times the normal risk of delivering pre-term, low birthweight babies.

* Use a Q-tip or your finger to apply *T36-C5 Melaleuca Oil* directly to the affected region of the gums. Melaleuca oil soothes inflamed gum tissues and, while it does not have one of the greatest tastes in the world, it does taste like it is working and accelerating the healing process. Not only for the benefits of healing, but for prevention as well, use the entire *Denti-Care System*. There are four toothpastes including a bubblegum tasting one for children. Any one of them will prove to be better than most store-bought brands, but *Classic Tooth Polish* is the one usually recommended for overall oral health.

Take *The Vitality Pak* for vital nutrients along with *Cell-Wise* to help repair connective tissue around the teeth. Take *ProVex* or *ProVex-Plus* to help reduce inflammation of the gum tissues, and to help prevent plaque buildup.

Taking good care of your teeth not only provides good oral hygiene, but also may help you to avoid disease you probably don't associate with your teeth and gums. Be sure to get adequate calcium and vitamin C to keep teeth and gums healthy. *The Vitality Pak*, which includes *Mela-Cal*, is an excellent place to start. Also, brush your teeth with a soft-bristled brush for at least two and a half minutes and then floss. Use a fine bristled rotary brush, if possible. Change your toothbrush once a month and get regular dental checkups.

DEPRESSION

One of the most common conditions experienced by adults and young people is occasional depression. This is exemplified by an attitude that "I don't feel like doing what I normally would like to do." It is normal for someone to feel blue or have an attitude of melancholy from time to time due to undesirable situations. It is another thing to see a black cloud cast over the future. Some people actually develop a sort of regular "gloom and doom" attitude if depression is allowed to persist. Nutritional deficiencies or fast foods often provoke such feelings. Exposure to household chemicals and food additives may also contribute. If a cause for the depressed mood can be identified, then the cause should be treated. Menopause can also increase the need for estrogen stabilization to control mild depression.

Fortunately mild depression is one of the most treatable mental conditions. The first step toward a cure is to recognize the symptoms:

A sullen mood
Feelings of hopelessness, guilt and anxiety
Loss of interest in things that used to be pleasurable
Change in appetite
Change in sleeping patterns
Inability to concentrate
Lack of energy or feeling run down

* Having a positive support group during times of depression is of great benefit. Take *Luminex*—1 three times each day, along with *The Vitality Pak*—2 each per day, *Cell-Wise with Natural E*—2 per day, and *ProVex* and/or *ProVex-Plus*. *EstrAval* can be taken as directed to reduce mild depression during menopause. A good nutritional system is essential to good health. Minerals are like catalysts; they are involved with almost all reactions in the body. Getting balanced minerals into the cells is critical. Studies have shown that these products can make a remarkable difference in not only mild depression, but also schizophrenia, bi-polar affective disorders and even fibromyalgia.

Drinking 1 to 2 cups of *G'Day Melaleuca Tea* daily and eating and exercising regularly each day can be very helpful. Allow approximately 2 to 4 weeks before you expect to see results.

Harmful household chemicals should be eliminated and replaced with Melaleuca's biologically safe ones.

DERMATITIS

Dermatitis is an inflammation that can be caused by an outside irritant that can produce itchy, red skin. It can, when irritated, ooze, crust, scale, and develop vesicles. These can develop suddenly and be short-lived or can become chronic in nature. In the chronic stages, dermatitis is evidenced by dry, scaly and thickened skin patches. Chronic dermatitis is commonly known as eczema. See the section on *Eczema* in this book.

Healthy skin is able to withstand exposure to many natural substances and some synthetic chemicals without harmful effects. It is designed to be our first line of defense against the outside world. Substances that irritate the skin include plants such as poison ivy or poison oak, some trees, fruits and vegetables. Other irritants include fabrics such as wool and synthetics, as well as toxic household cleaners and chemicals. In addition to these external sources, there are internal conditions such as allergies, sensitivities to foods, prescriptions, and over-the-counter drugs.

* Reduce the amount of toxins in the air in your home by converting your home to Melaleuca cleaning and personal care products. Many cases of dermatitis are greatly reduced by switching to the *EcoSense Laundry System* and laundering all clothing, linens, and towels. Try to identify the cause of the dermatitis before aggressively treating the symptoms.

As soon as possible after the symptoms begin, wash the area with *Antibacterial Liquid Soap* or *The Gold* or *Platinum Bar*. Additional soaking in a warm tub with 1 ounce of *Sol-U-Mel* and 1 ounce of *Renew Bath Oil* once daily is advised. Use *Renew Intensive Skin Therapy* twice daily. *Triple Antibiotic Ointment* is also effective. In addition, *Advanced Expressions Moisturizing Shampoo for Dry or Treated Hair* is highly recommended for a dry and scaly scalp.

CAUTION: Avoid using pure Melaleuca oil to treat any dermatitis condition.

DETOXIFICATION

To detoxify is to cleanse your body of toxic chemicals.

* There are many ways to detoxify your body. Some are very unpleasant. Using the Melaleuca products to detoxify is a much more pleasant experience and in many cases works just as well.

One suggestion is to stop taking *The Vitality Pak* and drink eight glasses of **Melaleuca G'Day Herbal Tea** each day for two weeks. It is important to exercise regularly and drink plenty of water.

FiberWise drink and bars are very effective at detoxification because of the high level of fiber. A high-fiber and low-fat diet is a good place to start. Using the **Attain** or **Sustain** will certainly help with the 20-35 grams of fiber you need daily. Adding fiber to your diet will not only remove the toxins, but also it will bind, dilute, and deactivate the carcinogens.

DIABETES

Juvenile-onset diabetes appears to be due to a defective gene that causes self-destruction of insulin-producing cells in the pancreas. Insulin must then be taken regularly to support life.

Adult-onset diabetes, on the other hand, appears to be due to suppression or inhibition of normal pancreas production. Being over 55 years of age, overweight, lacking exercise, and consuming large amounts of refined sugar and dietary fat (more than 20% of daily calories), is the typical picture. Usually, insulin is unnecessary but a pancreatic stimulant drug is often prescribed.

* Drink 2 to 4 cups of **G'Day Melaleuca Tea** each day, and take **The Vitality Pak**—2 each per day and **Cell-Wise with Natural E**—2 per day. Take **ProVexCV** at the therapeutic dose level (one capsule per 35 pounds of body weight daily). This increases circulation and reduces the incidence of many diabetic symptoms. Heart disease has been shown to be one of the most serious possible side effects of diabetes. These supplements are very important to protect the eyesight of diabetics and should be taken by any diabetic suffering from neuropathy, retinopathy, kidney problems, or circulation problems.

The **American Journal of Clinical Nutrition** reported when working with insulin-dependent diabetics that 45% of all insulin-dependent diabetics that they tested significantly reduced their insulin requirement after only 16 days on a high-fiber diet. Seventy-five percent of all insulin-dependent diabetics significantly reduced their insulin after only a few weeks. *CAUTION:* Monitor your blood sugar carefully. You may have to adjust your insulin accordingly.

NOTE: Be careful to work **FiberWise** into your food exchange because it does have some sugar.

Blood sugar levels can be somewhat regulated using the **Access Bars** and/or **Sustain**. (Try a small amount at first and adjust to fit your personal needs and tolerance level.) Make exercise and a low-fat, low-sugar diet a way of life. A healthy nutritional program is important no matter what the challenging condition.

For the best mouth health, use **Denti-Clean Classic Tooth Polish**, **Exceed Waxed Dental Floss**, and **Breath-Away Mouthwash** at least twice daily. For the quickest healing of wounds, use **Mela-Gel** and **T36-C5**. **NutraView** should be taken as directed to safeguard your vision.

---

*Please consult your health care provider before starting any course of supplementation or treatment, particularly if you are pregnant or currently under medical care. Make sure you carefully read and understand all product packaging prior to use.

Some find that taking *Luminex* three times each day and *ProVex-Plus* four times each day is also very helpful.

See the sections on *Dental – Gum Disease, Diabetic Foot Ulcerations*, and *Diabetic Gangrene* in this book.

DIABETIC FOOT ULCERATIONS

Ulcerations frequently occur in those who are over the age of 40 and have had diabetes for more than 10 years. Other contributing factors include obesity, lack of exercise and improper care of the feet. Diabetes causes blood vessel walls to thicken. This decreases the blood flow to the feet and lower legs. Some diabetics suffer from neuropathy and poor circulation. Neuropathy is a condition that causes damage to the foot and leg nerves. It makes feet numb and unable to feel heat, cold, pressure, cuts or bruises. These conditions can combine to create a situation where even routine cuts, blisters and scrapes can develop into gangrene. If not treated aggressively, gangrene will result in limb amputation.

* Soak your feet in a tubful of warm water to which you have added 1 tablespoon of *Renew Bath Oil* and 1 capful of *Sol-U-Mel*. After soaking for 10 to 15 minutes, dry and liberally apply *T36-C5* to any sores or lesions. As this is drying, apply a thin coating of *Renew Intensive Skin Therapy*, *Mela-Gel* or even *Moisturizing Hand Creme*. Taking time to soak your feet will give you an opportunity to conduct your requisite daily foot inspection. See also *Diabetic Gangrene*.

DIABETIC GANGRENE

Diabetic gangrene is a complication of diabetes, causing the tissue to die. As the condition progresses, amputation of the affected limb is the traditional course of action.

* Dr. A. Penfold was successfully using tea tree oil on severe cases of diabetic gangrene as early as 1936. It is recommended that *T36-C5* or *T40-C3* be massaged into the affected area and the surrounding tissue for as long as needed. The area can also be treated with *Mela-Gel* or *Triple Antibiotic Ointment*, preferably on top of the oil. Frequently, the longer the condition exists, the longer it may take to get results. Coordinate this with your health care provider.

DIAPER RASH

Diaper rash is caused by friction and irritation in the presence of moisture. It is a common skin irritation affecting babies, who have otherwise healthy skin. It triggers yeast to grow. This occurs naturally when wet diapers are not changed promptly. Babies will vary in their susceptibility to developing diaper rash. Keeping the skin as dry as possible is one of the best methods of prevention. Hospital nurseries often harbor resistant strains of these organisms, and you may bring them home in your new bundle of joy. Elderly or incontinent adults must also be aware of this challenge.

* Proper laundering of all baby clothing as well as diapers in **Mela-Power Laundry Detergent** enriched with 1 capful of **Sol-U-Mel** and 1 to 2 teaspoons of **Mela-Brite**, will ensure that both colors and whites will be bright and clean-smelling.

Antibacterial Liquid Soap or *The Gold* or *Platinum Bar* should be used to bathe your baby. After towel drying, allow the skin to air dry (in direct sunlight if possible) for a few minutes. Apply *Renew Intensive Skin Therapy* or *Moisturizing Hand Creme* to form a natural moisture barrier on the skin before diapering.

NOTE: *Sol-U-Mel* should not be used in a baby's bath water, as the green soap in it may irritate sensitive skin (newborn babies lack active sweat glands).

DIARRHEA

A sudden increase in stool volume, fluidity, or frequency of fecal excretion is seen with microbial infections, flu viruses, stress, food poisoning, laxatives, certain genetic and malabsorption problems, and electrolyte loss from vomiting or drugs. The greatest concern is depletion of body fluids resulting in vascular collapse (the heart has nothing to pump). Children under the age of 4 can dehydrate quickly and die from uncontrolled diarrhea.

* Determine the cause, if possible. If there is abdominal pain, fever, or if the diarrhea does not resolve rapidly, seek emergency help without delay. Otherwise, begin drinking *G'Day Melaleuca Tea*, 4 to 16 ounces every hour along with *Sustain* drink for energy and nutrient replacement.

DISINFECTANTS

Disinfectants work by selectively reducing the population of disease-causing germs to make room for the friendly germs without harming humans or household plants and animals. Sanitation engineers have taught us that in order to control the spread of disease, we must control the number and transportability of disease-causing germs. Several products are effective and especially stand out for their use in making safe toys, furniture, clothing, and bodies. See the *Appendix* in the back of this book for a comparison of the disinfectant properties of *T36-C5* to the agents.

* Sponge bathe a sick person with *Antibacterial Liquid Soap* or *The Gold* or *Platinum Bar* on a washcloth to reduce surface germs transported through perspiration. Rinse well. Disinfect the air by running a steam vaporizer with 10 drops of *T36-C5* and 2 capfuls of *Sol-U-Mel* in the sick room. For preventing the spread of germs through the skin, use *Clear Defense* throughout the day to sanitize and kill germs on your hands without the need for soap and water. A general disinfectant solution for cleaning a sickroom is a solution of 1 ounce of **MelaPower Laundry Detergent** plus 1 ounce of **Sol-U-Mel** in 1 gallon of warm water. Sponge, mop, or wipe floors, walls, doorknobs, lamp, and bed frames.

DIVERTICULOSIS

Chronic constipation, insufficient fluid intake, inadequate dietary roughage, and some medications can cause pressure in the lower bowel sufficient to cause bulges or sacs in the muscular wall. These bulging pockets, or diverticuli, can become impacted with fecal material and extend to over one inch in length. If improperly cared for, they can develop irritation, pain, and serious infections, a condition known as diverticulosis.

* Until about 20 years ago, a low-roughage diet was recommended for treating diverticulosis. However, puddings, white bread, Jell-O, and soft vegetables proved to do little to stop the surgeon's knife. Oat bran, wheat bran, and psyllium, along with adequate exercise and liquids are now the treatment of choice for diverticulosis. Drinking 2 to 4 cups of **G'Day Melaleuca Tea** each day and adding the roughage found in **FiberWise**, is a good way to increase bowel elimination and reduce pressure. **FiberWise** drink and bars will provide 5 grams of dietary fiber per serving, healthy biotics to maintain digestive balance and other natural extracts for regularity. The *American Journal of Digestive Disorders* found that 85% of the diverticulosis patients reported a complete disappearance of symptoms after going on a high-fiber diet.

The Vitality Pak, **Cell-Wise**, and **ProVex** are needed for healing and improved health. Drinking **Sustain** or **Attain** every morning is also a very good source of adding fiber to your diet. Those who want to avoid diverticulosis or diverticulitis should strive to eat from five to eight fruits and vegetables every day.

DOG BITE

As incredible as it may seem, over a million people are bitten by dogs every year. Any animal bite can readily become infected. This is because bites are a type of puncture wound where contaminated secretions are injected deep into the tissues. Dog bites are notorious for becoming infected, and the rule of thumb is that any dog bite that breaks the skin, no matter how superficial, will become infected.

* Wash the area with **Antibacterial Liquid Soap** and water and then apply **T36-C5**. Repeat three times each day for several days. Then apply it once each day until the wound is healed.

CAUTION: See your health care provider immediately if you cannot verify whether the animal has had a rabies vaccination.

---

*Please consult your health care provider before starting any course of supplementation or treatment, particularly if you are pregnant or currently under medical care. Make sure you carefully read and understand all product packaging prior to use.

DOUCHE

A douche is a jet of liquid applied externally or internally to the body. It is used for cleansing and for treatment of infections.

* *Nature's Cleanse* is by far the most effective douche on the market for fighting irritating gynecological conditions including yeast infections, vaginal itching, burning, and feminine discomfort.

If *Nature's Cleanse* is not available, 3-6 drops of *T36-C5* added to a bowl of water can be used. Mix it thoroughly and use as a douche or to bathe the affected area. See the *Sitz Bath* section in this book.

DRUG POISONING

Three out of every ten hospital admissions are due to either prescription or over-the-counter drug reactions. Sixteen hundred people die each year from aspirin poisoning alone. Be certain that your drug-oriented health care provider communicates all possible side effects from any needed medications. Eli Lily, pharmacist and founder of Lily Pharmaceuticals, is quoted as saying, "A drug without side effects is no drug at all." Dermatitis, nausea, accelerated heart rate, excessive sweating, stomach pains, and diarrhea are some of the milder reactions. Tumors, kidney failure, diabetes, ulcers, and sudden death are the more common severe reactions. It is estimated that only one third of prescriptions are taken in the proper dosage or for the length of time that they are prescribed. Authorities state that the overuse of prescription antibiotics has resulted in super-resistant strains of bacteria, which defy all known treatment and killed over 13,000 hospitalized patients in 1992 alone.

Some drugs react with others to provide baffling symptoms. When several health care providers are treating the same patient for different conditions, the risk of drug interactions increases. The most recent Physicians Desk Reference lists over 2,300 reactions from drugs. Most of these reactions were from the misuse of the drug. Be informed and realize that the majority of drugs are for "treating symptoms" only and do not offer a cure. If your health care provider says you will need to take the drug for the rest of your life, he or she is often referring to this philosophy. Only the body can cure. Prevention and common sense can reduce the need for many drugs and their potential side effects on us and on our environment.

* Always ask your health care provider or pharmacist to list the possible side effects of the prescription drugs you are asked to take. The speed of detoxification can be increased by drinking *G'Day Melaleuca Herbal Tea* every hour. Take *The Vitality Pak*, along with *ProVex* and/or *ProVex-Plus* daily for additional detoxification.

See the section on *Detoxification* in this book.

DRY HAIR

Whether your hair is dry, greasy or you simply have an itchy scalp condition, Melaleuca oil, and the hair products that are made with Melaleuca oil, will make you hair healthier and more manageable. It is an excellent conditioning treatment for the hair due to its fresh scent, gentle action, and powerful antiseptic properties. It helps to regulate the activity of the sebaceous glands, cleanses the scalp of bacterial fungal infection, and helps disperse dead skin cells.

*Shampoo your hair daily with *Advanced Expressions Moisturizing Shampoo for Dry or Treated Hair.* Work up a rich lather with a small amount of the shampoo and then rise and shampoo again. Shampooing with the *Melaleuca Advanced Expressions Shampoo* designed for your particular type of hair is very effective. These shampoos contain fifteen hair-healthy ingredients to nourish your hair while delivering a superior clean. They are very concentrated, so be sparing in your use.

For exceptionally dry hair, 5-10 drops of *T36-C5* can be applied directly to the hair strands or massaged into the scalp. See the sections on *Cradle Cap, Dandruff, Lice,* and *Ringworm* in this book.

DRY SCALP

See Eczema and Dandruff

DRY SKIN

Some people have dry skin due to hormonal or nutritional deficiencies, prescription medications or a deficiency of essential fatty acids in their diet. Dry skin can also be caused by aging, the sun, or environmental stress. Hands that work in caustic or cold environments or those that are washed frequently (food handlers or health care workers) can develop excessively dry, cracked skin. Women who are going through the menopause are very prone to dry skin and chapped hands. The decreased production of natural oils reduces moisture in the skin.

Dry skin is usually found on the heel of the foot and around the ball by the big toe. On the hands, it is found primarily on the palms, whereas on the elbows it is on the unprotected outside skin. Sometimes cracked and dried skin is the result of psoriasis. It can be traced to frostbite. There is a fungus that may contribute to it as well. It could be a viral skin infection. In short, there are many opinions when it comes to figuring out what causes cracked and dried skin.

*Wash the dry skin area in *Antibacterial Liquid Soap*, and then liberally apply *Renew Intensive Skin Therapy*. Apply *Triple Antibiotic Ointment* or *Mela-Gel* to the cracked or infected areas. *Moisturizing Hand Creme* should be used on your hands after washing to help restore moisture. When hand chapping has begun, apply *Renew Intensive Skin Therapy* every 4 hours until normal skin moisture is restored. Skin

---

dryness that has invaded deeper tissues or caused swelling will require treatment with **_Triple Antibiotic Ointment_** every 4 hours. This will help to control the infection until healing is accomplished. **_Pain-A-Trate_** has been used by some patients with poor circulation. Take **_The Vitality Pak_** as directed, as well as the **_ProVex_** and/or **_ProVex-Plus_** to help improve skin suppleness and elasticity.

When it is possible, protective gloves should be worn to prevent contact by water, chemicals and so on, with the skin.

DUODENAL ULCERS
See Gastric Ulcers

DUST MITES
See Hives

DYSENTERY
See Diarrhea

EAR
See Earaches, Ear Infections, Ear Infection (Outer), Earring Infection, Earwax, Swimmer's Ear, Tinnitus

EARACHES
Unlike adults, the ear canal in infants and small children inclines upward from the inner ear toward its exit in the throat. This anatomical uphill climb makes children more susceptible to earaches and inner ear infections. You do not have to have an infection to have an earache. Milk drinking after weaning, allergies, the common cold, and even teething can cause this problem. A cool breeze can set off ear canal muscle spasms. Many foreign substances have been removed from children's ear canals including beans, beads, blueberries, a live moth, and rocks. Using Q-tips to clean the ears can push wax and other materials to the back of the ear canal against the eardrum, causing damage. Rapid changes in air pressure (such as landing in an airplane) quickly identify the children and adults who have Eustachian tube congestion.

We should also be aware that the American Medical Association has stated that formaldehyde in shampoos and air fresheners causes earaches. As a result, a serious consideration should be made to convert your home to safer products such as those made by Melaleuca.

* Determine the cause of the pain, if possible. Cover a child's ears when out in cold or windy weather to prevent earaches. Loose cotton pushed into the outer ear canal can help protect sensitive ears. Holding the open end of Styrofoam cups firmly over the ears when landing in an airplane has a dramatic effect on preventing earaches in adults as well as children. A drop of warm **_T36-C5_** or **_T40-C3_** can be mixed with 5 to 10 drops of olive oil or other neutral oil to saturate the end of a cotton plug.

---

*Please consult your health care provider before starting any course of supplementation or treatment, particularly if you are pregnant or currently under medical care. Make sure you carefully read and understand all product packaging prior to use.

This inserted in the outside ear canal and left overnight will help minimize pain. (**CAUTION:** A cotton plug could become a choke hazard for very small children and babies. Instead, insert the oil mixture directly into the outside ear canal with a dropper 3 to 4 times daily.) *Renew Bath Oil* can also be used. Symptomatic relief is often given with anti-histamines, aspirin, *CounterAct Ibuprofen*, *CounterAct Extra-Strength Acetaminophen* or *CounterAct Kids Pain Reliever*.

NOTE: For children the mixture should be much weaker. Allow only one drop of *T36-C5* or *T40-C3* to 20 drops of pure virgin olive oil. The Melaleuca oil is very strong and if too strong a mixture is used, it creates irritation to sensitive tissues within the ear. **NEVER use straight Melaleuca oil in the ear.**

Diluted warm *T36-C5* can be dripped into an ear that has a live bug inside. This will kill the bug so it can be removed painlessly.

If congestion exists, use *CounterAct Night-Time Cold, Allergy, Sinus Medicine* as directed.

EAR INFECTIONS

Repeated ear infections with fever and pain, requiring cycles of antibiotics, are a sign of continual blockage of the ear canal. (See the section on *Earaches* in this book.) Infections of the outer ear (pinna) can travel into the ear canal where severe pain is produced. Permanent hearing loss or meningitis can result if treatment is delayed. If antibiotics are unsuccessful, fine Teflon tubes are often surgically inserted through the eardrum, which allows accumulating fluid and pus to drain outward from the ear. The tubes are occasionally expelled within a few days or weeks and constitute a major part of some pediatricians' practices. Other pediatricians refuse to use this technique because of questionable results and the rare chance that the tubes may travel deeper into the middle ear to create new problems. Swimmers, bottle-fed infants, and recently immunized children frequently experience ear infections.

* Don't overlook allergies as a cause of the ear infection. Identify the cause, if possible. See your health care provider for further advice. Never send a child with an ear infection outdoors if the air is cool.

To treat an ear infection, use a drop of *T36-C5* or *T40-C3* mixed with 12 to 15 drops of warm olive oil or neutral oil to saturate the end of a cotton plug. Carefully insert the plug directly into the outside ear canal and leave overnight. (**CAUTION:** A cotton plug could become a choke hazard for very small children and babies. Instead, insert the oil mixture directly into the outside ear canal with a dropper 3 to 4 times daily.) Avoid using full strength *T36-C5* in ears as local irritation can result. A hot water bottle or heating pad set on low should be put over the ear. Drink 4 to 16 ounces of *G'Day Melaleuca Herbal Tea* every hour to prevent dehydration from the fever. If congestion exists, use *CounterAct Night-Time Cold, Allergy, Sinus Medicine* as directed.

In addition, many have found that chronic ear infections can be significantly helped by consistently taking *The Vitality Pak* and *ProVexCV*.

(*NOTE:* The American Lung Association cites formaldehyde as a possible major cause of chronic ear infection in children. Formaldehyde is an ingredient in many cleaning and personal care products commonly found in the home.)

EAR INFECTION (OUTER)

Outer ear infections primarily afflict young adults and teenagers, and are a common compliant among swimmers. Bacteria, present in rivers, lakes, pool water and the ocean often affects the outer ear canal. Some researchers believe that an increased risk of developing a fungal ear infection may be related to long-term use of antibiotics or birth control pills.

* Dab several drops of *T36-C5* on a Q-tip and apply to the outer ear twice daily. **NEVER drip pure oil into the ear canal.** This Q-tip can be used in the same manner as the cotton earplug under *Ear Infections*. See the section on *Ear Infections* in this book.

EARRING INFECTION

Earring infections result from the invasion of bacteria at the piercing site.

* Wipe earring posts with *T36-C5*. Rub *T36-C5* on the front and back of the piercing hole. Repeat daily until the piercing site is healed. *Mela-Gel* or *Triple Antibiotic Ointment* applied around the earring will make it easier and safer to turn as the healing progresses.

EARWAX

Some people produce more earwax than others. There is some relationship between excessive earwax production and high blood lipids (cholesterol or triglycerides). Earwax may plug the ear canal and cause itching, pain, and temporary hearing loss.

* To clean excess or impacted wax from the ear canal, do the following. Apply one drop of *T36-C5* and one drop of *Sol-U-Mel* to a small piece of cotton, which has been pulled and twisted to a point. Insert the soaked point in the ear canal overnight. The next morning, remove the cotton and fill a rubber baby syringe (purchased at any drug store) with a solution of 1 teaspoon of *Sol-U-Mel* in 8 ounces of water heated to body temperature. Hold the syringe toward the side of the canal just inside the ear opening, leaving a space for the water to swish back out. Squeeze a firm stream of water into the ear canal several times to melt and dislodge the wax. Old wax may require the application of a heating pad to the ear for about 10 minutes before irrigating. If the wax is too hard or too large, consult your health care provider.

ECZEMA

Eczema is an inflammation of the skin where a known cause may not be readily apparent. It may be attributed to sensitivity, toxicity or an allergy. Eczema is characterized by an outbreak of papules that frequently cause considerable itching. See the section on *Dermatitis* in this book.

* Those with eczema recommend that you use only ***Renew Intensive Skin Therapy***. Avoid using the pure Melaleuca oil on the eczema sensitive skin. In addition to ***Renew Intensive Skin Therapy***, some have found that washing with ***Antibacterial Liquid Soap*** and applying Melaleuca's ***Moisturizing Hand Creme*** works just as well.

Some have also found that washing the area with ***The Gold Bar*** and then applying ***Renew Intensive Skin Therapy*** and/or ***Renew Bath Oil*** is very effective, even for children.

Of course, nothing stops the itching like ***CortiCare***. It contains the maximum strength itch-stopping power of hydrocortisone to help soothe irritated skin.

If you have eczema on your scalp, try washing your hair with ***Naturals Melaleuca Oil Shampoo***. Let the shampoo remain on your scalp during your entire shower. After you have dried your hair with a towel, work ***Renew Intensive Skin Therapy*** into your scalp. The next morning, wash your hair with ***Naturals Melaleuca Oil Shampoo*** again. The itching and bleeding should stop within a couple of days and if you continue with this program for another week, you should eliminate your challenge. Continue to use the ***Naturals Melaleuca Oil Shampoo*** on a regular basis.

EDEMA

Hot weather, lack of exercise, kidney, liver, or heart problems as well as drug toxicity can cause swelling due to excessive sodium and water retention. A sudden weight gain of 2 to 15 pounds in a few days may be the first signal. Obesity, fatty diet, salty foods, carbonated beverages, and excessive sugar tend to increase edema. Lower legs, ankles, and feet are the most often affected. Facial puffiness usually denotes kidney disease. One way to test for edema is to press on the inside of the ankle with moderate finger pressure. If a "pit" is seen when the pressure is released, this means there is excessive fluid trapped in the space between the cells. Edema that develops only toward the end of the day most often responds to diet, exercise, and stress control.

* Exercise regularly. Drink 2 to 6 cups of ***G'Day Melaleuca Herbal Tea*** each day and take ***The Vitality Pak***, ***Cell-Wise***, ***ProVex*** and/or ***ProVex-Plus*** as directed. Elevate the legs for 15 minutes in the mid-afternoon and evening. Wear support hose when standing or walking for prolonged periods.

EMPHYSEMA

Mature adults who have been exposed to air pollutants or who have smoked may develop emphysema. The germ and pollution digesting enzymes that are released by the white blood cells cause permanent damage to the tiny air sacs in the lung. The person has trouble exhaling and develops an enlarged or over-extended chest. A simple spirometry test (lung volume) and history usually tell a story of hard work and an abused life. If the person also has allergies, further development of asthma is common. See the sections on *Air Purification, Asthma*, and *Bronchitis* in this book.

* To prevent further damage stop smoking, get moderate exercise unless the heart is also damaged, drink 2 to 4 cups of *G'Day Melaleuca Tea* daily, and take *The Vitality Pak, Cell-Wise, ProVex* and/or *ProVex-Plus* as directed. At night use a vaporizer, steamer or humidifier that has had 8 to 10 drops of *T36-C5* added to the water. The warm and moist air can be very healing. (Adding the *T36-C5* to the water will help to prevent infections from bacteria, yeast and fungus.) Also try rubbing the chest with *T36-C5* followed by *Pain-A-Trate*. If congestion exists, use *CounterAct Night-Time Cold, Allergy, Sinus Medicine* as directed.

It is most important to remove toxins from the home by converting to Melaleuca personal care and home care products. Use *Sol-U-Mel* to clean all of your equipment.

ENCEPHALITIS

See Ticks

ENLARGED PROSTATE

See Benign Prostatic Hyperplasia

EPSTEIN BARR VIRUS

See Mononucleosis

EXERCISE

Why should we exercise? We should exercise because we are designed to be physical creatures as well as emotional and spiritual ones. A better word for this activity is play. Children expend more daily calories per kilogram of their body weight than adults because of their attitude about play. The purpose of exercise is to improve the efficiency of combining oxygen with fuel to produce energy. In the clinical laboratory this is measured as the VO_2 max, (maximum volume of oxygen used per unit of time). The word aerobics (done with oxygen) describes exercises that tend to improve or condition the body to do this more efficiently. In order to achieve the greatest benefit, an exercise must be chosen that is enjoyable, comfortable, and ideally performed at a level of exertion at which a casual conversation can be maintained.

---

*Please consult your health care provider before starting any course of supplementation or treatment, particularly if you are pregnant or currently under medical care. Make sure you carefully read and understand all product packaging prior to use.

Physically exhausting activities should be avoided if better health is the goal. Having an exercise target helps to get the most from your activity. Your target heart rate is based on an equation developed by exercise scientists. You must have a watch with a second hand and be able to take your pulse in your wrist or feel it in your neck.

220 – Your Age x 0.8 = Your Target Heart Rate

Example: If you are 50 years old,

220 – 50 x 0.8 = 136 beats/minute
(about 14 beats in 6 seconds)

This is 80% of your maximum attainable heart rate (at 100%, your heart is put under too much stress). Exercise helps to reduce the resting heart rate. The most complete body exercises are swimming, jumping on a trampoline, and cross-country skiing, because they use so many muscles. The next best exercises are walking, hiking, jogging, soccer, bicycling, aerobic dancing and skating. Court sports, such as tennis, racquetball, handball, basketball and volleyball are good, but do not keep the heart rate even enough to sustain the conditioning effect. Other activities usually need to be included in your weekly workout schedule if you want better overall health. Weight lifting, bowling, archery, baseball, and horseback riding are more anaerobic (done without oxygen) and are great sports, but they cannot provide the kind of activity to keep the blood and oxygen adequately supplied to all organs of the body. Always make sure that you have adequate hydration before your start to exercise (drink 1 quart of liquid before each daily workout).

* Take *The Vitality Pak*, *Cell-Wise*, *ProVex* and/or *ProVex-Plus* as directed. Mature adults should also be taking *ProVexCV* as a preventive measure. Eat an *Access Bar* preferably two hours after a meal and 15 minute before exercising. It should be eaten on an empty stomach. Do not drink sugar drinks or milk products with the *Access Bar*. Drink water throughout and after exercise. *Sustain* can be added to your water to help maintain a better blood sugar level.

EXERCISE STRAIN

There are several levels of muscle strain. Mild strain occurs regularly with all forms of exercise. Severe muscle strains can cause tearing and bruising. See the section on *Bruises* in this book.

* Overused muscles, tendons (connecting muscles to bones), and ligaments (connecting bones to other bones) are helped by immediately applying ice to prevent swelling. Keep the ice on for 5 to 10 minutes each hour, until the swelling is reduced. *Pain-A-Trate* gives dramatic relief from athletic strains.

EYE

The eye is the organ of sight.

*A major contributor to eye challenges is the typical high-fat, high sugar, preservative-laden American diet. Since the deficiency of just one vitamin or mineral can lead to a variety of eye challenges, *The Vitality Pak* along with *NutraView* is necessary to protect the eyes not only from macular degeneration, but it can often help with blurred vision, cataracts, eyestrain, floaters, itchy or tired eyes, thinning eyelashes, or vascular retinopathy. In addition, the glucosamine found in *Replenex* has shown to prevent some disease of the eye. People who are near-sighted (myopic) usually have much less glucosamine than people with normal vision.

See the sections on *Allergic Reactions, Cataracts, Eye Injuries,* and *Macular Degeneration* in this book.

EYE INJURIES

Never put T36-C5, Triple Antibiotic Ointment, or Mela Gel in the eye, as they can cause pain and dryness of the eyeball. None of the medicine chest products are approved for use in the eye. See the section on *Bruises* in this book.

* None of the Melaleuca products are approved for use in or near the eye. If the injury is due to caustic chemicals splashing in the eye, you should immediately wash the eye with fresh water for several minutes. Contact your eye doctor without delay. Foreign matter in the eye can scratch or even penetrate the cornea. Avoid rubbing the eyes, so as not to cause further irritation. Use only products that are certified ophthalmological grade.

EYE IRRITATION

See Allergic Reactions

FATIGUE

Fatigue is the second most common complaint doctors hear. Fatigue is more than tiredness; it is an inner feeling of difficulty in performing the most basic physical tasks and usually leads to a "bad attitude." It can be caused from serious disorders such as anemia, cancer, chronic viral infections, low thyroid, hormone production, hypoglycemia, diabetes, allergies, premenstrual syndrome, and the near-exhaustion phase of stress or emotional crisis. It can also be due to correctable factors such as inadequate sleep, malnutrition, or habitual sedentary lifestyle. Clinical depression is often associated with fatigue. See the sections on *Allergic Reactions* and *Anemia* in this book.

* Faithfully take *The Vitality Pak*—2 each per day, *Cell-Wise with Natural E*—2 per day, and *ProVex-Plus* at the rate of 1 capsule for each 25 lbs of body weight per day. Balance exercise with rest. Identify and

avoid possible allergic foods in your diet. Periodically see your health care provider for a good checkup.

FEET

See Bromhidrosis (Foot Odor)

FEVER

Consult your health care provider whenever a fever is present, and use the information below in conjunction with your doctor's advice. Fever is not an illness, but simply our body's healthy response to an infection. It increases the metabolism and strengthens the immune system. It signifies that you should rest your body and give it the time it needs to fight the cause. Melaleuca oil helps to support the immune system and thus the healing process because it promotes increased sweating (a process that causes the fever to go down on its own) and fights viruses and bacteria.

A rise in body temperature to 100.4 degrees (2 degrees above normal, the normal body temperature being 98.6 degrees) is considered a fever. A portion of the brain known as the hypothalamus measures the temperature of the blood. It stimulates hormones to increase the rate of burning fuel and directs blood flow away from the skin, causing chills. In this way, the body has its own internal thermostat. Bacteria and viruses give off hormone-like substances, known as pyrogens, which trigger the same body reaction.

A fever that comes and goes or lasts over two weeks may involve the "resetting" of the hypothalamus to a higher temperature. Certain types of cancer and brain tumors can cause this. Remember, however, that scientists generally agree that a fever, up to a point, is healthy and is the body's attempt to "burn" the foreign substance or organism out of the body.

* If a fever is less than 103 degrees, drink liquids, including *G'Day Melaleuca Tea*, every 1 to 2 hours and restrict activity. This will help to detoxify the body and prevent dehydration. Since fevers tend to reduce appetite, restrict solid foods. If a fever is above 103, a tepid enema is helpful to bring the temperature down. Wrapping the legs in cold cloths with a few drops of *T36-C5* on them can also help. If the fever is above 105 for more than 2 or 3 hours, emergency measures should be taken to reduce it and prevent brain damage.

Fever may also be reduced using: *CounterAct Extra-Strength Pain Reliever; CounterAct PM Pain Reliever Plus Sleep Aid; CounterAct Ibuprofen Pain Reliever and Fever Reducer; CounterAct Multi-Symptom Cold Plus Cough;* or *CounterAct Kids Pain Reliever and Fever Reducer*. If congestion exists, use *CounterAct Night-Time Cold, Allergy, Sinus Medicine* as directed.

Taking a lukewarm bath with three to ten drops of *T36-C5* (depending on your age) can help with the fever. Sponging is also

---

effective if you are too weak to bathe. Putting a few drops of *T36-C5* in a small bowl, in an aroma light or on your handkerchief or pillow will also help.

FEVER BLISTERS
See Cold Sores

FIBROMUSCULAR HYPERPLASIA
Fibromuscular hyperplasia is an overgrowth of the inner muscular wall of arteries, which causes a constriction of the blood flow, increasing blood pressure and the likelihood of clots.

* This condition has responded well to *ProVex*, *ProVex-Plus*, and particularly *ProVexCV*. If you are taking *ProVex* or *ProVex-Plus*, start with a saturation dosage, which is one capsule for every 25 pounds of body weight. After a couple of weeks, you should be able to return to the maintenance dosage of ⅓ of that amount. However, the regular dosage of *ProVexCV* should be sufficient.

FIBROMYALGIA
Fibromyalgia is not a form of arthritis but a medical condition that causes widespread pain and tenderness (soreness to the touch) at specific body sites. Some attribute its cause to an overload of toxic chemicals in the body. Others think it is caused by chronic fatigue syndrome or injury. What is known is that it results in pain, muscle aches, headaches, depression, bladder trouble, insomnia, anxiety, and sometimes numbness or tingling. The discomfort can be located in such unusual places as the neck, outside of the hip joints, upper buttocks, top of the shoulder and inside of the knee. Fortunately, fibromyalgia is not progressive and does not lead to other serious diseases or destruction of body tissue.

People with fibromyalgia have been found to have low serotonin and tryptophan levels. It has been suggested that 5-HTP might be useful, such as is found in Melaleuca's *Luminex*. A larger dose may be even more useful. *Luminex* may also help the depression associated with fibromyalgia, as will moderate exercise. Do simple stretches and flexing.

* Not much is known as to a definitive treatment for this condition; however, a healthy diet, rest, and good nutritional supplements seem to be the most effective. Diet, exercise, and nutritional supplements will be more likely to relieve your pain than painkillers.

Start with a high-fiber, low-fat diet. Eat as many raw fruits and vegetables, whole grains, raw nuts and seeds as you possibly can. Eat skinless chicken, turkey, or deep-water fish. Drink fresh juices, herbal teas, such as *Melaleuca's G'Day Herbal Tea*, and lots of water. These foods create energy and immunity. Eat four to five small meals a day. *Sustain* is the ultimate "fatigue buster," and the *Access Bar* is a tremendous energy booster as well.

One of the best and most convenient sources of fiber on the market is Melaleuca's *FiberWise* drink and bars. Fried foods, animal fats, soft drinks, caffeine, sugars, and alcohol—all of these have to go. Be aware that stress seems to aggravate fibromyalgia appreciably.

It has been suggested that someone with fibromyalgia take 2 each per day of *The Vitality Pak*, which will increase the magnesium level, 2 per day of *Cell-Wise with Natural E*, and 3 per day of the *Replenex*. Magnesium supplementation has produced very good results, which may also be due to its importance in serotonin function. Take the *Mela-Cal* part of your *Vitality Pak* at night to facilitate deep tissue repair, which is largely accomplished while you are sleeping. Be sure to get sufficient rest—at least eight hours of sleep each night. *RestEZ* is an excellent choice if you need a sleeping aid. For those really rough times, you can add *Counteract PM Extra Strength Pain Reliever*.

ProVexCV is an outstanding supplement that contains certain nutrients that are essential for your wellness. It is also recommended that the body be rubbed with *Renew Bath Oil* and that you eat one *Access Bar* each day.

Taking a saturation dose of the *ProVex* and/or *ProVex-Plus* should also help the arthritic pain. (Take 1 capsule for each 25 pounds of body weight daily for approximately two weeks. Then begin to decrease the number of daily capsules until a maintenance dose is determined.)

Alternate between hot and cold water while showering. Studies have shown cold showers to be beneficial for relieving the pain of fibromyalgia. Massage therapy can also be beneficial. A bath in Melaleuca's *Renew Bath Oil* will relieve muscle aches to an amazing degree because of the Melaleuca oil. Also, the patented *Pain-A-Trate* will help significantly with muscular pain.

If you feel that you are coming down with a cold or the flu, take *Activate* at the first symptom. Put 2 drops of *T36-C5*, lemon juice, honey, and some hot water in a cup and drink it. It is not too tasty, but it helps. If you really feel you are going downhill, make sure to get as much rest as possible, and double up on your *ProVex*.

Get a Value Pack to change your entire household to an environmentally safe atmosphere. Expect 12 to 16 weeks on the above regimen before any change is noted.

FINGERNAIL INFECTIONS
See Paronychia

FLEAS
See Insect Bites

FLU
See Influenza

FOOT ODOR
See Bromhidrosis

FOOT PAIN
See Aches and Pains

FOOT ULCERATIONS
See Diabetic Foot Ulcerations

FOUL TASTE IN MOUTH
See Mouth - Foul Taste

FROSTBITE
Exposure to freezing temperatures can cause ice crystals to form in and between cells, which causes cell damage. The skin stings, itches, burns, and sometimes turns red and/or numb. Peeling or blistering may occur in 24 to 72 hours. Lifetime sensitivity to temperature may develop.

* Protecting the body with warm, dry clothing can usually prevent frostbite. Pay close attention to the hands and feet. When frostbite is suspected, immediate action must be taken to warm the affected area. Since numbness can be an advanced symptom, care should be taken to not overheat the area. Soaking for 30 minutes in water 100 to 110 degrees Fahrenheit is advisable. Then apply *Pain-A-Trate* to maintain microcirculation. Repeat the soaking and application of *Pain-A-Trate* every hour for four hours. *Sole to Soul Revitalizing Foot Scrub* and *Revitalizing Foot Lotion* can also be used to cleanse and stimulate circulation. In addition to following these conservative measures, be sure to check with your health care provider.

The affected body part can become sensitive to cold after one attack and can easily suffer other attacks. Regular exercise and massage can help improve circulation in the area.

FUNGAL INFECTIONS
Several considerations are involved in understanding fungi. These organisms belong to the plant kingdom and are found on all healthy skin. Opportunistic forms of fungi that take advantage of a person's weakened immune system cause many infections. As such, fungal infections are common in people receiving x-ray therapy, taking birth control drugs, steroids, or antibiotics, diabetics, burn victims, and people with tuberculosis or emphysema. Many infections develop during tropical vacations or military service. Severity can vary from a mild rash on the skin to fatal overgrowth in the lungs. When the infection is localized, it is more easily treated than if it has invaded a major organ. Because of the many forms of fungal infections, microscopic examination of the affected tissue, hair shaft, or sputum is helpful in making a diagnosis. Fungal infections fail

---

to respond to antibiotics and can successfully be treated with Melaleuca oil. Fungal infections have different names depending on the area of the body affected:

Face and Neck (Tinea barbae)	See the section on *Barber's Rash* in this book
Feet (Tinea pedis)	See the section on *Athlete's Foot* in this book
Groin (Tinea cruris)	See the section on *Jock Itch* in this book
Nails (Tinea ungium)	See the section on *Paronychia* in this book
Scalp (Tinea capitis)	See the section on *Ringworm* in this book
Skin (Tinea corporis)	See the section on *Ringworm* in this book

* For common fungal infections, wash the affected areas with **Antibacterial Liquid Soap**. Dry the area and apply **Renew Intensive Skin Therapy** or **Moisturizing Hand Creme**. For acute outbreaks apply **T36-C5** followed by **Mela-Gel** or **Triple Antibiotic Ointment**. Repeat at least 2 to 3 times daily for 7 to 10 days.

An alternate choice would be to use **Dermatin Antifungal Creme** with clotrimazole and Melaleuca oil. Consult your health care provider for further advice.

FURNICLES
See Boils

GANGRENE
Gangrene is a medical term for the death of tissue resulting from loss of blood supply or a diminished blood supply caused by the narrowing of arteries and vessels. It is a progressive bacterial infection that if, untreated, will require amputation. While it can affect any area of the body, gangrene generally appears on the feet, legs, fingers and arms. The majority of the estimated 50,000 non-traumatic amputations annually in America are performed on diabetics. Amputation is not always required, particularly if aggressive treatment can be initiated immediately.

If caused by the clostridium bacteria, moist gangrene causes blisters, oozing fluid, and putrid odors; thus the term gas gangrene. It also has the symptoms of dry gangrene where the affected area turns black, loses feeling, and has red, inflamed surrounding tissue. Some of the causes of gangrene are bad wounds and infections, reduced blood supply to an extremity, diabetes, frostbite, drug reactions and swelling from large burns. Sclerosis of the arteries, thrombosis, and embolisms can also cause it. Warning symptoms include pain in the area when at rest and black, blue, or purple colored skin surrounding the affected area. See the sections on *Disinfectants, Diabetes,* and *Frostbite* in this book.

* See your health care provider if symptoms are suspicious. Depending upon the location and advanced state of the infection,

antibiotic therapy may be ineffective and often fails to stop the disease. If caught in the early stages, soak the body part in a solution of 1 ounce of *Sol-U-Mel* and 4 tablespoons of Epsom salts in one gallon of very warm water (106 to 110 degrees) for 20 minutes, every 2 hours. The wound should be allowed to drain as much as possible. Keep the area warm, since the tissue usually feels hot and swollen. Apply *T36-C5* or *T40-C3* every 2 hours to the affected part. *Pain-A-Trate* can increase local blood circulation to the area and should be applied immediately after *T36-C5* or *T40-C3*.

Of course, a good nutritional program is always recommended. The *Daily for Life Pack*, (*The Vitality Pak*, *Cell-Wise* and *ProVexCV*), is a good start.

GARGLING

Gargling is a very useful treatment for mouth ulcers, sore throats, bad breath, or other mouth and gum infections.

* Use *Breath-Away Mouthwash* as directed or as strong as you can tolerate it. 'As directed' is too strong for some people. Another excellent gargle is to combine 5-10 drops of *T36-C5* in a glass of warm water. Mix this solution well and then use for a mouth rinse and/or gargle.

GAS

See Abdominal Distress

GASTRIC ULCERS

Stress, aspirin, or spinal nerve irritation, as well as a poor diet, can lead to ulcers by stimulating the Vagus nerve, which controls production of stomach hydrochloric acid. Some scientists insist that the taking of antacids, while giving temporary relief from stomach acid, in the long run actually elevates production of stomach acid. Statistics show that while antacids are being taken at ever-increasing frequency, ulcers continue to be one of the most frequently treated conditions. Starting as indigestion and stomach pain, this condition can lead to referred back pain, anemia, and fatigue if uncorrected. Our high-stress lifestyle appears to be the most contributing factor.

* For people who have had ulcers for several years, lifestyle should be closely evaluated. The flavonoids in *ProVex* and *ProVex-Plus* help heal ulcers by reducing histamine secretion and by binding to and protecting connective tissue in mucous membranes of the stomach, so take as directed. Drink 2 to 4 cups of *G'Day Melaleuca Tea* each day. Begin an exercise program. Practice relaxation breaks for 20 minutes each day. For acute attacks, drink one cup of *G'Day Melaleuca Tea* every hour. Eat one half of a *FiberWise* bar every two hours between meals. *FiberWise* drink and bars are excellent ways to increase dietary fiber. Eat cole slaw or have boiled cabbage every four hours (compound U in cabbage stops production of stomach acid). Avoid alcohol, caffeine, smoking, and rich or fatty foods, as these stimulate the production of stomach acid.

GASTRITIS

Gastritis is an irritation in the stomach and/or small intestine, usually caused by gas. Overeating, eating in a hurry, or eating rich foods late at night are the usual causes. Severe gastritis can trigger pains in the chest, which are often mistaken for a heart attack.

* Celebrate eating by giving thanks and having soft music and candlelight. Take time between bites to have casual conversation, and quit eating just before you are full. If gastritis is common, in spite of these preventive measures, avoid eating anything 3 hours before bedtime, and avoid drinking anything within 1 hour before bedtime. Have only liquids between meals including **G'Day Melaleuca Tea**. Persistent discomfort should be brought to the attention of your health care provider.

GASTROESOPHAGEAL REFLUX

See Hiatal Hernia

GENITOURINARY INFECTIONS

Genitourinary infections are a general classification for infections of the genital and urinary organs. The antiseptic, bacterial, anti-itching, anti-fungal, anti-viral, and immune system stimulating properties of tea tree oil make it an excellent agent for dealing with genitourinary infections.

* See the *Cystitis* or *Thrush* section in this book.

GERDS

See Hiatal Hernia

GERMAN MEASLES

See Rubella

GINGIVITIS

Gingivitis is an inflammation of the gum tissues that affects nine out of ten people to some extent. It is usually caused by a buildup of plaque. Some believe that toxins within the plaque irritate the gums and cause gingivitis. It often leads to infection and swollen gums that bleed easily during or after even gentle to moderate brushing and flossing. If not checked, this condition may lead to inflammation of the connecting bone tissue and possible tooth loss.

According to a study at the State University of New York at Buffalo, adults who consume less than the recommended 60 mg per day (about one orange) of vitamin C have nearly one and a half times the normal risk of developing severe gingivitis as those who consume three times the RDA (more than 180 mg).

 * Brush your teeth a minimum of twice a day with *Melaleuca's Tooth Polish* and floss with *Exceed Waxed Dental Floss*. If the condition is severe enough, apply *T36-C5* to your finger or a Q-tip and dab it on the affected gum areas. Rinsing with *Breath-Away Mouthwash* and using *Hot/Cool Shot Mouth Spray* may also help alleviate gingivitis. Swishing several times each day with 3-5 drops of *T36-C5* in water or *Breath-Away Mouthwash* can be very effective.

Take *The Vitality Pak* for vital nutrients along with *Cell-Wise* to help repair connective tissue around the teeth. Take *ProVex* or *ProVex-Plus* to help reduce inflammation of the gum tissues, and to help prevent plaque buildup. See your dentist for regular checkups.

GLOSSITIS

Inflammation of the tongue is a sign of a local irritation or, more often, a disease elsewhere. Local causes can include mechanical trauma from jagged teeth, ill-fitting dentures, or repeated biting during convulsive seizures. Other irritants include alcohol, tobacco, hot foods, and spices, or sensitization to chemicals in toothpaste, mouthwashes, breath fresheners, candy dyes, or dental materials. The most common general cause of glossitis is malnutrition or avitaminosis (a deficiency in specific B vitamins). A few rare disorders produce tongue inflammation but are determined by first ruling out these common causes.

 * Take *The Vitality Pak* as directed. Also take *ProVex* and/or *ProVex-Plus* to help reduce inflammation. Stop smoking. Use only safe dental hygiene products such as *Classic Tooth Polish*, *Breath-Away Mouthwash,* and *Exceed Dental Floss*. Drink 2 to 4 cups of *G'Day Melaleuca Tea* each day. Have dental checkups regularly.

GOUT

A condition with painful joints of the toes, fingers, or other areas, along with elevated blood uric acid, is typically know as gout. Sharp crystals cause physical damage to the cartilage. Once known as a "rich man's disease," gout affects those who are usually overweight and consume alcohol, large quantities of red meat, and rich foods. It is frequently characterized by a sudden onset of extreme pain with the big toe swelling and becoming highly inflamed. While there sometimes is a headache and other times a fever that accompanies it, the most pronounced symptom is that huge, painful swollen big toe. Have a thorough physical examination performed and begin following the recommendations of a health care provider.

 * Start a low-stress diet consisting of more vegetables (a "greens and beans" diet) and fewer animal products. Take *Replenex Joint Replenishing Complex* to help rebuild damaged cartilage. Drink 2 to 4 cups of *G'Day Melaleuca Tea* each day. Apply *Pain-A-Trate* to any affected joint 2 to 4 times each day at first, then each morning and

evening until painless mobility is achieved. Take a hot soak with 1 capful of *Sol-U-Mel* in 1 quart of water 30 minutes each morning to minimize damage to cartilage.

It has been suggested that someone with gout take 2 each per day of *The Vitality Pak*, 2 per day of *Cell-Wise with Natural E*, 3 per day of *Replenex* and 2 per day of *ProVex Plus*. It is important to decrease uric acid levels in the blood. When the body is deficient in certain vitamins (such as B5, A and E) excessive amounts of uric acid may be produced. *The Vitality Pak* will help to prevent these deficiencies. Candida infections will also increase a uric acid blood level, which is why adding *G'Day Melaleuca Tea* to your diet each day may help.

GROIN FUNGAL INFECTION
See Jock Itch

GROWING PAINS

Growing pains are usually associated with a child complaining about leg pains at night. It is generally thought that growing pains are not severe even though they make the leg muscles tighten-up to a degree where one thinks they are severe. However, if your have any doubts about this, be sure to check with your child's pediatrician or health care provider for guidance. See the section on *Osgood-Schlatter's Disease* in this book.

* Be aware of your child's overall nutritional needs. Be sure she/he is taking the *Vita-Bears Children's Supplements*. For the actual pain, try the *CounterAct Kids Pain Reliever* and/or massage the legs with *Renew Intensive Skin Therapy* or *T36-C5*. Mixing *Pain-A-Trate* with one of the other Melaleuca lotions makes a very pleasant massage as well.

GUM DISEASE
See Bleeding Gums, Dental-Gum Disease, Sore Gums

HAIR
See Dry Hair, Hair Loss, Ingrown Hair, Oily Hair

HAIR LOSS

One cause of hair loss can be an inherited trait seen in middle-aged men. A receding hairline is caused by an accumulation of male hormones, which alters the natural fats secreted in the scalp and stunts hair growth. The characteristic pattern is thinning and baldness beginning in the front and progressing backward over the head. Research has recently shown that men who begin this pattern in their 20s or early 30s instead of the mid-40s have a greater risk of developing heart disease early in life. Male pattern baldness or slow hair loss due to aging has no known proven treatment. It appears to be nature's conservative desire to reduce unneeded plumage as we get older. We do know that protein metabolism (hair is pure protein) slows down by about one-half after the sixth decade of life. We also know that maximizing our nutrition in youth helps avoid or postpone many genetic weaknesses called inborn errors of metabolism.

In conditions other than male pattern baldness, we find quite an array of causes. Doctors have seen partial hair loss in children who were malnourished; patched hair loss due to heavy metal poisoning such as lead; thinning or splitting and lifeless hair due to harsh chemical hair care products; total body hair loss due to stress; and intermittent hair loss in people experiencing bowel parasitic infections. After giving birth, some women will lose up to one-third of their head hair but will quickly grow it back within a year if properly nourished. There have been a few cases of head lice and dog and cat fleabites that have produced immune reactions in the scalps of children, causing temporary hair loss. Dandruff sufferers, due to scratching, often have mild to heavy hair loss. See the section on *Dandruff* in this book. Your health care provider should evaluate complicated or unresponsive hair loss.

* After ruling out the pathological conditions causing hair loss, many people slow down or stop hair loss when simple steps are taken. A daily scalp massage with *T36-C5* or *Renew Intensive Skin Therapy* is often helpful. Use *Naturals Melaleuca Oil Shampoo* to maintain healthy hair and scalp. Above all else, get adequate nutrition including protein. *ProFlex20* is an easy and delicious way to add protein to your diet. Take *The Vitality Pak* as directed. Adequate rest to prevent stress is essential. Include moderate exercise in your daily schedule to keep the pores of the skin clean and circulation optimal. It has even been suggested that you try rubbing your scalp with *Nature's Cleanse*. Drink *G'Day Melaleuca Tea* on a daily basis.

After an extensive study of about one thousand plant extracts, researchers in Japan discovered that proanthocyanidins extracted from grape seed "promote proliferation of hair follicle cells isolated from mice by about 230% relative to controls (100%)." And that proanthocyanidins "possess remarkable hair-cycle-converting activity." So consider taking *ProVex*, *ProVex-Plus*, or *ProVexCV* for possible hair growth benefits along with all the other health benefits of these supplements.

HALITOSIS
See Body Odor

HANDS
See Chapped Hands

HARDENING OF THE ARTERIES
See Atherosclerosis

HAY FEVER

Hay fever is one of the most commonly seen conditions. It is seasonal symptoms of tree, weed, and grass pollen hypersensitivity. Symptoms include runny, red, and itching eyes and a runny, stopped-up nose. When possible, avoid exposure to the pollens to which you are allergic. Due to cross-sensitivity, food allergies may reinforce pollen allergies. For example, eating wheat may aggravate a wheat pollen allergy. In that case, avoid eating wheat, oats, rye and barley from May until August.

 * The flavonoids in *ProVex* have been shown to have an anti-histamine action as well as anti-allergic action, so take *ProVex* and/or *ProVex-Plus* at the rate of one capsule for every 25 pounds of body weight daily. This should be in addition to your daily *ProVexCV* intake. Each night before retiring, swab each nostril of your nose with a Q-tip containing *Renew Intensive Skin Therapy*. This will reduce the accumulated pollen from the day and moisten dry mucous membranes. Take *The Vitality Pak* as directed to boost your immune system. Drink 2 to 4 cups of *G'Day Melaleuca Tea* each day.

A cold mist humidifier with ½ capful of *Sol-U-Mel* will have an almost immediate affect on breathing and coughing due to allergies and hay fever. During allergy and hay fever season, it is advisable to use it at night in the bedroom of the person who is affected. Some use as much as two capfuls of *Sol-U-Mel* combined with 10 drops of *T36-C5* in the humidifier.

HEADACHES

There are many types, degrees of severity, and locations of headaches. About 80% of all headaches are due to muscle tension or nerve restriction from stress or injury, which inhibits blood flow out of the brain. These respond well to chiropractic adjustments of the vertebral spine and massage of tense muscles. Allergies, eyestrain, sinus or dental infections, viruses, high blood pressure, reduced blood oxygen, low blood sugar, or toxemia (constipation, alcohol, chemical fumes, caffeine addiction, etc.) are other common causes. Brain tumors can also cause slowly developing, continual headaches. Migraine headaches usually are one-sided and can be severe enough to cause nausea and reduced vision. Migraine sufferers get dramatic relief from identifying and eliminating specific sensitized foods from their diet. See the section on *Migraine Headaches* in this book.

 * For a tension headache, a gentle massage for 2 to 5 minutes to the back of the neck, on the temples, and on the sinuses over and under the eyes using *Pain-A-Trate* often relieves local muscles and promotes blood circulation. Special care should be taken to keep *Pain-A-Trate* away from your eyes. Apply a hot moist pack to the back of the neck or over the eyes afterward. Most tension headaches are relieved within 10 to 15 minutes with this technique. If symptoms do not improve, keep a log of the frequency, severity, and duration of your headaches and see your health care provider.

Remember, do the simple things first! Begin an exercise program to reduce tension. Take *The Vitality Pak* and *Cell-Wise* as directed. Drink 2 to 4 cups of *G'Day Melaleuca Tea* each day. Take a *FiberWise* drink or bar to maximize bowel elimination. Take *Sustain* drink between meals to maintain blood sugar. Drink water and get plenty of rest. If congestion exists, use *CounterAct Night-Time Cold, Allergy, Sinus Medicine* as directed. *ProVex* and/or *ProVex-Plus* have been found to be effective in relieving or reducing migraine headaches. *Luminex* often reduces the incidence of migraine headaches, as it boosts the level of 5-HTP, which has been shown to be very helpful in decreasing the number of attacks.

HEAD COLD
See Sinus Congestion

HEAD LICE
See Lice

HEARING LOSS
See Earwax

HEART DISEASE
See Cardiovascular Disease

HEMORRHOIDS
Hemorrhoids are varicosities of the veins of the hemorrhoidal plexus in the anus, often accompanied by inflammation, reddening, and bleeding. Seldom are they painful unless accompanied by more advanced conditions such as fissures (tears) or fistulas (burrow-like tracts from the inner anus to non-healing sores around the anal area). Hemorrhoids bother over 50% of all adults. There are Biblical accounts of piles (hemorrhoids). Hemorrhoidal veins contain blood that is not emptying properly into the portal circulation to the liver. Constipation, laxative-induced diarrhea, pregnancy, and occupations requiring long periods of sitting on hard or cold objects tend to cause this itching, burning irritation.

Constipation causes excessive lower bowel pressure and can cause the external hemorrhoid veins to enlarge suddenly. Thin or flat-on-one-side stools or a full feeling immediately after a bowel movement is a good indication of internal hemorrhoids.

* Preventing this condition is best. Get adequate exercise and water each day. Take *ProVex*, and/or *ProVex-Plus* each day as recommended. *FiberWise* drink or bars are excellent fiber supplements and should be taken every day to prevent constipation. A cotton ball or a 2x2-inch gauze pad soaked with *T36-C5* or *Pain-A-Trate* held in the anal opening can quickly reduce the itching and burning. *Mela-Gel* applied to the area can also bring quick relief.

Chronic hemorrhoids are best treated as follows: Add 1 ounce of *Sol-U-Mel* and 1 ounce of *Renew Bath Oil* to 1 quart of warm water. Sponge the solution onto the hemorrhoidal area. Leave for several minutes. Pat day. Apply *Mela-Gel, Renew Intensive Skin Therapy*, or *Triple Antibiotic Ointment*. Repeat the procedure morning and night for seven days. A hot sitz bath each evening with the above solution may be very helpful in shrinking any external hemorrhoids.

Stubborn hemorrhoids may require conservative therapy beyond the use of Melaleuca products. Contact your health care provider about non-surgical hemorrhoid treatments.

HERPES SIMPLEX TYPE 1
See Cold Sores

HERPES ZOSTER
See Shingles

HERNIA
See Hiatal Hernia

HIATAL HERNIA
Hiatal hernia is a condition in which the stomach pushes upward through an opening in the diaphragm in the thorax. This condition is also associated with gastroesophageal reflux, in which the muscle that circles the point of juncture between the stomach and the esophagus fails to keep acid and food from coming back up into the esophagus from the stomach. When this happens, the esophageal tissues are irritated, causing heartburn, belching and great discomfort behind the breastbone.

Hiatal hernias affect approximately 50% of adults over 40 years of age. Because most of these hernias are quite small, the majority of these people are unaware of their condition because they do not have any symptoms.

* The *Daily for Life Pack* is especially helpful because it contains all the nutrients necessary to create balance. Included in this pack are the very important protcolytic enzymes, pancreatin, grape seed extract, zinc, vitamin B complex, and vitamin C, which can significantly improve digestion and promote tissue repair and healing.

Because extra fiber helps this condition, *FiberWise* drink and bars are excellent choices. Drink a large glass of water every three hours, and at the first sign of heartburn drink one or two large glasses of water to help wash the acid out of the esophagus.

Eat six or seven small meals daily. Do not consume spicy foods. Avoid fats and fried foods. They delay digestion and prolong the stomach's emptying time. Also, avoid coffee, tea, alcohol, soft drinks, and smoking.

Avoid heavy lifting and bending. Give the stomach at least two hours to empty before lifting or other exertion. Do not eat within three hours of bedtime. If you have indigestion at night, raise the head of your bed 6 to 10 inches. Do not lie down during the day if you are bothered by heartburn. Standing or sitting helps to keep the stomach acids in the stomach. Allergenic foods can aggravate symptoms. Obesity can contribute to the challenges as well.

HIGH BLOOD PRESSURE

No single cause is known for hypertension. Whatever the cause, it will lead to either a restriction of blood flow in the blood vessels or increased heart pumping. Family tendencies are often seen as the most common trait. Lifestyle factors such as type "A" personalities (high stress), smoking, high blood cholesterol and triglycerides, alcohol consumption, and caffeine consumption predominate. Contrary to popular belief, salt consumption in healthy people does not increase blood pressure. (Low blood pressure, however, is often due to a deficiency of salt.) Those who are under high stress and have high blood pressure benefit from restricting salt intake. Actually, deficiencies in many other essential nutrients including magnesium, potassium, and B vitamins are known to be present in people who have high blood pressure, and they are helped by supplementation. See the section on *Cardiovascular Disease* in this book.

* Progressive exercise helps high blood pressure by reducing stress hormones and increasing the efficiency of the vascular system. Take **The Vitality Pak** and **Cell-Wise** as directed. Take **ProVexCV** to regulate platelet activity and increase vascular integrity. Drink 2 to 4 cups of **G'Day Melaleuca Tea** each day.

HIVES

Hives are a form of skin rash that consists of raised white welts mixed with red patches on the skin. Burning, itching and the formation of smooth patches characterize it. The cause of hives is an allergic or hypersensitive reaction to drug allergies, severe stress, insect stings or bites, exposure to weeds or weed venom, and ingestion of certain foods (particularly eggs, shellfish, nuts or fruits). Desensitization injections can cause hives due to a hypersensitive reaction. Certain virus infections such as hepatitis, mononucleosis, and measles can be announced by the sudden appearance of hives. Hives lasting two weeks or longer can be caused by an allergic reaction to drugs or chemicals such as penicillin in milk, non-prescription drugs, food preservatives, dyes or other food additives. Hives can also result from animal dander. Determine the source and avoid it in the future.

* The flavonoids in **ProVex** have shown to have an antihistamine action as well as an anti-allergic action, so take **ProVex** and/or **ProVex**-

---

*Please consult your health care provider before starting any course of supplementation or treatment, particularly if you are pregnant or currently under medical care. Make sure you carefully read and understand all product packaging prior to use.

Plus at the therapeutic dose of 1 capsule for every 25 pounds of body weight per day until relief is found. Application of *T36-C5*, *Mela-Gel*, *Pain-A-Trate*, or soaking in a warm bath with 4 ounces of *Sol-U-Mel* and 4 ounces of *Renew Bath Oil* usually returns normal circulation to the affected area. Drink *G'Day Melaleuca Tea* 2 to 4 times each day to assist in detoxification. If congestion exists, use *CounterAct Night-Time Cold, Allergy, Sinus Medicine* as directed. Chronic hives can be due to an underlying disease and should be brought to the attention of your health care provider.

Use *CortiCare* to take the sting out of poison ivy, hives, and rashes. Its unique formula includes pharmacist-recommended hydrocortisone for itch relief plus naturally soothing Melaleuca oil.

Obviously one should determine the source that causes the hives and than avoid it. This might be a good time to consider making the necessary changes to turn your home into an environmentally safe, Melaleuca household.

HOARSENESS

Hoarseness is due to inflammation of the voice box (larynx) and can be caused from simply overuse, such as yelling at an athletic event, or other disorders such as viral or bacterial infections.

* Inhale steam made from adding 10 drops of *T36-C5* and 2 capfuls of *Sol-U-Mel* to the water in a steam vaporizer. Drink hot *G'Day Melaleuca Tea* 2 to 6 times each day. Resting the voice usually reduces the symptoms within a few days and prevents further inflammation. For serious cases, see your health care provider.

HORSEFLIES

See Insect Bites

HOT FLASHES

Not to be confused with a fever, hot flashes can appear suddenly with a stiflingly stuffy hot feeling and reddened sweaty head, face, and neck skin lasting from a few second to several minutes. Chills often follow them. Hot flashes occur in over 75% of women at menopause and may occur for more than 5 years. Pregnant women may also experience hot flashes. Menopausal-aged women frequently experience these sudden hot spells with profuse perspiration during the day or night. Adrenal-pituitary "storms" create an unstable hypothalamus, which brings about inadequate thermal regulation. Insomnia and resulting anxiety can be a complication. Apparently, the hypothalamus of the brain becomes unable to coordinate with other hormone fluctuations and body temperature changes, due to declining estrogen levels. Busy lifestyles and inadequate rest may intensify the general symptoms. Stress also can play a moderate part.

---

* Reduced stress is vital for control of hot flashes. Avoid sugar, caffeine, red meat (arachadonic acid), and chocolate. Use cold-pressed olive oil as a salad dressing. Get enough rest (night sleep and mid-day nap) and aerobic exercise. Take *EstrAval* and *Luminex* as directed. Maintain proper nutrition including *The Vitality Pak*, *Cell-Wise*, and *ProVex* and/or *ProVex-Plus*. Also enjoy 2 to 4 cups of *G'Day Melaleuca Tea* each day.

HYPERTENSION
See High Blood Pressure

HYPOGLYCEMIA (LOW BLOOD SUGAR)

Low blood sugar accounts for more behavioral symptoms than any single condition. Afternoon fatigue, forgetfulness, dull headaches, multiple food allergies, anti-social behavior, difficulty losing weight, bad dreams, sweet or alcohol cravings, sudden loss of energy, eating disorders, fits of anger or depression, body aches, poor protein digestion and slow physical reflexes are the more common symptoms.

Stress, overconsumption of refined sugar, and nutritional deficiencies of minerals and B vitamins appear to be the causes of hypoglycemia. Up to 50% of Americans randomly tested with a 6-hour glucose/insulin tolerance test had an abnormal response. Since the nervous system cannot store fuel, it must constantly be bathed in glucose for normal function. (One judge in California is known for not granting a divorce to couples until they have both taken a glucose tolerance test.) Children experiencing hyperactive behavior following a sugary holiday are well documented by teachers. In adults, sudden drops in blood sugar or low fasting levels (before breakfast) stimulate instinct to eat something or somebody! Many convicted criminals have a story of sugar abuse. Alcohol is the simplest form of sugar. Untreated, hypoglycemia in some people tends to produce adult-type diabetes.

* Eat nourishing meals with the insurance of *The Vitality Pak*. Eating smaller, more frequent meals is also very helpful. Start with a high-fiber, low-fat diet. Lots of fiber cleanses the body, removes toxins and helps to dilute, bind, and deactivate many carcinogens. It removes excess bile from the stomach and intestine, prevents obesity, lowers cholesterol, stabilizes blood sugar, and increases energy. Avoid refined sugar, caffeine, and cooked fats. Exercise moderately after eating an *Access Bar*. Take *Sustain* drink between meals to prevent sudden blood sugar drops.

IMMUNE SYSTEM

The immune system is what protects the body from damage due to infection, disease, or other traumas that can harm the body. Many things, including environmental influences and stress, can weaken the immune system. Once it is damaged, viruses, bacteria, or fungi easily access it.

T36-C5 is a valuable and effective way to support the body's defense against infection because it directly influences the microorganisms that attack the body.

It also stimulates and improves the activity of the impacted body cells, thereby improving the entire immune system. Using Melaleuca products containing *T36-C5* is an excellent way to strengthen the entire body before surgical procedures and during long-term debilitating illnesses such as glandular fever, hepatitis, and chronic fatigue syndrome. The value of *T36-C5* in slowing down the development and furthering the treatment of AIDS is also undergoing investigation with some success.

* Entirely converting your home to safer products such as those available through Melaleuca can provide a more conducive environment for a healthy lifestyle.

In addition, there are several specific things that can be done to help build up resistance levels: 1. Take a bath at least once a week with 8-10 drops of *T36-C5* in the water. 2. Massage the palms of the hands and soles of the feet once a day with **Renew Bath Oil**. 3. Use *T36-C5* in a cold air humidifier at night, put a few drops on your pillow, or leave some to evaporate in a dish. 4. Take **The Daily for Life Pack** as directed. (Vitamins should be taken not because we are sick, but to move us from not being sick to being really healthy.) 5. Drink several cups of **G'Day Melaleuca Herbal Tea** each day. (It is also delicious as iced tea.)

It has been found that any illness that ends in "itis" such as sinusitis, bronchitis, colitis, and so on, responds well to **ProVex-Plus**. Take a saturation dose of 1 capsule for every 25 lbs. of body weight for the first two weeks and then begin to taper off every few days until a maintenance level is reached.

Take **Activate Immune Complex** at the onset of symptoms. Then discontinue use when the illness has run its course. Take as directed.

One other point of interest: if you or anyone you know is susceptible to infection, they should be discouraged from using commercial furniture polish. Most commercial furniture polishes have a two-week half-life, which means that two weeks after you have used the polish, the toxic chemicals are still half as strong as they originally were. By that time, you have probably used it again! Use **Rustic Touch Furniture Care** instead.

IMPETIGO

This highly contagious skin disease is recognized by eruptions of pustules or blisters. Caused by the streptococcus or staphylococcus bacteria, the infection primarily affects children. Spots or inflamed patches break out on the scalp, neck and face. Blisters that sometimes crust over will appear on the knees and on the hands.

* Use a cotton ball to apply *T36-C5* to all pimple and blister areas. When dry, treat the area carefully by applying *Mela-Gel*, *Renew Intensive Skin Therapy*, or *Pain-A-Trate*. Repeat several times each day.

Since Impetigo is an extremely contagious infection, steps must be taken to assure that others in the household aren't infected. Wash the affected person's clothes and bedding separately using *MelaPower* and a capful of *Sol-U-Mel*.

INDIGESTION

Gas, belching, or a bloated feeling is a sign of inadequate digestion in the stomach. Eating on the run, inadequate chewing, dilution of digestive juices with copious amounts of liquids, and stress all play a great part in causing indigestion. Many antacids make the problem worse. Malabsorption, ulcers, constipation, and low bowel conditions including hemorrhoids and cancer are seen frequently in people who have a history of indigestion.

* Sit down. Give thanks. Surround yourself with people you love as often as you can. Savor each bite. Use just enough seasoning to bring out the natural taste. Use *Calmicid Antacid Plus* for fast relief of acid indigestion, heartburn, and gas. Take *The Vitality Pak*, *Cell-Wise*, *ProVex* and/or *ProVex-Plus* for overall good nutrition. Drink 2 to 4 cups of *G'Day Melaleuca Tea* each day between or after meals. For more serious digestive challenges, consult your health care provider.

INFECTIONS

See Dry Skin, Ear Infections, Fungal Infections, Genitourinary Infections, Gingivitis, Jock Itch, Paronychia (Fingernail), Skin Wounds, Urinary Tract Infection and Yeast Infection

INFLUENZA (FLU)

Influenza is an infectious disease caused by a virus. Its many symptoms may include chills, fever, coughs, headache, and aches in the joints, weakness, and stomach distress. Much more severe than the common cold, the flu can progress to total exhaustion, acute bronchitis, pneumonia, and sometimes death. Since the virus is spread from one person to another, controlling the environment is important. Keeping one's immune resistance up is the best prevention.

*Upon the first signs of the flu, immediately take *Activate Immune Complex*—3 per day. Start drinking a cup of *G'Day Melaleuca Tea* every hour. Drink hot *Sustain* to prevent exhaustion. To reduce painful muscles, frequently bathe with *Renew Bath Oil*. Use *CounterAct Cough Relief Medicine* as directed. If congestion exists, use *CounterAct Night-Time Cold, Allergy, Sinus Medicine* as directed. Go to bed and get all the rest you can.

Use *Calmicid Antacid Plus* if indigestion or gas is present. Begin a steam vaporizer with 10 drops of *T36-C5* and 2 capfuls of *Sol-U-Mel* in the infected person's room. Take ***The Vitality Pak***—2 each per day, ***Cell-Wise with Natural E***—2 per day, and ***ProVex-Plus***—2 per day for an antioxidant effect, which reduces pain of muscles, chest and abdomen.

INGROWN HAIR

When a hair that has not grown beyond the skin's surface folds back under the surface and begins to grow inwardly, it is known as an ingrown hair. Bacterial growth around the hair shaft can cause a painful eruption below the skin.

* Apply ***T36-C5*** to the specific area of the infection. Continue applications every two hours until the infection has disappeared. Consult your health care provider if the condition persists.

INGROWN TOENAILS

Ingrown toenails are usually due to poorly fitting shoes. One method of preventing a recurrence is to file a V notch on the middle of the nail so that the point nearly touches the quick. This will cause the nail to draw towards the center and prevent the embedding of the edges of the nail. Trimming in a rounded fashion is not recommended, as this actually causes further ingrown toenails. If possible, carefully remove the ingrown part of the nail.

* Soak the foot for 15 minutes in a solution of 1 ounce of ***Sol-U-Mel*** per quart of hot water. Dry thoroughly. Apply ***T36-C5*** followed by ***Mela-Gel*** or ***Triple Antibiotic Ointment***. Repeat morning and night. ***Sole to Soul Revitalizing Foot Scrub*** and ***Revitalizing Foot Lotion*** can also be used to cleanse and stimulate circulation. If there is an infection, see the section on *Abscesses* in this book.

INJURIES

See Eye Injuries, Athletic Injuries

INSECT BITES

Most plagues and life-threatening communicable diseases have had biting insects (or other families of bugs) as carriers. From the fleas carrying black plague throughout Europe to the malaria-carrying mosquito that took the life of Alexander the Great, insect bites should not be taken lightly. Many unexplained itches and tiny sores on sleepers have been due to nocturnal flying and crawling bugs attracted by body heat. These insects can remain dormant in an unattended dwelling for years awaiting their next (or first) meal.

* When staying in a cabin or beach house, immediately fumigate the area with 10 drops of ***T36-C5*** in a pan of boiling water. The insect repellent properties of Melaleuca oil are international, thus this works anywhere. Apply ***T36-C5*** to children's clothing or spray with diluted ***Sol-U-Mel*** when going to natural parks or walking in the forest in the spring. Mix a few drops of ***T36-C5*** in ***Renew Intensive Skin Therapy***

or *Moisturizing Hand Creme* to spread over the skin.

Inspect your children and yourself daily for small breaks in the skin indicating bites. If you discover an attached "tick" upon your inspection, cover the tick in *T36-C5*. The tick should "let go," and you will be able to remove it easily. Apply *T36-C5*, *Mela-Gel*, or *Triple Antibiotic Ointment* and cover with a bandage for 24 hours.

For simple insect bites, use *Mela-Gel*, especially if you have already started scratching. *Renew Intensive Skin Therapy* will also provide relief.

INSECT REPELLENT

These are great alternatives to those awful toxic and poisonous insect repellents that you buy at the store. Melaleuca products are not pesticides and therefore will not stop the varmints from landing on you, but they will greatly reduce the incidence of bites and the reactions that accompany them. They also do not make you feel like you need to take a shower after you use them. Frequent use enhances their effectiveness and your skin will be healthier because of it. It is also important to note that different body types respond differently to the different formulas. Some even say that just taking Melaleuca vitamins has stopped mosquito bites. So, do not be afraid to experiment, find your own solution, and pass it on.

It is, however, important that you make the time to find your personal solution, as the danger of insect bites is often underestimated. Someone dies every 30 seconds because of an insect bite.

* For humans, mix 1 teaspoon of *Moisturizing Hand Creme* and 5 drops of *T36-C5* and apply to any exposed skin.

Another very effective insect repellent is to mix ¼ cup of *MelaMagic*, ¼ cup of *Tough & Tender*, 2 capfuls of *Sol-U-Mel*, and 5 drops of *T36-C5*. This has been used effectively in the rainforest, so it should work well for most of us.

An alternate solution would be to combine 2 ounces of *Renew Bath Oil* with 2 ounces of *Sol-U-Mel*, 1 ounce of *Tough & Tender* and 20 drops of *T36-C5*.

You might also try mixing 2 capfuls of *Sol-U-Mel* with 10 to 15 drops of *T36-C5* in 16 ounces of water in a spray bottle. *PreSpot Plus* is another great repellent lotion.

INSECT STINGS
See Bee and Wasp Stings

INSOMNIA

Insomnia is a condition characterized by the inability of a person to fall asleep or by wakefulness in the middle of the night. Approximately one third of all American adults at one time or another suffer from insomnia. The most common cause of sleeplessness is worry. A stressful lifestyle, indigestion, over-excitement, pain, discomfort, drugs, coffee or

---

*Please consult your health care provider before starting any course of supplementation or treatment, particularly if you are pregnant or currently under medical care. Make sure you carefully read and understand all product packaging prior to use.

other stimulants are other possible causes. General good health is the best approach in preventing insomnia.

* Avoid caffeine, nicotine, alcohol, sugar, and a sedentary lifestyle. Regular daily exercise, deep breathing, drinking most liquids early in the day, and practicing a philosophy that lives life in one-day segments are good habits to ensure good sleep. A relaxing walk after dinner helps digestion and promotes good sleep. Take **Calmicid Antacid Plus** if heartburn, acid indigestion, or gas is present. Taking **The Vitality Pak** and **Cell-Wise** as directed and using **Sustain** before stressful activities will help you feel better overall. If insomnia is a habit, try enjoying a warm cup of the **Herbal Evening G'Day Melaleuca Tea** at bedtime. Take your **Mela-Cal** and a **RestEZ**. Breathe slowly and deeply as you begin to relax. Massage your feet with the **Sole to Soul Revitalizing Foot Lotion**. Yawnnnnnnnnnnnnnnnnnn.

ITCHING

For itching that is on the skin, see the appropriate section on *Athlete's Foot, Barber's Rash, Chiggers, Dermatitis, Dandruff, Dry Hair, Head Lice, Hives, Insect Bites, Itching and Flaking Skin, Lice, Mosquito Bites, Poison Ivy, Poison Oak, Poison Sumac, Prickly Heat, Pruritis Ani (Itching Anus), Psoriasis, Ringworm, Sand Flies and Ticks* in this book.

For itching that is due to sexually transmitted infections or in the genital region, see the appropriate section on *Jock Itch, Leucorrhoea, Pruritis, Genitourinary Infection,* or *Vaginitis* in this book.

ITCHING AND FLAKING SKIN

Itching and flaking skin can be caused by many different health conditions. Those suffering from psoriasis or allergies can experience this challenge with their skin. This condition may also be seen in people whose diet is deficient in essential oils and some who are post-menopausal. Also see the sections on *Allergic Reactions* and *Psoriasis* in this book.

* Regularly take **The Vitality Pak** and **Cell-Wise**. **ProVex** and/or **ProVex-Plus** will help to restore skin suppleness and elasticity. Bathe with **Renew Bath Oil** or **The Gold** or **Platinum Bar**. Apply **Moisturizing Hand Creme** or **Renew Intensive Skin Therapy** to the troubled areas. During the day be sure to use **Sun-Shades** to protect your skin and keep it moisturized. Continue this at least twice a day for 10-14 days. See your health care provider for further instructions.

ITCHING ANUS
See Pruritis Ani

---

*Please consult your health care provider before starting any course of supplementation or treatment, particularly if you are pregnant or currently under medical care. Make sure you carefully read and understand all product packaging prior to use.

ITCHING SCALP

See Dry Hair

JOCK ITCH

Fungal infections of the groin, commonly known as jock itch, can form ring lesions around the sides of the crotch. Scratching of the area can cause secondary infections or chronic dermatitis. The lesions may be complicated by secondary bacterial or yeast infections such as candida. The occurrences are chronic since the fungus may persist indefinitely or may repeatedly infect susceptible individuals. It occurs more often during the summer or when humidity is high.

 * Bathing in 1 ounce of *Sol-U-Mel* and using the *Antibacterial Liquid Soap* or *The Gold* or *Platinum Bar* is helpful in controlling the fungus. After patting dry, apply *Dermatin Antifungal Creme* as directed. *Mela-Gel*, *T36-C5*, and *Triple Antibiotic Ointment* are also effective.

It has also been suggested that *Nature's Cleanse* be used as a deterrent to jock itch, as it is very effective on yeast.

Reduce your chances for re-infection by cleaning the bathroom areas using a 16 ounce spray bottle containing 2 capfuls of *Tough & Tender*, 10 drops of *T36-C5* and 2 capfuls of *Sol-U-Mel* in water. Wash all contact clothing in *MelaPower* and *MelaBrite* for additional protection.

JOINTS

See Arthritis, Athletic Injuries

KIDNEY STONES

Kidney stones can be formed in the kidneys, ureter, bladder, prostate, or urethra. Their movement down the urinary tract can produce pain, bleeding, obstruction, and secondary infection. Milk drinkers and those who do not drink enough water tend to make stones from super-saturated urine. Patients who have passed stones describe them as "a red hot bowling ball with razor blades," while other say it is "ten times worse than having a baby."

One third of a million Americans are hospitalized each year with kidney stones. Some people have had 3 or more surgeries over the years for stones. Modern ultrasound shattering (lithotripsy) is being performed but can damage the kidneys, spleen and lymph nodes as well. Since kidney stone formation conforms to the rules of chemistry, they can usually be prevented. About 80% of stones in Americans are composed of calcium salts, about 5% are uric acid, and 2% are made up of the amino acid cystine, with the rest being made up of a mixture of phosphates released during infections or from medications. Many stones are "silent" until they begin to move. Some produce back pain or radiating pains into the groin area. Occasionally nausea, chills, fever and abdominal swelling are present.

* If there is a family or personal history of stone formation, avoid dairy products completely. Drink plenty of water and 2 to 6 cups of **G'Day Melaleuca Tea** per day. Take **The Vitality Pak**, **Cell-Wise**, **ProVex** and/or **ProVex-Plus** as directed. Ask your pharmacist about the side effects of all medications you are prescribed. If back or abdominal pain is present, apply **Pain-A-Trate** to the affected area along with a hot pad. Take a long, hot bath. The stone will pass more easily if you are relaxed and comfortable.

KNEES
See Arthritis

LARYNGITIS
See Hoarseness

LEG CRAMPS
Leg cramps are due to either a deficiency in circulating calcium or reduced oxygen to muscles. Muscle cramps tend to appear after unconditioned physical activity. Stretching a "crampy" muscle can prevent knotting.

* Exercise in three steps: warm up for 5 minutes to stretch muscles, do your workout, then cool down by moving slower or walking until the heart returns to its pre-exercise rate. Eat an **Access Bar** 15 minutes before beginning exercise. Take **The Vitality Pak**—2 each per day. Drink **G'Day Melaleuca Tea** and **Sustain** before, during and after exercise to reduce stress on the body. Take **Cell-Wise with Natural E**— 2 per day, to properly oxygenate muscle cells during exercise without free radical formation. It is also recommended that **ProVexCV** be taken at the rate of one per 35 lbs of body weight per day. Persons who are bedridden may need the assistance of external pneumatic compression boots to maximize circulation and prevent leg pains. Consult your health care provider.

LEG ULCERS
See Ulcers, Varicose

LEUCORRHOEA
Leucorrhoea is an inflammation of the vagina caused by an overabundance of unwanted bacteria or fungi. It can have a variety of causes. Symptoms often include a thick white or yellow discharge and severe itching of the vaginal area.

Pruritis or itching is an irritating condition, which generally accompanies any type of mild vaginal infection, such as trichomonal vaginitis or cervicitis.

---

* Bath daily in a warm water bath to which you have added 8-10 drops of *T36-C5*. This will not only act as an antiseptic but will help with the itching and irritation. Sit in the warm water for 5-10 minutes.

Avoid tight clothing, nylon underwear, and harsh bubble baths. Keep tea, coffee, alcohol, and spices to a minimum. See the sections on *Bladder Infections, Pruritis and Thrush* in this book.

LEUKOPLAKIA

Leukoplakia is white lesions on the skin inside the mouth. They are occasionally pre-cancerous. While no certain cause is known, suspicion is aimed toward chemical irritations from smoking tobacco, chewing tobacco, food additives, food preservatives, food colorings, and dental materials, as well as toothpastes, mouthwashes, and oral medications that contain alcohol, which tends to dry the mucosa. This condition is seen in people of all ages.

* Discontinue contact of questionable substances with the oral mucosa. Use *Classic Tooth Polish*, *Breath-Away Mouthwash*, and *Hot/Cool Shot Mouth Spray*. Drink 2 to 6 cups of *G'Day Melaleuca Tea* daily. Take *The Vitality Pak*, *Cell-Wise*, *ProVex* and/or *ProVex-Plus* as directed.

LICE

Lice infestation (Pediculosis) involves the head (P. capitus), the trunk or extremities (P. corporis), or the genital area (P. pubis). Originally, lice prefer birds and almost any hairy mammal other than man. They will settle for second best (humans) when a warm puppy or chicken is absent, but will selectively crawl to these animals if given a choice. The lice live directly off blood after biting and puncturing the skin; hence it can easily spread a multitude of diseases. It lives in hairy areas including eyebrows, eyelashes, or beards, where it lays its grayish-white eggs (nits), which can be seen with a magnifying glass on the hair follicles. The eggs hatch in three to fourteen days where the sluggish, overweight-looking insects seem eager for their first meal. Multiple families of lice cause excruciating pain, irritation and itching. Lice are transmitted by contact with objects such as combs, hats and shared garments. For this reason it is common among school children. Fortunately, Melaleuca oil products are a safe alternative to the prescription drug Lindane.

* Immediately upon suspecting or seeing evidence of lice, shampoo with *Naturals Melaleuca Oil Shampoo* and bathe in a mixture of 1 ounce of *Sol-U-Mel* and 1 ounce of *Renew Bath Oil*. Afterwards, massage *T36-C5* into the scalp and hair to soften and dislodge the nits (the eggs of the lice). Don't be stingy with the oil! Comb the oil through the hair. To fumigate the live insects, wrap your hair in a hot moist towel for 10 minutes. Repeat every second day for at least 5 treatments (10 days). (Do this even if you don't notice any additional head lice.)

It has also been suggested to spray the hair with **Sol-U-Mel**, followed by shampooing with **Naturals Herbal Shampoo**. Let it set for about 10 minutes before rinsing. Using a nit comb, the eggs should come out easily. Repeat this procedure to be sure that all the lice are gone.

To avoid re-infection, wash all clothing and bedding with **MelaPower Laundry Detergent** plus **Sol-U-Mel** in hot water. Add 2 ounces of **Sol-U-Mel** to 16 ounces of water and spray the entire house, especially affected areas.

LIPS
See Chapped Lips

LIVER DISORDERS

The liver is the master chemist of the body. Every bit of food, every ounce of non-food chemicals (Americans ingest more than 11 pounds per year), and every waste product of the cells in the body is processed through the liver. The liver is so vital to life that we have been given one that is seven times larger than needed. Yes, we could actually have six-sevenths removed surgically and still live. The liver would respond by regrowing to its original size, a feat that no other organ can do. Besides genetic defects, two main types classify disorders of the liver: toxic and infectious. Liver toxicity occurs from alcohol consumption as well as storing substances in the liver that are unable to be detoxified. Infectious damage occurs from such conditions as mononucleosis, hepatitis, and parasites. Once the liver is damaged, it begins to affect every other function and system of the body. Protecting the liver is of vital concern in these days of environmental pollution and untreatable infectious diseases.

* Drink plenty of water. Prepare food in a safe manner and demand safe handling by food establishments. Drink 2 to 4 cups of **G'Day Melaleuca Tea** each day. Take **The Vitality Pak**, **Cell-Wise**, **ProVex** and/or **ProVex-Plus** as directed.

NOTE: Allowing the liver to detoxify is essential for health. Our great grandmothers used to give the family sulfur and molasses, along with cod liver oil, each spring. Unless you are a child, pregnant, nursing or hypoglycemic, you may want to do the following spring and fall liver cleanse:

Eat only raw, steamed, or juiced vegetables, or vegetable soup and rice for one week. Drink one quart of apple juice along with 2 to 4 cups of **G'Day Melaleuca Tea** each day. On the sixth and seventh day, take one-fourth to one-half cup of olive oil followed by 1 tablespoon of Epsom salt dissolved in citrus juice. Stay close to home those days. Some nausea may occur due to the release of bile. Consult your health care provider before beginning this regimen.

LONGEVITY

The human body and mind are designed to last one hundred and twenty years. Illnesses, stress, and accidents can shorten that span. Much of our ability to live a full and active life has to do with planning to be well and taking preventive measures against disease early in life. Using health-building Melaleuca products enhances wellness and enjoyment of life. We all will get older, but aging can be slowed significantly using these products.

* Drink plenty of water. Drink 2 to 4 cups of *G'Day Melaleuca Tea* each day. Take *The Vitality Pak*, *Cell-Wise*, *ProVex* and/or *ProVex-Plus* as directed. The antioxidants in *Cell-Wise* and the *ProVex* products are the best defense available against free radical activity, which causes aging. Take *ProVexCV* as directed to help support normal platelet activity and thus give you superior heart protection. Use *Access Bars* daily to help burn stored fat and maintain muscle tone. Take *NutraView* to prevent macular degeneration and cataracts. Use *Nicole Miller Skin Care* to fight aging and maintain healthy skin.

Convert your home to the environmentally safe Melaleuca products to stop the poisoning of you and your family by all the dangerous chemicals found in the grocery store brand products.

Be happy, smile, laugh and let the significant people in your life know how much you love them. Each day is a gift. Treat it as one. Attitude does make a difference.

LOW BLOOD SUGAR

See Hypoglycemia

LUPUS

Lupus is an immune system disorder of unknown origin occurring predominantly in young women but also in children and older adults. It may begin abruptly with fever simulating an acute infection or it may develop over a period of months or even years. It is characterized by inflamed connective tissue and skin lesions.

Nearly 1.5 million Americans have lupus. It is more common than muscular dystrophy, multiple sclerosis, or leukemia. Lupus can be mild to life threatening, depending on what organs are involved. There is no cure, but symptoms can be treated. It is often misdiagnosed until severe damage has been done. As a result, it is known as the "Great Imitator."

*Take *The Vitality Pak* and *Cell Wise*—2 each per day (morning and evening). Also, saturate with *ProVex-Plus* by taking one capsule for every 25 lbs of body weight for the first 2-4 weeks. Then after 3-5 weeks, decrease by one each day. Continuing decreasing until you reach the level of four. Never go below four. If you feel that you are slipping, increase the *ProVex-Plus* by one per day. This is not an exact science, so you will need to pay attention to your body and listen to what it is telling you that it needs. Only you can determine your maintenance level.

Another suggestion is to take *Replenex*—3 per day, *The Vitality Pak*—1 per day, and *Cell Wise*—3 per day. Take one capsule of *ProVex* three times each day for the first two weeks. At the end of the first two weeks, change to *ProVex-Plus* and take two capsules 3 times each day.

Drink eight glasses of water each day and drink a cup of hot *Melaleuca G'Day Herbal Tea* before bedtime. Stay away from highly inflammatory foods, and stay away from all sugar. Give it time. It will take 14 to 21 days for this regimen to saturate the tissue.

Sustain is the ultimate "fatigue buster" and does not make you feel wired like caffeine or sugar. The *Access Bar* is also a tremendous help with energy.

MACULAR DEGENERATION

Macular degeneration is the deterioration of the central focal region of the back of the eye called the macula, and it results in impaired vision. The symptoms can be gradual or sudden, with objects usually appearing distorted in one eye. Upon examination, degeneration is often found in the normal-appearing eye as well. Both men and women, mostly elderly, contract this condition and seldom have any other eye problems. There may be a hereditary link. Since the condition involves lack of nurturing of this normally blood-rich tissue, some scientists believe that it is similar to brain tissue degeneration taking place in senility and atherosclerosis. Laser treatments are often used to treat advanced cases.

See the *Eye* section, as well as the sections on *Atherosclerosis* and *Cardiovascular Disease* in this book.

* Take *NutraView*—1 per day, which promotes long-term macular health and visual acuity with lutein, bilberry, blueberry, and Vitamin C. Take *The Vitality Pak*—2 each per day, and *Cell-Wise with Natural E*— 2 per day. Take *ProVex-Plus* to promote vascular integrity. Drink 2 to 4 cups of *G'Day Melaleuca Tea* each day. If you are older than 60, get a visual field evaluation test performed by your eye doctor every year.

MANIC DEPRESSION

See Depression

MASSAGE

This is not a condition as much as it is a preferred treatment. It is a truly wonderful remedy for easing life's aches and pains. In addition, massage helps revive the flesh and motivates the circulation. It increases the production and release of the body's natural healing chemical called oxytocin.

Massage is one of the oldest and most widely practiced health-preserving therapies known. (See the section on *Bathing* in this book.)

Part of its benefit is the mechanical effect of "rubbing" and "kneading" tensions from the body. Many times we are not aware of these tensions until we are actually being massaged. Often, we can massage certain muscles on our own bodies. However, the greatest benefit is generally received when a trained pair of gentle hands does it. There are several different techniques, each having certain advantages in specific situations. Massage is especially recommended for those who are bedridden or who are unable to exercise. Well-muscled people can usually withstand more vigorous techniques, while those with less muscle will be comfortable with more gentle techniques. Modern massage therapists are trained in multiple techniques to meet our level of need and comfort.

* Start by taking a hot bath with 1 to 2 ounces of *Renew Bath Oil* for 20 to 30 minutes. Light a few *Sun Valley Candles* and put on some soft, soothing music. Relax. Feel the smoothness of your skin. The person receiving the massage must be in a comfortable position, usually face down. The person giving the massage must not feel hurried or uncomfortable when bending at the waist. Apply ample amounts of warmed *Moisturizing Hand Creme* to one extremity, neck, upper back, or lower back area at a time. Rub *Pain-A-Trate* into tender muscles and over stiff or painful joints. A few drops of *T36-C5* can be massaged into areas that feel cold and need better circulation. Massage the limbs toward the heart area, not away from the center of the body. When done gently, you can do no harm.

MEASLES

Rubeola, also known as red measles, is a highly contagious viral infection characterized by fever, bronchial cough, sneezing, and irritated eyes that are sensitive to light. A brownish-red rash starts around the ears, on the face and neck, and then spreads over the trunk and occasionally over the limbs. The primary symptoms usually last 4 to 7 days before the rash appears, and from 2 to 5 days after the rash disappears. In most cases, a person only has the measles once. Some people who are weakened by the measles suffer complications such as lung or middle ear infections. See the sections on *Rubella, Ear Infections* and *Disinfectants* this book.

* In well-nourished children and adults, measles usually pass without complications. In malnourished or unhealthy individuals, great care must be taken to prevent a weakened immune system. Preventing ear infections (see *Ear Infections*), bacterial infections (See *Disinfectants*), and pneumonia is a primary goal. To prevent respiratory complications, use a warm steam vaporizer in the person's room with 10 drops of *T36-C5* and 2 capfuls of *Sol-U-Mel*. Drink *G'Day Melaleuca Tea* 3 to 6 times each day.

---

*Please consult your health care provider before starting any course of supplementation or treatment, particularly if you are pregnant or currently under medical care. Make sure you carefully read and understand all product packaging prior to use.

MENOPAUSE

Menopause (stopping of flow) may be natural (average age 45-51), artificial (radiation or surgery), or premature (illness or stress-induced). In a state of health, natural menopause has mild symptoms, such as the ovaries ceasing to produce eggs and shriveling up like gray colored prunes. When a woman undergoes premature menopause, there are underlying causes that need specific attention. The greatest concern during and for about 5 years after menopause is the rapidly dwindling levels of estrogen to the cells of the body. Various lifestyle factors can have a great effect on estrogen production at this time of life, including stress vs. rest cycles.

Hot flashes, sweating, or light-headedness affect approximately 75% of menopausal women and last for about a year. (See the section on *Hot Flashes* in this book.) Approximately 25% to 50% of these women have these symptoms for 5 years or more. Other symptoms of tiredness, weight gain, headaches, irritability, insomnia, and nervousness may be related to both estrogen deprivation and the stress of aging and changing lifestyle roles. Lack of sleep due to disturbances from hot flashes makes the fatigue and irritability worse. Occasional dizziness, numb or tingling sensations, palpitations, and fast heart rate may occur. The risk of heart disease increases. Urinary incontinence and urinary tract infections increase. Nausea, low bowel gas, constipation or diarrhea, and joint and muscle pains are also common complaints. The major health risk is osteoporosis at this time. (See the section on *Osteoporosis* in this book.) Preventing this challenge should be every woman's primary health concern.

* See your health care provider and begin following his/her advice for controlling stress. Take ***EstrAval Natural Support for Menopause***—2 per day. Take ***The Vitality Pak***—2 each per day, ***Cell-Wise with Natural E***—2 per day, and ***ProVexCV***—1 per 35 lbs of body weight per day for cardiovascular protection. Begin a daily exercise program using the ***Access Bar*** and ***Sustain*** drink to prevent low blood sugar and fatigue. Drink 2 to 4 cups of ***G'Day Melaleuca Tea*** each day to prevent urinary tract infections. Communication is very important during this time. Overwork and continued stress can prolong symptoms.

MENSTRUAL PAIN
See Cramps

MIGRAINE HEADACHES
See Headaches

MILIARIA
See Prickly Heat

MITES
See Hives

MONONUCLEOSIS

The presence of fatigue, fever, sore throat, and enlarged lymph nodes signifies the illness known as "Mono," which is caused by the Epstein-Barr virus. About 50% of children contract the virus before the age of five and have mild or no symptoms. Recovery is rapid. When infection occurs in young adults, an immune system battle results. Damage is done to human lymphocytes, the spleen, and the liver. Relapses are common if activity is resumed too soon. Many high school and college students miss school because of not heeding the necessary "rest and recover" treatment. No medicines are known to treat this illness.

The incubation time of the virus is not fully known, but one week to two months is common. The illness can take up to three months to run its course. Complications may occur if it is not properly treated. "Mono" can go on to cause seizures, meningitis, psychosis, chronic fatigue syndrome, respiratory disease, jaundice, and hepatitis. Blood testing can detect past infections for several years after the illness has passed.

* Complete bed rest for the first several weeks is often necessary to ease symptoms and prevent complications. Mild activity with mid-day rest periods is recommended for the first 4 o 6 weeks. Drink 2 to 6 cups of *G'Day Melaleuca Tea* each day. Take *The Vitality Pak*, *Cell-Wise*, *ProVex* and/or *ProVex-Plus* with juice or broth for the first 2 to 3 weeks, then with meals. Breathe *T36-C5* enriched steam vapor to prevent respiratory complications. Thirty-minute hot baths, with 1 ounce of *Sol-U-Mel* and 1 ounce of *Renew Bath Oil*, are helpful in the absence of a fever. Do not do heavy lifting, bending at the waist, or jumping for 3 months, as permanent damage to the liver or spleen may occur.

MORNING SICKNESS

On about the tenth day after conception, the developing placenta begins producing the hormones HCG and estrogen, which may cause mild to severe nausea and vomiting in susceptible mothers-to-be. This, along with tender breasts and no menstrual period, is strong (but not absolute) evidence of pregnancy. A self-administered pregnancy test can be performed on urine, and these tests are now sensitive enough to be accurate only a few days after conception.

* There are no FDA-approved drugs for morning sickness. Any anti-nausea drugs can cause damage to the developing baby. Drink and eat small amounts of bland food (steamed vegetables, baked potato, dry bread, etc.) throughout the day to not stretch the stomach and trigger the very sensitive gag reflex. The first food and drink should be before getting out of bed in the morning. *Sustain* drink is a helpful supplement at this time. Small amounts of *G'Day Melaleuca Tea* taken throughout

the day are very calming to the stomach. The need for vitamin B-6 and magnesium is great and can be supplied from *The Vitality Pak Prenatal* (they may need to be ground up and put in a drink or taken in the middle of the night). Ginger is a very good herb for controlling nausea and has no side effects. Take *Calmicid,*which contains a natural stomach-calming herbal complex which includes ginger and chamomile. Take as directed. The use of wrist straps fitted with acupressure beads help some women with morning sickness.

MOSQUITO BITES

In many parts of the country, summer is well known as "Mosquito Season." The pesky little creatures cannot only ruin an evening on the porch, but your sleep as well. Prevention is the best method of control. Check the recipe for *Mosquito Spray* in this book.

* Apply *T36-C5* to bites and follow with *Mela-Gel* on any bites where the skin is broken. If the skin is itching significantly without a break occurring, use *Renew Intensive Skin Therapy* or *Moisturizing Hand Creme* to alleviate the itching and the pain. See the section on *Insect Bites* in this book.

MOSQUITO SPRAY

This is called a mosquito, black fly and "no see'em" spray. One of the most important things to remember when using Melaleuca products is that they are NOT pesticides and therefore will not stop the varmints from landing on you. They will deter them and greatly reduce the incidence of bites and the reaction that accompanies them. Melaleuca products also do not make you feel like you need to take a shower after you use them, but will actually enhance the healthiness of your skin. It is also important to note that different body types respond differently to the different formulas. Some say that simply taking the vitamins has stopped mosquito bites. Do not be afraid to experiment and find your own solution and then pass it on!

* Mix 4 ounces of *Sol-U-Mel* with 4 ounces of *Renew Bath Oil* and 5 ounces of *Moisturizing Hand Creme*. This formula can be spread on the exposed body skin or over the entire body.

An alternate choice might be to blend 2 ounces of *Renew Bath Oil* and 2 ounces of *Sol-U-Mel* with 1 ounce of *Tough & Tender*, 20 drops of *T36-C5* and 6 to 12 ounces of water. Apply this frequently with a spray bottle.

Keep in mind that shampooing with *Naturals Melaleuca Oil Shampoo* or *Naturals Herbal Shampoo* and using *Sun-Shades* sun block affords insect repellent protection as well.

For babies and children, combine 3 ounces of *Sol-U-Mel* with 16 ounces of water in a spray bottle and spray on their skin, clothes and holders.

MOUTH – FOUL TASTE

The human taste buds are highly developed in some people. Certain food tastes are pleasant to some and not so pleasant to others. Disorders of taste can be caused from sinus infections, reduction in smell due to nasal congestion, smoking, or facial nerve damage. Other conditions causing foul tastes are poor dental hygiene, chemical poisoning, heavy metal poisoning, viral infections or psychological depression. Reduced taste can be due to a zinc deficiency in the diet.

* If organic causes for the foul taste cannot be determined, begin a systematic treatment plan of your own. Proper daily dental care with *Classic Tooth Polish, Breath-Away Mouthwash,* and *Hot/Cool Shot Mouth Spray* can be very helpful in restoring normal taste. Have regular dental checkups. Take *The Vitality Pak, Cell-Wise, ProVex* and/or *ProVex-Plus* as directed. Drink 2 to 4 cups of *G'Day Melaleuca Tea* each day. Avoid being around pesticides and herbicides as well as solvents, paints, or petroleum-based products. If you experience frequent nasal congestion, consult your health care provider for allergy testing.

MOUTH AND GUM INFECTIONS

See Gingivitis and Dental-Gum Disease

MOUTHBURN RELIEF

Biting something which is too hot can cause a burn inside the mouth.

* Immediately flush your mouth with ice water. Follow with a dab of *T36-C5* on the burned area.

MOUTH ULCERS

See Canker Sores

MUCOUS

Thin, watery mucous is a product of healthy membranes in the body and is needed to protect soft tissues from damaging environmental substances. Thick, discolored or stringy sputum (phlegm), and vaginal, eye, stool, or nasal mucous are signs of irritation or infection. Mild bacterial growth, viruses, chronic yeast or fungal infections, digestive problems, stress, allergies and chemical sensitivities can produce this type of mucous.

* Drink 2 to 6 cups of *G'Day Melaleuca Tea* each day to reduce the number of harmful organisms in the bowel and urinary tract. Use *CounterAct Cough Relief Medicine* as directed. If congestion exists, use *CounterAct Night-Time Cold, Allergy, Sinus Medicine* as directed. Breathe steam and *T36-C5* to clear tear ducts, nasal, and sinus mucous membranes. Douche with *Nature's Cleanse* as directed to reduce vaginal viruses, yeast, molds, fungus, and bacteria. Repeat any of the above to maintain healthy mucous.

---

*Please consult your health care provider before starting any course of supplementation or treatment, particularly if you are pregnant or currently under medical care. Make sure you carefully read and understand all product packaging prior to use.

MULTIPLE SCLEROSIS

Multiple sclerosis (MS) is an illness diagnosed in over 350,000 people in the United States today. Even now, much is to be learned. In brief, what is known about MS is that it is signified by more than one (multiple) area of inflammation and scarring of the myelin in the brain and spinal cord. Myelin is the tissue that covers and protects our nerve fibers. When this damage occurs, nerve "communication" is disrupted. Thus, a person with MS experiences varying degrees of neurological impairment depending on the location and extent of the scarring. Although there is no known cure for MS at this time, there is much that can be done to make your life easier.

* The following suggestion has been recommended for MS: *The Vitality Pak*—2 each per day (morning and evening) and *Cell-Wise with Natural E*—2 per day (morning and evening). For the first 2-4 weeks, take a saturation dose of *ProVex-Plus*—1 per 25 lbs. of body weight per day or *ProVexCV*—eight per day. Take half in the morning and half in the evening. After 3-5 weeks, you should be able to decrease by one per day and gradually decrease until you are taking four each day. Never go below four. However, if you are decreasing and you seem to be "slipping" a little, increase the dosage by one each day. This is not an exact science, so you will need to pay attention to your body and listen to its needs. *Sustain* is the ultimate "fatigue buster" and will not make you feel wired like caffeine or sugar. The *Access Bar* is also a tremendous help with energy.

Dr. Royce Frank, head of the Department of Neurology at the University of Oregon, put 146 incurable MS patients on low-fat, high-fiber diets (approximately 30-40 grams of fiber per day), with a vitamin supplement and found that 90% of the early stage MS patients had a complete arrest of the progress of their disease. In fact, they showed improvement even over a twenty-year span of the illness. He then looked at the intermediate stage and had a 65% success rate in that it significantly slowed the progression of the disease. This regime was continued for seven years, and it arrested the progression of the MS in patients at the intermediate stage of this disease. In the advanced stages, Dr. Frank found that there was a 30% arrest of the progression

Adding fiber to your diet is easy if you use *Sustain*, *Attain*, and *FiberWise* drink or bars provided by Melaleuca. It is not only easy, but they taste good as well!

MUSCLE

See *Aches and Pains, Athletic Injuries, Cramps, Leg Cramps and Muscle Strain*

MUSCLE ACHES

See *Aches and Pains, Muscle Strain*

MUSCLE CRAMPS
See Cramps and Leg Cramps

MUSCLE PAIN
See Athletic Injuries

MUSCLE SPASMS
See Athletic Injuries

MUSCLE STRAIN
There are several levels of muscle strain. Mild strain occurs regularly with all forms of exercise. Severe muscle strains can cause tearing and bruising. Overused muscles, tendons (connecting muscles to bones), and ligaments (connecting bones to other bones) are helped by immediately applying ice to prevent swelling. Keep the ice on for 5 to 10 minutes each hour, until the swelling is reduced.

* *Pain-A-Trate* gives dramatic relief from athletic strains and soreness. Soaking in a hot bath with *Renew Bath Oil* is very relaxing for aching muscles.

NAGA SORES
See Ulcers, Tropical

NAILS, INFECTED
See Paronychia

NAPPY RASH
See Diaper Rash

NASAL CONGESTION
Nasal congestion comes from a partial blockage of a nasal passage caused by an inflammation of the mucous membrane. Congestion can be caused by infection of the passageway as a result of a cold, an infection coming from the sinuses, or allergies. See the section on *Sinus Congestion* in this book.

* Place two caps of *Sol-U-Mel* and 10-12 drops of *T36-C5* in a cool mist humidifier in your bedroom and breathe deeply all night. A warm air vaporizer will work as well, but it will not last as long and thus is more expensive, especially if you run it every night to prevent early morning stuffiness.

If the blockage is severe, take a cloth and drip 4 to 5 drops of *T36-C5* on it and place it on or near your pillow. Placing a few drops of *T36-C5* or *T40-C3* in hot water and making a tent with a towel over your head is also very effective.

NASAL ULCERS

Nasal ulcers are open sores or lesions of the mucous membrane, which are accompanied by sloughing of inflamed tissue.

* Dab *T36-C5* onto the infected area with a saturated Q-tip. This will not only help with the infection, but will aid with the pain as well.

NECK PAIN

See Athletic Injuries

NERVOUSNESS

"A sound mind in a sound body" was the Greek ideal for a healthy person. We now know that what impairs one part of our being will affect the other. Nervousness (mild anxiety) can be due to worry about an unfounded or unlikely situation or event. Deprivation of sleep, clinical depression, and the aches and pains that often accompany tense muscles are typical with nervous people. Nervousness tends to be a learned behavior that depletes the body of valuable nutrients, which in turn perpetuates the condition. Chemical addictions, including nicotine (nervous stimulant) and alcohol (nervous depressant), as well as long-term prescription drugs, should be avoided and corrected before permanent improvement can take place. A healthy body makes its own chemicals for awareness and response to real problems. Nervousness is one way the body responds to stress. Nearly all mental disorders include nervousness as a component of the diagnosis. See the section on *Exercise* in this book.

* See your health care provider and follow his/her recommendations for stress control, exercise, and diet. Take *Luminex*, which contains St. John's wort, Griffonia seed, folic acid and B-12, daily as directed. Take *The Vitality Pak*, *Cell-Wise*, *ProVex* and/or *ProVex-Plus* as directed as well. Drink 2 to 4 cups of *G'Day Melaleuca Tea* each day. Practice relaxation and breathing exercises. Believe that you can train your body, with help, to be less nervous.

NETTLE RASH

See Rashes

NEURODERMATITIS

So far, not much is known about this illness except that the number of people suffering from it has been increasing continuously in the industrial countries of the world. The main symptoms range from severe itching and reddening of the skin to papules and pustules. Experts do agree that its causes are in some way connected to the immune system. It could be a result of overreaction similar to what happens to allergies. It has been observed that people who suffer from neurodermatitis are frequently affected by illnesses that are also caused by an overreaction of the immune system, like allergic asthma and hay fever.

---

*Please consult your health care provider before starting any course of supplementation or treatment, particularly if you are pregnant or currently under medical care. Make sure you carefully read and understand all product packaging prior to use.

In nearly 90 percent of all cases, neurodermatitis appears for the first time before a person is six years of age. The risk of getting the disease is increased by inheritance, the mother smoking during or before pregnancy, or such socioeconomic standards such as excessive hygiene, stopping breastfeeding sooner, or the stress of holding down two jobs.

Neurodermatitis occurs intermittently and can be triggered by synthetic materials that irritate the skin, rapid changes of temperature, showering or bathing too frequently, contact allergens, natural allergens, food allergens, and stress.

* People with neurodermatitis have very dry skin. Bathe in body temperature water. Taking oil baths in body temperature water and *Renew Bath Oil* can be very helpful. *Renew Intensive Skin Therapy* as well as the *Renew Bath Oil* directly on the skin is very effective for dry skin.

One of the basis rules for dealing with neurodermatitis is "moist on moist and dry on dry." This means that if acute phases are accompanied by discharges, you should apply moist compresses and cooling ointments and lotions. Contrary to this, during healthy intervals, you should use, as needed individually, the oil, ointments and cremes.

Products with Melaleuca oil are very effective in treating neurodermatitis because they work as a local anesthetic and cool the skin. It can also fight the skin infections that are frequently caused by the damaged immune system.

NOTE: Some doctors have had excellent results using Melaleuca oil and are in favor of using it with neurodermatitis. However, others are critical of it and claim that it may cause a contact allergy. Discuss this with your health care provider.

NEUROPATHY

One of the complications of diabetes is neuropathy. In the early stages of neuropathy there is a tingling and numbness of the hands and feet. In severe cases, the tendon reflexes are decreased or absent. Vibration sense may be diminished or lost. A constant aching type of pain is frequent and is usually worse at night.

* It has been recommended that people with neuropathy take *The Vitality Pak*—2 each per day, *Cell-Wise with Natural E*—2 per day, and *ProVex Plus*—1 capsule for each 25 lbs of body weight per day. Diabetics must take very good care of their feet. See the section on *Diabetic Foot Ulcerations* in this book.

NICOTINE WITHDRAWAL

The question is often asked, "How can I quit smoking?" The answer is different for each individual. Some people make up their mind to quit and have no symptoms of withdrawal. Others have neurological and psychological symptoms typical of drug addition. Depression, anxiety, and behavioral changes are common. Since nicotine is of the

alkaloid family, along with morphine and codeine, chemical detoxification and emotional support are important to recovery. The
appetite-suppressive effects of nicotine are well known. Compulsive
eating during recovery must be compensated for with exercise and
adequate nutrition.

* See your health care provider and begin following his/her advice.
Take *The Vitality Pak, Cell-Wise, ProVex* and/or *ProVex-Plus* as
directed. Drink 2 to 4 cups of *G'Day Melaleuca Tea* each day. Take one
FiberWise bar or drink each day to speed detoxification. Exercise and
drink plenty of water. If needed, do not hesitate to get professional
guidance. If congestion exists, use *CounterAct Night-Time Cold, Allergy,
Sinus Medicine* as directed.

NIPPLES, SORE
See Sore Nipples

NUTRITION
Nutrition is more than just getting enough food. It is getting enough
of the right food at the right time for the prevailing needs of the body.
Nutrition is the miracle the body performs when changing the molecular
structure of food into living human tissue. Everyone has slightly different
needs for nutrition based upon genetics, lifestyle, temperament,
geographic location, past illnesses, digestive and absorptive capacity,
and stress effects. The best thing you can do (after choosing the right
parents) is to determine your unique nutritional needs. Waiting until you
have a health problem before getting concerned about nutrition is like
waiting until your car engine runs out of oil before becoming interested
in engine lubrication. Just do it!

Not getting enough of the right kinds of food causes malnutrition.
On the average, Americans are overfed and undernourished. Ninety-
seven percent of Americans have some sort of nutritional deficiency. In
any one day 47% of Americans do not consume even one fruit. Twenty-
four percent have not chosen any milk products and 18% have avoided
consuming even one vegetable. In addition, choosing "brands" that are
heavily advertised in place of foods in their original state is often due to
clever marketing and advertising techniques. An example is potato chips
in place of a baked potato.

Why is the topic of nutrition so important to us? The Surgeon
General's Report in 1990 disclosed that, "...eighty percent of all current
diseases are due to chronic degenerative states in the body either
directly or indirectly related to diet and nutrition." Twenty-five years ago,
in spite of volumes of published clinical studies, medical scientists
lacked "conclusive" evidence that heart disease and cancer (number 1
and 2 leading causes of death) were related to diet. More recently, only
a few physicians would deny that diet and nutrition are the leading cause
and the best prevention for these conditions. This sudden awakening of

---

*Please consult your health care provider before starting any course of supplementation or treatment, particularly if you are
pregnant or currently under medical care. Make sure you carefully read and understand all product packaging prior to use.

the public to the "new" nutrition has paved the way for fad diets, quick vitamin cures, and overnight experts who have had little training and often less experience in using nutrition as "the" first medicine of choice. As Hippocrates said, "Let your medicine be your food and let your food be your medicine." This should not be too difficult to understand.

 * Consult your health care provider. Learn where your weaknesses are and design a plan to promote wellness. There is a big difference between preventing disease and promoting wellness, and we certainly want to work on the latter. So take *The Vitality Pak*, *Cell-Wise*, *ProVex* and/or *ProVex-Plus* as directed. *ProVexCV* should be a regular part of your health care plan as well. Drink *G'Day Melaleuca Tea* daily. Get enough rest. Learn how to relax. Practice playful activities (those that make you talk, laugh and breathe deeply) every day. The desire for self-nurturing exists when body, mind and spirit are healthy. Some people may need a little help to get started.

OBESITY

 The underlying causes of clinical obesity (being more than 20% above your optimum weight, or having more than 40% of your body weight as fat) often stems from boredom eating, stressful eating, childhood or sexual abuse, drug effects, or improper nutrition. See the section on *Nutrition* in this book. Less than 10% of obesity involves glandular conditions. The obvious problem is in storing more calories than are being burned through metabolic need and exercise. All chronic degenerative diseases are accelerated when obesity is present.

 Obesity increases the chances of becoming seriously ill. High blood pressure, stroke, coronary heart disease, and other conditions are more common in an obese person than in someone who is lean. Diabetes is five times more likely in those who are obese. Women who are overweight show a corresponding increase in the risk of developing breast, uterine and cervical cancer. Osteoarthritis is aggravated by obesity. Obese men have a greater risk of developing cancer of the colon, rectum and prostate.

 Our ancestors earned and burned 4,000 to 6,000 calories each day just in living, working and walking to school. Because of our automated lifestyle, we earn and burn between 1,200 and 2,000 calories each day. Our nutrient needs for vitamins, minerals and cofactors common to food remain the same. What is wrong with this picture?

 Many people have lost hundreds of pounds over the years only to gain it right back. This is due to a physiological condition called "set point." The hypothalamus gland in the brain constantly monitors the temperature of the inside of the body compared with the outside surface of the body. The appetite center, also located in hypothalamus, is activated when factors begin to lower blood sugar. Our bodies are then conditioned or "set" to burn less when apparent reserves begin to drop. We actually slow down our rate of calorie burning to conserve fuel. This is why people can go on a water diet for a week and not lose more than one or two pounds. Fatigue is the most common complaint when total calories are restricted. The set point must be changed so that the body is satisfied with fewer intakes, while it is burning more of its reserves. Restricting dietary fats to less than 20% of daily intake decreases free radicals and hunger sensations. Continuing exercise establishes a new set point, which is the permanent way to control weight. See the section on *Exercise* in this book.

   * See your health care provider and begin following his/her advice. Start with a high-fiber, low-fat diet. Lots of fiber cleanses the body, removes toxins, and helps to dilute, bind, and deactivate many carcinogens. It moves excess bile from the stomach and intestine, prevents obesity, lowers cholesterol, stabilizes blood sugar, and increases energy.

   Eat an *Access Bar* 15 minutes before exercise. This will allow your body to actually burn stored fat. Plan your meals ahead of time. Remove all unhealthy snack foods from your home. Enjoy *Attain* as a healthy meal replacement. It is especially effective for weight loss when it is mixed with water or rice milk. *Attain* can also be mixed with *ProFlex10* for added protein. Protein helps lower appetite cravings and cholesterol while it increases strength and endurance. *Attain* is a great replacement for Slim Fast and Ensure. *Luminex* would be helpful in boosting the level of 5-HTP, which is known to help in obesity.

   Use exercise, instead of eating, as a means of handling stress. If childhood stresses are present to any extent, contact Overeaters Anonymous and get involved. This non-profit group is an excellent source of free support. If necessary, see a counselor or a health care provider for appetite suppressive-herbs, acupuncture, or specific metabolic testing. Seeking help in getting started is far better than reading a "how to" book and doing it alone. They don't work for 99% of the people who buy them. The weight simply slips back, with interest!

ODOR

   See Body Odor and Bromhidrosis (Foot Odor)

OILY HAIR

   Oily hair is often the body's reaction to overwashing. The more often the hair is washed, the more oil our body tends to produce. When the hair is frequently washed it removes much of the hair's natural oils, causing the oil glands to overact.

   * Wash your hair daily with *Advanced Expressions Volumizing Shampoo For Oily or Limp Hair*. If the oily condition persists after two weeks, cut back to washing your hair every other day. At first this may seem to exasperate the problem, but the body will slow down its oil production when there is an ample amount of oil in the hair. This is one

condition which often gets worse before it gets better. Fortunately, a few days of abstinence will pay off in the long run.

ORAL THRUSH
See Thrush

OSGOOD-SCHLATTER'S DISEASE *(Growing Pains)*

Young athletes have muscles that are stronger than the actual bones to which they are attached. Heavy track and field events, especially broad jumping, puts an unusual amount of strain on the thigh muscles as they connect with the tibia just below the knee. Some young athletes develop this crippling disorder due to an avulsion (fracture), which tears away soft bone. This causes pain and swelling in the damaged area. This pain was once called "growing pains." Knee supports are often used to prevent injuries in 14 to 18-year-olds. See the section on *Growing Pains* in this book.

* Apply an ice pack for 5 to 10 minutes to acute pain areas. Take **Mela-Cal** with each meal, as well as before and after exercise to maximize bone development. **Mel-Vita**, taken as directed, will enhance growth and healing of injuries. **ProVex** and/or **ProVex-Plus** will reduce pain and inflammation. Apply **Pain-A-Trate** directly to the affected area before and after exercise to minimize swelling and pain. Rub exercised thigh muscles with **Pain-A-Trate** to relax tension and stimulate circulation. Jacuzzi or whirlpool massage is excellent for reducing tension. Do not overtrain. You have a long life ahead of you.

OSTEOARTHRITIS

A degeneration of joint material, including cartilage and bone, take place when complex systems of mechanical injury, biological stress, biochemical irritation, and enzymatic or nutritional deficiencies are upset. There is no single cause for osteoarthritis. Healthy joints have such little friction that without some precipitating condition, they will never wear out. Apparently the amount of friction in the joint increases after repetitive injury, taking drugs for other conditions (many drugs affect joint and bone metabolism), toxic reactions to environmental pollution (pesticides, herbicides, food additives, etc.) trace nutrient deficiencies, or dietary habits that promote nutritional deficiencies (excessive coffee drinking, alcohol, limited diet selection. etc.). Osteoarthritic joints have less flexible cartilage and more infiltrated bones, causing the telltale enlarged joints on fingers. Exercise tends to pump nutrients in and wastes out of healthy cartilage. See the section on *Arthritis* in this book.

* Exercise and movement are imperative. Some people who have complained of painful hands, especially in cold weather, have found relief by taking up knitting. Start each morning by washing the evening

---

snack dishes by hand in hot water. Apply *Pain-A-Trate* to the affected joints. Take *Replenex Joint Replenishing Complex* for cartilage growth. *ProVex* and/or *ProVex-Plus* will help to reduce inflammation.

It has been suggested that someone with osteoarthritis take 2 each per day of *The Vitality Pak*, 2 per day of *Cell-Wise with Natural E*, 3 per day of the *Replenex*, and 2 per day of the *ProVex Plus*. Drink 2 to 4 cups of *G'Day Melaleuca Tea* each day. Consult your health care provider.

OSTEOPOROSIS

There are two major types of osteoporosis, primary and secondary. The primary type occurs more often in women and progresses with age. Known as the "shrinking disease," it affects more women over the age of 65 than breast and uterine cancer combined. The loss of calcium prematurely is due to a combination of factors. Women who are slight of build, smoke cigarettes, consume caffeine and animal products, fail to exercise, and do not ingest enough usable calcium from vegetable sources are prone to develop fractures of large weight-bearing bones after menopause. The spine, pelvis, and femoral hip joint areas are most often affected. School-aged girls are often deficient in dietary calcium from vegetable sources. Most are at great risk of never attaining 100% of their expected bone calcium density. Since the expected life span of a woman born in the 1990s is 90+ years, more emphasis should be placed on teaching girls how to prevent this disease

Secondary osteoporosis is less common and can be due to malabsorption of calcium, endocrine imbalances, prescription or other drug reactions, liver disease, or kidney disease. Recent studies indicate that a deficiency of vitamin D is the real cause of osteoporosis. Vitamin D allows your body to absorb calcium. Without it, you can take all the calcium supplements in the world and it would not help.

* If you are having any of these challenges, see your health care provider and begin following his/her advice. Limit or eliminate all dairy and other animal products. Also eliminate soda pop from your diet. If you are a woman of menopausal age and have lost ½ inch or more of height since you were 18, begin a program to minimize osteoporosis. If more than 1 inch of height has been lost, consult your health care provider for a calcium metabolism evaluation.

Women of all ages can benefit from taking *EstrAval* daily as directed. Take *The Vitality Pak* and *Cell-Wise* to ensure adequate trace nutrients. Drink 2 to 4 cups of *G'Day Melaleuca Tea* each day to detoxify. Take *ProVex* and/or *ProVex-Plus* daily as directed. The ingredients in *ProFlex20* are powerful stabilizers of collagen structures, which is the major protein structure in bone.

OTITIS
See Ear Infections

PARKINSON'S DISEASE

Parkinson's is an incurable neurological disorder. It occurs when brain cells that produce dopamine, an important neurotransmitter (message-carrying chemical), are destroyed in a part of the brain known as the substantia nigra.

In a recent study presented to the American Academy of Neurology it was stated that people who had been exposed to pesticides were twice as likely to develop Parkinson's Disease as those not exposed. Whether this proves to be conclusive or not, it is reason enough to convert your home to the safer Melaleuca products. Why take a chance on exposing yourself and your family to toxic chemicals unnecessarily? See the section on *Insect Repellent* in this book.

* Convert your home to Melaleuca products and start your family on a healthy nutritional supplement program such as the *Daily for Life Pack*.

PEDICULUS HUMANS CAPITIS

See Lice

PAIN

See Aches and Pains, Athletic Injuries, Cramps and Growing Pains

PARONYCHIA

Paronychia is an infection or inflammation of the tissues around a fingernail or toenail. Some researchers maintain that yeast such as Candida albicans or bacteria such as Pseudomonas or Proteus cause it. However, the most common cause is usually staphylococcus, with Candida as a secondary invader.

It enters through a break in the skin. It will usually first appear as white patches or a lifting or thickening of one edge of the nail plate. The infection may follow the nail margin and may extend beneath the nail where the infection penetrates more deeply into the finger or toe. Tissue breakdown into the tendons and muscle in the finger or toe may result. Eventually the infected nail may become distorted and lose normal function if not treated promptly.

* Early detection and treatment is important. Wash the affected area with *Antibacterial Liquid Soap*. Soak for 15 minutes in 1 quart of warm water and 1 ounce of *Sol-U-Mel*. Pat dry. Apply *T36-C5* to the fingernail or toenail morning and night, and then follow with *Triple Antibiotic Ointment* or *Mela-Gel*. Cover the area with a loose bandage. Chronic infections may require repeated applications for several months. If Candida albicans is the causative agent in a female, douching with *Nature's Cleanse* may be needed to reduce the fungus. Drink *G'Day Melaleuca Tea* 2 to 4 times each day.

An alternate choice would be to clean the affected area with *Antibacterial Liquid Soap* and then apply *Dermatin Antifungal Creme*, or *Zap-It Acne Medication*. In addition to the normal nutritional

---

*Please consult your health care provider before starting any course of supplementation or treatment, particularly if you are pregnant or currently under medical care. Make sure you carefully read and understand all product packaging prior to use.

supplements, also take *ProVex Plus* (1 capsule per 25 lbs. of body weight each day).

PEPTIC ULCERS
See Gastric Ulcers

PERIODONTITIS
See Dental-Gum Disease

PHARYNGITIS
See Hoarseness

PIERCED EARS
See Abscesses

PILES
See Hemorrhoids

PIMPLES
See Acne

PLAQUE
Bacteria in the mouth cause a thin, sticky film on the tooth enamel called plaque.

*Gently brush the teeth and tongue after every meal with *Denti-Clean Classic Tooth Polish*. Swish your mouth with *Breath-Away Mouthwash* to reduce mouth microbes. Floss frequently with *Exceed Waxed Dental Floss* and chew *Insta-Fresh Gum*. Take *ProVex* and/or *ProVex-Plus* to help prevent plaque buildup. Have regular checkups with your dentist to maintain healthy teeth.

PLANTAR WARTS
This common wart, usually located on the sole of the foot, can become quite tender when pressure is applied. Plantar warts can be distinguished from corns and calluses by their pinpoint bleeding when the cap is shaved away.

*Apply *T36-C5* to the specific area daily. *Renew Intensive Skin Therapy* will help to decrease and soften cornified tissues around the wart.

PNEUMONIA
See Sinus Congestion

POISON IVY, POISON OAK, POISON SUMAC
Complex chemical agents in certain plants are capable of producing acute dermatitis in sensitized individuals. Poison ivy, poison oak, or

---

*Please consult your health care provider before starting any course of supplementation or treatment, particularly if you are pregnant or currently under medical care. Make sure you carefully read and understand all product packaging prior to use.

sumac's blistery rash is a result of coming in contact with the plant itself, or handling the clothing of someone who has been in contact with it. Some people are more sensitive to the oily plant juices than others. Many substances other than poison oak, poison ivy, or sumac cause this acute reaction, including ragweed and primrose. Shoe dyes, formaldehyde in clothing, penicillin, sulfonamides, neomycin, anesthetics, food stabilizers and cosmetics can also produce severe dermatitis.

When out of doors, be aware of these three plants. Poison ivy appears as a plant, bush or vine and has three shiny leaves on each stem. The leaves turn red in the fall. In late summer, it has white flowers or cream-colored berries. Even in winter when the leaves have dropped, the plant can still be quite toxic.

Poison oak is commonly found in sandy soil and pinewoods along both the West and East Coasts. Poison oak has shiny green oak-like leaves clustered in groups of 3 or 5.

Poison sumac has the same characteristics of the two preceding plants. It is a short shrub or small tree having smooth gray bark and branches with 7 to 13 dull green leaflets. The leaves turn yellow in autumn. White berries distinguish it from the harmless sumacs. The poison variety predominantly grows in swampy areas or along streams.

* Immediate removal of the affecting agent is necessary for any treatment to be effective. Immediately wash the area thoroughly with *Antibacterial Liquid Soap* and warm water. Pat (don't rub) dry. Apply *Triple Antibiotic Ointment* and cover with a loose gauze bandage three times each day until resolved. If the rash or blistering has appeared before treatment can be started, soak gauze in cool *G'Day Melaleuca Tea* and cover the affected area. Re-soak the gauze and apply every 15 minutes until the pain subsides. Apply *Triple Antibiotic Ointment* three times each day until resolved. Draining the blisters can be done, but do not remove the covering skin. If pain does not reduce, apply *Pain-A-Trate*. Contact your health care provider, especially if improvement is not seen after 4 days.

Another solution would be to try *Corticare*. It is designed to take the sting out of poison ivy, oak and sumac, as well as hives and rashes. This unique formula includes pharmacist-recommended hydrocortisone for itch relief plus the naturally soothing Melaleuca oil.

NOTE: *Sol-U-Mel* very effectively stops the itching and dries up poison ivy, oak or sumac. Please note that this is the **ONLY** time it is appropriate to use *Sol-U-Mel* without diluting it.

POISONING
See Drug Poisoning

PORES
See Clogged Pores

POULTICE

A poultice is a hot, soft, moist mass applied to a sore part of the body. It is designed to extract pus from an abscess or to remove an infected splinter. It will disinfect, soothe pain, and speed up the healing process. See the *Compress* section in this book.

* Mix a small amount of healing earth (from your pharmacy) with water and add 3-6 drops of *T36-C5*. Apply the mixture to the affected area and cover with a bandage.

PREGNANCY

Pregnancy is a natural process, yet one out of every eleven pregnancies produces an abnormal baby. The best thing to do to have a healthy, happy baby is to have healthy, happy parents. External factors that are known to greatly affect a normal pregnancy include the nutrition of the mother and the safety of the environment. Exercise should be continued during pregnancy to maintain muscle tone and prevent back problems from the added 20 to 30 pounds of normal weight gain.

Since the baby is made from molecular building blocks, maximizing nutritional needs and minimizing non-nutritional chemicals is vital. Nutritional needs for the expectant mother increase for all of the known nutrients. A lack of folic acid is now known to cause spinal cord defects in babies of deficient mothers. It is estimated that 85% to 90% of all pregnant women take prescriptions or over-the-counter drugs during their pregnancy, with 3% to 12% of abnormal pregnancies resulting from their side effects. Drugs and babies do not mix well. Other dangerous substances include carbon monoxide from cigarette smoke, alcohol, and fumes from paint or toxic household cleaners. Actually, common sense gives us good direction in avoiding these things. The heightened sense of smell and taste during pregnancy gives a woman a great defense for her baby. Remember, if it bothers you, it will bother the baby. See the sections on *Nausea* or *Morning Sickness* in this book.

* Plan for your baby at least one year before you intend to get pregnant. Begin taking *The Vitality Pak Prenatal* as directed. *The Vitality Pak Prenatal* satisfies all of the minimum recommendations for 18 vitamins and minerals, including folate, during pregnancy. See your health care provider and follow his/her advice. Exercise for 30 minutes daily. Walking is the best exercise prior to the birth of the baby. Eating low on the food pyramid automatically gives adequate roughage to prevent constipation and water retention. Minimizing stress while balancing activity with rest best prevents toxemia during pregnancy.

PRICKLY HEAT

Prickly heat is a skin eruption caused by inflammation of the sweat glands. Some factors that can cause or worsen the challenge are personal hygiene, nutritional deficiencies, clothing that does not breathe, emotional or physical stresses, detergents, underarm deodorants, cosmetics, and allergic reactions. It is important to identify and remove the cause of this inflammation.

*Massage *T36-C5* into the affected area. It will help to reduce the inflammation and speed the healing.

For general care of the inflamed areas, wash your face with *The Gold* or *Platinum Bar* and bathe with *Renew Bath Oil*. Dry the skin gently and then apply *T36-C5* followed by *Renew Intensive Skin Therapy*. By using products that contain *T36-C5*, you can continue the healing process.

PROSTATE HEALTH
See Benign Prostatic Hyperplasia

PRURITIS
Itchy skin is certainly annoying, yet it can also be an indication of serious disease. However, it is usually a manifestation of a relatively minor ailment such as an allergic reaction or dry skin.

Some of the illnesses and diseases that may cause pruritis include: hepatitis, cancer, kidney failure, kidney infections, liver failure, food allergies, contact allergies due to poisonous plants, soaps and metals, internal fungal infections, skin fungal infections, essential fatty acid deficiency, and vitamin A deficiency.

* Melaleuca's products that contain Melaleuca oil are excellent for pruritis, as the oil is one of nature's finest anti-itch remedies. Some conditions warrant the direct use of *T36-C5*, while others will respond more readily to *CortiCare* or *Dermatin*. See the particular section in this book that applies to the condition you are experiencing, such as *Leucorrhoea* or *Candida Albicans*.

PRURITIS ANI
Pruritis ani is Latin for "itching anus." This area of the body tends to have an almost built-in "readiness to itch." Itching around the anus can be caused from something as simple as pinworms in children, or as complicated as rectal cancer in adults. Internal hemorrhoids are often discovered as a cause in adults. Many causes stem from chemical irritation with perfumed soap or toilet tissue. Food allergies (particularly eggs or milk) are frequently associated with this condition and often produce a red ring around the anal opening. Food additive sensitivities (colorings, flavorings, and preservatives) are among the most common causes in children. Other causes include fungal growths such as Candida albicans, psychological responses in anxiety patients, skin problems such as psoriasis or contact dermatitis, heavy coffee or cola drinking, poor hygiene, vitamin deficiency, and overly meticulous cleaning with soaps and perfumed powders.

---

* Try to treat the cause. Soaking in a warm bath with 1 cup of Epsom salt and 1 ounce of **Renew Bath Oil** often reduces anal muscle tightness, which contributes to the itch. Avoid applying or consuming chemical conditioned substances. Drink 2 to 6 cups of **G'Day Melaleuca Tea** each day. Take **The Vitality Pak**, **Cell-Wise**, **ProVex** and/or **ProVex-Plus** as directed. **Pain-A-Trate** can be dabbed around the anus during extreme cases to minimize itching. **Renew Intensive Skin Therapy** often gives lasting relief from pruritus ani while the true cause is being corrected. If itching persists, consult your health care provider for further evaluation.

PSORIASIS

Psoriasis is a chronic and recurrent disease of the skin that affects up to 3% of Americans. Dry, well-circumscribed, silvery, scaly patches of various sizes characterize it. The patches can vary in severity from one or two lesions to a widespread dermatosis. The cause is unknown, but it appears to be related to inadequate detoxification possibly through the kidney or the alimentary tract. Thick scaling is probably due to an increased rate of epidermal cell growth. This cosmetic deformity proves socially embarrassing although it is not contagious.

Psoriasis usually involves the scalp and the upper surface of the extremities, particularly the elbows, knees, back, and buttocks. The nails, eyebrows, armpits, abdomen, or groin region may also be affected. Occasionally the illness is generalized.

The lesions are more sharply localized and usually heal without scarring. Hair growth does not appear to be affected. Extension of lesions sometimes produces large plaques up to one-half inch thick. Nail involvement may resemble fungal infections, causing a separation of the nail with thickening, discoloration, and debris under the nail plate. Allergies, stress, and environmental sensitivities should be evaluated. Nutritional needs tend to be elevated.

* Bathe using **Antibacterial Liquid Soap** and soak in **Renew Bath Oil** for 30 minutes each night. Pat dry. Do not rub. Apply **Renew Intensive Skin Therapy** to the scaly areas. Use **T36-C5** on newly inflamed or red areas. Cover the area with **Mela-Gel**. Daily sunlight exposure for 15 to 20 minutes is helpful. Practice relaxation. Eat healthy food. Take **The Vitality Pak**, **Cell-Wise**, **ProVex** and/or **ProVex-Plus** as directed, and drink 2 to 6 cups of **G'Day Melaleuca Tea** daily to help detoxify. It has also been suggested that you dab straight **Nature's Cleanse** on a small area of the psoriasis. If it does not turn red, repeat several times. Consult your health care provider for further advice.

RADIATION BURNS

Radiation burns can occur to skin that has been exposed to prolonged doses of radiation, such as is frequently used in the treatment of cancer.

---

* There are many prescriptions that are recommended to aid in this painful condition. However, it has been found that simply using *Renew Intensive Skin Therapy* has proved just as effective. It is certainly worth a try.

RASHES

Rashes can be caused by many things. They should be treated to prevent secondary infections and reduce any stinging or itching. See the section on *Dermatitis* in this book.

* Take a hot bath with 1 ounce of *Renew Bath Oil*, plus 1 ounce of *Sol-U-Mel*. Soak for 20 to 30 minutes. Pat dry and apply *Renew Intensive Skin Therapy*, *Triple Antibiotic Ointment* or *Pain-A-Trate* to the affected area.

If you don't have time for a nice relaxing bath, try adding one capful of *Renew Bath Oil* to a cupful of water and dabbing it on the rash. Pat dry and then apply *Renew Intensive Skin Therapy*, *Mela-Gel* or *T36-C5*. Of course, nothing stops the itch of a rash like *CortiCare*. It is an anti-itch cream formulated with the #1 pharmacist-recommended itch-stopping ingredient, hydrocortisone, plus Melaleuca oil.

When outdoors, be sure to use *Sun-Shades Waterproof Sunblock* (SPF 15 or SPF 30) and *Lip Balm* (SPF 15). If exposed to the sun for any length of time, use the *Sun-Shades After Sun Hydrogel E* when you go inside.

Another suggestion is to mix *T36-C5* with olive oil and put it on the skin of someone with poison ivy, oak or sumac. This works particularly well on the skin of children. Within 24 hours they will usually start healing and they will feel better immediately. Mix a few drops of the oil with 1/4 cup of olive oil and apply it with cotton balls several times each day.

The preceding addresses treating the results of the condition rather than dealing with the cause of the condition. A program of regularly taking *ProVex* and/or *ProVex-Plus* along with *The Vitality Pak* has been suggested for allergies of all kinds. However, if you think you have too many rashes, you may want to talk with your health care provider about the possibility of having allergy tests done. Undergoing a series of allergy tests can point toward determining the challenge.

NOTE: Anyone with contact dermatitis should NOT use a Melaleuca alternifolia oil product. Even if a situation seems to be improving, it may grow worse.

For other types of rash, see the *Diaper Rash* and *Shaving Rash* sections in this book.

RAZOR BURNS

Razor burns can happen when the skin is not sufficiently protected before being shaved. This can be caused by not enough lubrication or ineffective lubrication.

---

*Please consult your health care provider before starting any course of supplementation or treatment, particularly if you are pregnant or currently under medical care. Make sure you carefully read and understand all product packaging prior to use.

* *Melaleuca Essentials Shave Creme* can protect your skin when you shave by moisturizing it. It's unique blend of aloe vera, and algae forms a moisturizing film. This solution also contains nine essential oils including Melaleuca alternifolia oil. Combined, your sharp razor will glide over your skin.

Both men and women use *Melaleuca Essentials Shave Creme*. However, men may prefer what is referred to as the "ultimate shaving protection" by using *Mate Classic Conditioning Shave Gel*. It is a proprietary formula that gives you the closest shave possible while combining gel technology and soothing Melaleuca oil.

REPELLENT
See Insect Repellent

RESPIRATORY TRACT INFECTIONS
See Cold, Sinus Congestion, Cough, Fever, and/or Flu

RHEUMATISM
Soreness in the joints and muscles, red and swollen joints, backaches, a stiff knee, and many other ailments can identify rheumatoid conditions. The term 'rheumatism' is used to describe a whole range of disorders, which involve these symptoms. Rheumatism refers to muscular pain, whereas arthritis and gout are associated with pain located within the joints themselves. To arrive at a more specific diagnosis and to find the remedies best suited to you, check with your health care provider.

* Because of pain-relieving properties, products with Melaleuca oil are very effective in treating rheumatism. They also improve blood circulation and flexibility. Since rheumatism, like arthritis, is aggravated by an accumulation of toxins in the system, your diet and lifestyle should be evaluated.

A warm bath can provide instant pain relief. Add 8 to 10 drops of *T36-C5* to your warm bath water and bathe with *Renew Bath Oil* as it, too, has pain-relieving properties. Massage the aching areas twice a day with *Pain-A-Trate* to increase circulation and dispose of pain-causing toxic substances.

Since rheumatism is worsened by an accumulation of toxic substances in the body, consider changing your diet. 1. Eat as little protein from animals and eggs as possible. 2. Eat a lot of raw vegetables and fruit. 3. Take *The Vitality Pak* as directed daily. See the sections on *Arthritis* and *Aches and Pains* in this book.

RHEUMATOID ARTHRITIS
See Arthritis

RINGING IN THE EARS
See Tinnitus

RINGWORM

A round, reddened, often bulls-eye appearing rash anywhere on the skin is evidence of ringworm. Dermatophytes fungi cause the superficial infection (those that invade only dead tissue of the skin, nails, or hair). At least three different strains of fungi can cause ringworm. Household pets such as cats and dogs carry these fungi on their fur and skin. Some cases produce only mild inflammation and often go unnoticed and untreated, then gradually reappear in hot weather. Other types cause a sudden outbreak of a violent-looking rash with vesicles and swelling of the tissue due to a strong immunological reaction of the body against the fungi.

Severe itching, especially in the groin area, provokes scratching, which tends to spread the infection by the fingernails or causes skin damage and produces a secondary infection from bacteria. (See the section on *Jock Itch* in this book.) Since differentiation of these types of fungi is difficult, these infections are approached according to the sites involved. Your health care provider can make a diagnosis after he/she scrapes a sample of skin and either examines it under a microscope or sends it to the lab for culture.

*As in most infections, prevention is the best thing to stop the spread of the infection. Family members must take precautions to not pick up the infection from other family members. Always wear shower sandals when in public showers such as athletic locker rooms or in swimming pools where the fungi grow readily and cross with other strains. Bathing is advised over showering. Always put 1 ounce of *Sol-U-Mel*, along with *Renew Bath Oil*, in the tub. Use a clean washcloth with *Antibacterial Liquid Soap* or *The Gold* or *Platinum Bar*.

Cracking or oozing skin should receive a generous amount of *Renew Intensive Skin Therapy*. Apply *Dermatin*, *T36-C5*, *Mela-Gel*, or *Triple Antibiotic Ointment* on any suspicious areas of the skin immediately after showering or bathing. Direct sunlight and thoroughly air drying the body after showering or swimming is a great preventive act also.

Take *The Vitality Pak*, *Cell-Wise*, *ProVex* and/or *ProVex-Plus* as directed to optimize trace nutrients. Drink 2 to 3 cups of *G'Day Melaleuca Tea* daily.

Bathe your cat and dog regularly with *Sol-U-Mel* during warm weather. Treat any pet rashes or "hot spots" with *T36-C5*, *Triple Antibiotic Ointment*, or *Mela-Gel*.

ROSACEA

Rosacea is a skin disease of the face that usually appears after the age of 40. Small, red veins and inflammation of the skin develop on the nose,

---

*Please consult your health care provider before starting any course of supplementation or treatment, particularly if you are pregnant or currently under medical care. Make sure you carefully read and understand all product packaging prior to use.

cheeks, or forehead and are sometimes accompanied by papules, or small knots, with fine scales on up to festering pustules.

The cause of this disorder has not been fully identified, but it appears together with certain other complaints, such as gallbladder disorders, chronic infections, genetically caused vascular weakness, and high blood pressure.

* Avoid coffee, excessive alcohol or tobacco, and exposure to heat, as they can all intensify this skin disease. Treating the skin as though it has acne has proven to be quite effective. The *Zap-It* skin care program certainly should be considered. See the section on *Acne* in this book.

Check with your health care provider for an accurate diagnosis.

RUBELLA (German Measles or Three-Day Measles)

Fourteen to twenty-one days from the time of exposure to rubella, susceptible persons will feel tired and may have slightly swollen lymph nodes under the eyes, behind the ears, and in the neck. Other symptoms of rubella include the development of a headache, moderate fever and runny nose, and a finely textured pinkish rash which starts on the face and neck, moves to the trunk and limbs, and lasts for about 3 days. The virus is spread through the air or by physical contact. See the sections on *Measles* and *Air Purification* in this book.

Rubella is much milder in children and adults than "red" measles, which not only differs in the color of the rash from rubella, but displays a painful cough and Koplik's spots on the inside of the mouth.

Women in their first three months of pregnancy who are susceptible to rubella, can contract the virus (usually from children) and naturally abort or give birth to developmentally defective and often mentally retarded (congenital rubella) infants.

In children up though teenagers, the illness is generally mild. Except for the risk of congenital rubella, some scientists question the risk/benefit ratio of immunizing children. An immunization offers about 15 years of protection and may pose risks.

Rubella may be difficult to properly determine without a trained health care provider using laboratory testing, as some of the symptoms can resemble other illnesses.

* Since the active virus can be spread from about one week before to one week after the eruption of the rash, epidemics of rubella sweep through susceptible children quickly. By then the virus has spread throughout the body. Only palliative care can be given to ease discomfort and prevent secondary infections such as pneumonia. Soaking in a hot bath with 1 ounce of *Renew Bath Oil* and 1 ounce of *Sol-U-Mel* for 20 minutes may help diminish the rash. Chicken soup, *G'Day Melaleuca Tea* and *Vita-Bears Children's Supplement* are the rations of choice. Solid food can be given upon request, which is usually after the rash subsides.

See also Measles.

SAND FLEAS

Sand fleas are fleas found in sandy places. They are sometimes known as beach fleas.

* Applying *T36-C5* to the sting area can be very effective in not only the healing, but it will help with the pain as well. *Triple Antibiotic Ointment* or *Mela-Gel* can be used on larger areas.

SAND FLIES

Sand flies are a particularly irritating insect, generally found in sand locations. Their small size allows them to easily get through most protective defenses one sets up. The itching and scratching they cause can create open wounds or sores.

* *T36-C5* gives fast relief for sand fly bites. It not only soothes the itching, but also prevents the possibility of infection. Apply *T36-C5* to the affected area every 4 hours as needed. It is also very helpful to add 8-10 drops of *T36-C5* to a warm bath and relax in the tub for at least 10 minutes. The use of *Mela-Gel* will protect the area and help with the itching as well.

T36-C5 applied directly to exposed skin, and clothing such as scarves, socks, collars, and cuffs on pants and shirts will serve as an effective sand fly repellent. Sand flies will also avoid your tent or home if your put *T36-C5* on a hanging ribbon or use it in a vaporizer.

SCABIES (Crabs)

Scabies, or crabs, are transmittable parasitic infections characterized by intensive itching and secondary bacterial infections. They are caused by the itch mite known as Sarcoptes scabiei, which burrows under the skin to feed and lay its eggs. The itching is usually most intense when the person is in bed. The characteristic initial lesions of the burrow are seen as fine wavy dark lines a few millimeters to a half-inch long with a minute papule at the open end. A red lesion occurs on the finger webs, on the under-surface of the wrists, about the elbows and under arms, around the nipple area of the breasts in females, on the genitals in males, along the belt line, and on the lower buttocks. The face is not usually involved in adults but may be in infants. The burrow may be difficult to find, especially when the disease has been persistent for several weeks, because it is often obscured by scratching or by secondary lesions. Diagnosis is confirmed by seeing the parasite under a microscope after a scraping is taken from the burrow. The mites can remain dormant in infected bedclothes or blankets for months awaiting a warm victim to bring them back to life. Scabies are nothing to ignore. See the section on *Chiggers* in this book.

NOTE: Treatment of scabies with lindane-containing medications (Kwell) has multiple hazards to children. Nervous system disturbances have been observed and reported in the scientific literature.

---

*Please consult your health care provider before starting any course of supplementation or treatment, particularly if you are pregnant or currently under medical care. Make sure you carefully read and understand all product packaging prior to use.

* Soak in a hot bath for 20 minutes each night with 1 ounce of **Renew Bath Oil** and 1 ounce of **Sol-U-Mel**. Apply **T36-C5** to the affected areas each morning and night. Apply **Renew Intensive Skin Therapy** or **Triple Antibiotic Ointment** to give long-term protection against infection. Apply **Pain-A-Trate** to extremely itchy areas. Consult your health care provider for further advice.

Be sure to wash all clothes, towels and bedding separately. Add 2 ounces of **MelaPower Laundry Detergent**, two capfuls of **Sol-U-Mel** and 2 ounces of **MelaBrite** to your wash water. Line dry rather than tumble dry, since these parasites are so easily transmittable.

SCALDS

Hot water, steam, liquid nitrogen, or liquid propane can produce scalds. Immediate blistering and light colored skin is characteristic. Care should be taken to not dislodge delicate superficial skin. Painful blisters may appear within a few minutes indicating second-degree penetration. Loose, swollen skin without blistering is evidence of third-degree penetration. See the section on *Burns* in this book.

* Immediately apply cold water to hot water scalds and warm water to cold scalds. Pat dry and apply **Mela-Gel**, **T36-C5**, or **Pain-A-Trate** to the affected area. Wrap the area with a sterile dressing. Begin treating as a second- or third-degree burn.

SCALP

See Dandruff, Dry Hair, Eczema

SCHIZOPHRENIA

See Depression

SCRAPES

See Abrasions

SCRATCHES

See Abrasions

SEBORRHEA

This is a scaly inflammation of the skin that occurs around the scalp, face, and occasionally on other areas of the body. Seborrhea primarily affects adults and usually appears as dry or greasy scaling and is often misdiagnosed as thick dandruff. In the most severe cases, a yellow or red scaling with papules around the rash appears usually along the hairline and behind the ears. If is often found in the ear canal, on the eyebrows, on the bridge of the nose, in the nasal folds, or on the upper chest. Seborrhea dermatitis does not cause hair loss.

Infants in the first month of life may develop seborrhea dermatitis,

---

often called cradle cap, which results in thick yellow-crusted scalp. In severe cases, cracks and yellow scaling behind the ears and red facial papules may be present.

Nutritional deficiency is a contributing cause of seborrhea. Deficiencies of vitamin A, biotin, vitamin B-2 (riboflavin), vitamin B-6 (pyridoxine), essential fatty acids, zinc, sulfur and selenium have all been documented, and treatment with these nutrients invariably results in improvement. In particular, the development of seborrheic dermatitis is a sign of severe essential fatty acid deficiency. Zinc, B-2, B-6, and biotin are all required for optimal digestion and utilization of essential fatty acids.

Optimal results are achieved when antimicrobial treatment is combined with nutritional therapy. The diet should be high in natural fats and protein and low in sugar, particularly refined sugar. Daily doses of essential fatty acids, zinc, selenium, vitamin A, B-6, biotin, and riboflavin should be taken. Genetic and climatic factors, in addition to chemical and allergic sensitivities, seem to affect the incidence and severity of the disease. It is more prevalent in the winter when more time is spent indoors and household chemicals are more concentrated. Some cases of seborrhea miraculously improve with the avoidance of coffee.

* Take *The Vitality Pak*, *Cell-Wise*, *ProVex*, and/or *ProVex-Plus* as directed. Drink 2 to 6 cups of *G'Day Melaleuca Tea* daily for detoxification. Bathe using *Antibacterial Liquid Soap* in a tub containing one ounce of *Renew Bath Oil* and one ounce of *Sol-U-Mel*. Shampoo with *Naturals Melaleuca Oil Shampoo* or *Naturals Herbal Shampoo* daily. Some feel that the *Advanced Expressions Moisturizing Shampoo for Dry and Treated Hair* is even more effective. Continue the bathing procedure once a day, but apply *T36-C5* with either *Renew Intensive Skin Therapy* or *Mela-Gel* after each bath.

SHAVING RASH

A rash is an eruption of spots on the skin, in this case caused by shaving. It can lead to a bacterial or fungal infection or be compounded into an outbreak of acne.

* Avoid commercial aftershaves and harsh soaps. Use *Melaleuca Essentials Shave Creme* or the *Mate Conditioning Shave Gel*. Follow with *Renew Intensive Skin Therapy* or *Mate After-Shave Balm*. Putting a drop of *T36-C5* on the blade of your razor occasionally will also help.

SHINGLES

The same virus that causes chicken pox in children causes shingles in adults. It manifests as small, very painful clusters of blisters, which form along a sensory nerve on the skin of the chest, neck, face, stomach or limbs. These pink or white blisters contain a clear fluid, which may later become pus. They dry up and disappear in about a week, but the irritation may remain for a longer period of time. See the section on *Chicken Pox* in this book.

   * Shingles can be treated similarly to chicken pox, except for the use of more *Sol-U-Mel* and *Renew Bath Oil*, detoxification, and satisfying the increased nutritional need for B vitamins. Take *The Vitality Pak*, *Cell-Wise*, *ProVex* and/or *ProVex-Plus* as directed. Drink 2 to 6 cups of *G'Day Melaleuca Tea* to reduce virus growth. Add 2 ounces of *Renew Bath Oil* and 2 ounces of *Sol-U-Mel* to a warm tub of water. Soak for 30 minutes. Pat dry. Apply a drop of *T36-C5* to pustules, followed by *Triple Antibiotic Ointment*. If the pustules are particularly sensitive, apply the *T40-C3*, as it is a rarer and therefore a more gentle form of Melaleuca oil. Continue this once or twice a day for 6 days. Consult your health care provider for further advice.

SINUS CONGESTION

   Sinus congestion can be due to mild infections or generalized irritations caused from allergies, chronic airborne pollutants, dust, grasses, pollens, cigarette smoking, or other chemicals. Often, bacterial sinus infections are caused by repeated use of antihistamines, which dry mucous membranes and create opportunity for other infections. Inflammation from mold sensitivity or anemia can also be an underlying cause. When frontal sinuses, found above and behind the eyes, are affected, headaches may occur. Coughing is often associated with deeper irritations in the nasal pharynx and can lead to ear infections in children or nose bleeds in older children and adults. If repeated episodes of sinus congestion occur, your health care provider should determine the cause. If bacterial infections are present, the condition is termed sinusitis. When it is not properly treated, pneumonia can result. Prescription antibiotics are becoming less effective against these types of infections due to their overuse.

   * Drink 2 to 6 cups of *G'Day Melaleuca Tea* each day as a decongestant. (*Note:* For adults only: To ¼ cup of warm *G'Day Melaleuca Tea*, add ⅛ tsp. of sea salt. From a cup, snort the mixture into your nose. Tilt your head back and hold it in your sinuses for 10 to 15 seconds. Expel the mixture through your nostrils into a sink. Blow your nose gently. Repeat morning and evening.)

   Dab *T36-C5* directly under each nostril. Breathe the enriched steam from a vaporizer or a bowl of very hot water. To do this, add 10 drops of *T36-C5* and 2 capfuls of *Sol-U-Mel* to the water. Form a tent over your head and the vaporizer, breathing the aromatic vapors through your nose and mouth deeply and gently into your lungs. Keep your eyes closed. Add 1 to 2 drops of *T36-C5* every 5 minutes for 15 to 20 minutes. Repeat each morning and evening, or use the vaporizer all night.

   Apply *Pain-A-Trate* on the temples and forehead to reduce pain from

---

*Please consult your health care provider before starting any course of supplementation or treatment, particularly if you are pregnant or currently under medical care. Make sure you carefully read and understand all product packaging prior to use.

the congestion. Repeat every 2 to 4 hours for relief. As long as congestion exists, use *CounterAct Night-Time Cold, Allergy, Sinus Medicine* as directed. See also the section on *Sinusitis* in this book.

SINUS PASSAGES, BLOCKED
See Sinus Congestion, Sinusitis

SINUSITIS
Sinusitis is an inflammation of the mucous-lined air spaces often caused by an infection spreading from the nose. While often a bacterial infection, Mayo Clinic's Otorhinolaryngology Department published results that suggest fungi caused 96.6% of all chronic sinusitis. You may want to check your home for fungus growth. Also remember that Melaleuca alternifolia oil is excellent in opening closed respiratory passages as it kills both bacteria and microbes.

* Follow the directions under *Sinus Congestion* above.

SITZ BATH
A sitz bath is a therapeutic bath in which only the hips and buttocks are immersed. It is used to soothe itching sensations in the genital area, soothe hemorrhoidal discomfort, and produce healing effects on bladder infections. Some are used in conjunction with a douche to bathe the external genitalia. It will increase the effectiveness of the treatment, particularly in extreme or prolonged cases of infection.

* Put 6 to 8 drops of *T36-C5* into a bowl or bathtub containing warm water. Sit in the bath for 5-10 minutes. For genital itching, rinse the area with a mixture of 4 or 5 drops of *T36-C5* in a container of warm water. Let the mixture run slowly over the genital area.

SJOGREN'S SYNDROME
Sjogren's syndrome is an autoimmune disease where you don't make tears or saliva. See the *Immune System* section in this book.

* With any autoimmune disease, your immune system is compromised and the result is that you will usually catch everything that is going around. Because of the poorer health, energy levels are frequently low. By taking the *Daily for Life Pack*, overall health can be enhanced and energy levels can be boosted. The *Denti-Care Dental Program* will also help with the dental challenges caused by Sjogren's, and *Insta-Fresh Dental Gum* provides great relief from the dry mouth by increasing salivation.

It is also important that your home be converted to safer products, such as those provided by Melaleuca.

SKIN
See Dry Skin, Itching and Flaking Skin, Skin Care, Skin Wounds

---

*Please consult your health care provider before starting any course of supplementation or treatment, particularly if you are pregnant or currently under medical care. Make sure you carefully read and understand all product packaging prior to use.

SKIN CARE

Good skin care is important. Your personal appearance is your own best advertisement, and your health is reflected in your skin. The *Nicole Miller* skin care program does make a difference. Much like fructose compounding, *Nicole Miller* uses a deliver system called liposome encapsulation that delivers vitamin C and E to the epidermis. In addition, it delivers even greater amounts of vitamins A, B, C, D, and E to the second layer of the skin. This is important because the dermis is where the new cells are born. *Multi-Action Vitamin Complex* has every vitamin and antioxidant known to have a beneficial effect on the skin in a delivery system. *Age-Defying Serum* is a revolutionary breakthrough in skin care, as it is a powerful antioxidant blend which shields your face to protect it against damage caused by free radicals and harsh environmental elements.

Nicole Miller uses ingredients in her products that actually reduce lines and wrinkles or plump the cells as opposed to fillers, binders or preservatives. And, remember, good skin care is not just for women. Men want it and need it just as much as women do.

* In addition to using a good skin care system, such as *Nicole Miller* provides, a proper nutritional program is essential. The *Daily 4 Life* plan is a good place to start. Add a positive mental attitude, sound sleep (with *RestEZ*), plenty of water and regular exercise, and you can enhance and enjoy that good skin that you inherited.

SKIN WOUNDS

These are individual punctures, scrapes, scratches and cuts that break the skin's surface. The top layers of skin are damaged, causing nerves, blood vessels, and lymph vessels to be exposed to the air. This causes immediate pain and creates an opportunity for germs to enter the body. When an injury occurs, the immediate area can become red and inflamed. The infectious fighting white blood cells rush to the site and begin the healing process. A dry protective scab will usually form within a few hours, as nature's protection against infection. Unfortunately, scabs will occasionally obscure secondary infection, so treatment needs to continue as long as redness is present. See the section on *Abrasions* in this book.

* Wash the area gently, yet thoroughly, with *Antibacterial Liquid Soap* and cool water. Cool water quickly reduces the pain. (Warm or hot water increases nerve stimulation and thus pain in most people.) Allow the stream of water to wash off all visible particulates. Pick out any embedded material if possible. Pat dry and apply *T36-C5*. Because of its ability to kill bacteria, *T36-C5* will help treat the infection and the soreness created by the inflammation. As this dries, apply *Renew Intensive Skin Therapy*, *Mela-Gel* or *Triple Antibiotic Ointment* and try to allow the wound to remain open to the air. If a bandage is necessary, saturate it with *Triple Antibiotic Ointment* or *Mela-Gel* to prevent

*Please consult your health care provider before starting any course of supplementation or treatment, particularly if you are pregnant or currently under medical care. Make sure you carefully read and understand all product packaging prior to use.

sticking. Repeat this as needed until the wound is adequately covered with a scab and all redness has disappeared.

WARNING: If the skin wounds are deep or contaminated and if it has been five years or more since your last tetanus shot, immediately contact your health care provider. Older adults are much more susceptible to tetanus because they are not as likely to be current on their booster shots.

SMOKING
See Cigarette Smoking

SNEEZING
Irritations in the nasal pharynx stimulate local histamine production that increases mucous secretion and triggers the central nervous response to expel the irritant. Food or chemical allergies, sensitivities such as hay fever, and viral infections provoke this response. A sneeze is the most efficient way to spread viruses and bacteria to your family, workmates, and friends. The velocity of air and atomized mucous exiting the nose and mouth approaches the speed of sound! Studies show that particles can be projected up to 20 feet across a room from a sneeze. See the section on *Air Purification* in this book.

* Take *The Vitality Pak*, *Cell-Wise*, *ProVex* and/or *ProVex-Plus* as directed. A therapeutic dose of *ProVex* (1 capsule for every 25 pounds of body weight per day) may be helpful. Drink 2 to 4 cups of *G'Day Melaleuca Tea* each day. Launder handkerchiefs with *MelaPower Laundry Detergent* and rinse in a solution of 1 ounce of *Sol-U-Mel* per gallon of rinse water. Air dry. For acute sneezing attacks, put 1 to 2 drops of *T36-C5* on a Q-tip and swab the inside of each nostril. If congestion exists, use *CounterAct Night-Time Cold, Allergy, Sinus Medicine* as directed.

SORE GUMS
Damage from rough foods, overzealous flossing, or from a toothbrush needs immediate attention to prevent secondary infections and canker sores. Poor dental hygiene or accumulated plaque below the gum line can lead to periodontal infections. See your dentist or dental hygienist without delay. Many health problems stem from improper dental health. See also the sections on *Bleeding Gums* and *Dental - Gum Disease*.

* Following an injury, immediately swish your mouth with *Breath-Away Mouthwash*. Follow the printed directions. Apply *T36-C5* to the sore area with your finger or a Q-tip to reduce the soreness. Take *ProVex* and/or *ProVex-Plus* to strengthen gum tissues, reduce inflammation, and to help reduce plaque buildup.

Use the *Denti-Clean Classic Tooth Polish*. It combines the anti-bacterial properties of propolis, myrrh, and fluoride with Melaleuca alternifolia oil. Not only does it fight bacteria, which often is the cause

---

of sore gums, but it also works against plaque buildup.

Sore gums may also be caused by a mineral deficiency that can be alleviated by switching to products from the *Melaleuca Vitality for Life Nutritionals*. In addition to changing your oral care to the *Denti-Care* line of products, be sure to have regular dental checkups.

SORE MUSCLES

See Aches and Pains, Muscle Strain

SORE NIPPLES

Sore nipples caused by dry or cracked skin respond well to *T36-C5*. If breastfeeding, make sure the oil residue on the skin is removed before the feeding. While *T36-C5* is considered safe, ingestion of pure Melaleuca oil is not recommended.

* *Renew Intensive Skin Therapy* is very soothing and healing for nipples that are sore, dry, or cracked. Massage a small amount into the sore areas three times each day until the condition improves. As a preventive measure, apply *Renew Intensive Skin Therapy* daily.

SORE THROAT

The challenge to our body's immune system comes partly from the air we breathe, the fluids we drink, and the food we eat. Viruses, bacteria, allergens, pollutants, prescription drugs, and overusing our voice can produce a sore throat. Many people get a sore throat if they do not get enough rest. Sore throats are often the body's first indication of an oncoming cold or flu. In children, a sore throat can precede chicken pox, mumps, colds or measles.

Whatever the cause, proper treatment is necessary to prevent the condition from escalating. Cancer of the throat starts with a mild, chronic sore throat with or without a cough. If a sore throat continues for longer than several days, your health care provider should be contacted. See the sections on *Coughs* and *Hoarseness* in this book.

* Gargle with *Breath-Away Mouthwash* or *T36-C5* to reduce bacteria and viruses. Swab the back of the throat and tonsil area with a Q-tip saturated with *T36-C5*. Spray the throat with *Hot/Cool Shot Mouth Spray*, as often as needed. Drinking large amounts of *G'Day Melaleuca Tea* will help, along with getting plenty of rest. In a bedside vaporizer add 2 capfuls of *Sol-U-Mel* and 10 drops of *T36-C5*. Begin taking *Activate*, as directed, immediately.

You might also try this suggestion: As soon as soreness is felt in your throat and it begins to become painful to swallow, take a trace of *T36-C5* on your finger and apply it to the saliva on the upper surface of your tongue. Move the saliva to the back of your throat where the tonsils are bathed by the oil and its infection-fighting strength. Then swallow everything. The entire process takes less than 20 seconds and within seconds you should feel a noticeable relief from the discomfort in your

---

*Please consult your health care provider before starting any course of supplementation or treatment, particularly if you are pregnant or currently under medical care. Make sure you carefully read and understand all product packaging prior to use.

throat. It will feel slightly anesthetized.

Repeat this process every minute for ten minutes. In addition, apply a few drops externally twice at five-minute intervals: one drop along each lateral surface of the neck, behind the ears, and below the corners of the lower jaws. These ten internal applications and two external applications are all completed in less than 15 minutes, and you will see amazing results. Try it. What do you have to lose?

SORE TONGUE
See Glossitis

SPASMS
See Athletic Injuries

SPIDER BITES
See Insect Bites

SPRAY
See Insect Repellent, Mosquito Spray

STINGS
See Bee and Wasp Stings

STOMACH ULCERS
See Gastric Ulcers

STRAIN
See Exercise Strain, Muscle Strain

STRESS
Ninety percent of all visits to health care providers are due to stress-related challenges. Disease, anxiety and the resultant stress in our fast paced society are taking their toll. But it doesn't have to. Stress isn't always bad, but it is always a choice. Simple things can make a difference. Things like:

Take a lunch break every day.
Make time for family and friends.
Listen to your body. Rest when it says rest.
Keep things in perspective.
Wear clothes that make you feel good.
Prepare the night before.
Live one day at a time.
Be sure the clock and telephone belong to you—not you to them.
Laugh, love and choose to be happy.

*Please consult your health care provider before starting any course of supplementation or treatment, particularly if you are pregnant or currently under medical care. Make sure you carefully read and understand all product packaging prior to use.

* Drink hot or ice-cold *G'Day Melaleuca Tea* each day. On a regular basis, take *Luminex*. It helps promote emotional health and is definitely important for anyone suffering from stress. Carefully consider a good nutrition program from the *Melaleuca Vitality for Life Nutritionals*. The *Daily For Life Pack* is a good place to start. A wholesome balanced diet and regular exercise can help you stay calm. Breathing and relaxation exercises are important stress relievers, too. Give yourself 15 minutes each day that belongs to no one but you. Do anything you want to do with it: read, walk, stare or suck your thumb! It doesn't matter as long as you know that those 15 minutes are all yours. MAKE time for fun! Your body needs to be healthy both mentally and physically for peak performance. Remember, this is your life—your only life. It is not a practice run.

STROKES

See Cardiovascular Disease

SUNBURN

See Burns

SURGERY

Surgery is a medical procedure concerned with the correction of deformities, defects and the repair of injuries. It is the treatment of diseases by surgical methods.

* When you are anticipating surgery, begin taking a double dose of your vitamins to build up your immune system. Stop taking all *ProVex* three days before surgery, and restart only when any chance of bleeding has past. Many people have found that using *T36-C5* on the incision as soon a possible has helped with the healing, the pain, and the scarring. See the *Immune System* section in this book.

SWIMMER'S EAR

Swimmer's ear is a common type of outer ear infection. It affects mainly children and teenagers and occurs almost exclusively during the summer months.

Water in swimming pools, lakes, or seas may become contaminated with pathogens. These water-borne pathogens readily infect the outer ear canal. They include viruses, bacteria, bacteria-like organisms, fungi, protozoans, amoebas, and parasitic worms. Bacteria and fungi cause the vast majority of outer ear infections.

In acute infections, symptoms include pain, aching, and discharge. With chronic infections, the symptoms are primarily fullness in the ear, excessive wax, irritation and itching.

* To treat these conditions apply one drop of *T36-C5* onto a Q-tip and wipe the outer ear region morning and night. **Do not drip Melaleuca**

---

oil directly into the ear. Continue this twice a day until symptoms disappear. If no improvement is noted within 72 hours, discontinue and check with your health care provider if you haven't already. See the section on *Ear Infection (Outer)* in this book.

TEETHING

Tooth bud swelling and eruption through the gum is often a stressful experience for parents as well as infants. Teething often is accompanied by a runny nose and loose stool in 6-month-olds to 2-year-olds.

* The cold, mushy consistency of a piece of banana or grape, held so the baby can gum it, is a quick way to speed tooth eruption. *ProVex*, opened and dissolved in distilled water, juice, or breast milk can give relief from teething pain. *CounterAct Kids Pain Reliever and Fever Reducer* can be used in severe cases where the more "natural" remedies don't give enough relief.

It has also been suggested that a 1:10 solution of *T36-C5* and water can be rubbed on the gums several times daily to ease the pain of teething.

TEMPOROMANDIBULAR JOINT DYSFUNCTION (TMD)

Temporomandibular Joint Dysfunction Syndrome, or TMD for short, is an extremely painful inflammatory condition caused by improper jaw development, improper dental bite, traumatic injury to the face and jaw, or muscle tension in the neck and jaw muscles. Your jaws are capable of generating 5,000 pounds per square inch of force. The jaw joint in front of our ear must also carry this force. Damage to the TMJ disk is a direct cause of the aggravating pain. If left untreated, complete degeneration of the joint can take place, requiring surgery.

If the TMJ itself is not injured, the condition is called myofascial pain-dysfunction (MPD) syndrome. This condition is common and is aggravated by emotionally stressful situations. The individual usually has a history of clenching and grinding their teeth. People with MPD may have tenderness to the touch in one or more of the chewing muscles, limited ability to open the mouth, and clicking or "popping" sounds are quite common.

* TMJ syndrome requires professional advice from your health care provider or dentist. Management may consist of the use of a night guard splint and therapy by several specialists. In the meantime, apply *Pain-A-Trate* 2 to 3 times per day to the affected muscles around the jaw joint. This is especially effective for MPD syndrome. Get an upper body massage weekly to relieve neck and facial muscle tension. Take *The Vitality Pak* and *Cell-Wise* as directed and drink 2 to 4 cups of *G'Day Melaleuca Tea* each day. Avoid foods that are hard to chew. Take *ProVex* and/or *ProVex-Plus* each day to help reduce inflammation.

---

*Please consult your health care provider before starting any course of supplementation or treatment, particularly if you are pregnant or currently under medical care. Make sure you carefully read and understand all product packaging prior to use.

THREE-DAY MEASLES
See Rubella

THROAT
See Sore Throat, Tonsillitis

THRUSH
Thrush is a fungal infection of the mouth or throat, caused by the Candida albicans organism. Oral yeast infections are common in persons who are on drug therapy. The condition causes the tongue, gums, inside of cheeks, and throat to have a white patched and swollen appearance. Repeated use of anti-yeast drugs tends to produce resistant strains.

* Use **Breath-Away Mouthwash**, as directed, every 2 hours. Brush with **Classic Tooth Polish**. Drink 2 to 6 cups of **G'Day Melaleuca Tea** daily. Take **The Vitality Pak**, **Cell-Wise**, and **ProVex** or **ProVex-Plus** with each meal. For severe infections, dab **T36-C5** on the area or apply with a finger or cotton-tipped swab. Avoid sugar, alcohol, yeast bread products, cheese, and vinegar products. (Those with sensitive mucous membranes may want to use a 5-10% concentration of the pure oil. **T36-C5** may also be used by infants and pregnant women in a **VERY** diluted form.)

TICKS
Ticks are small, 8-legged bugs that attach themselves to human (or animal) skin where they feed on the blood. They thrive in a warm, moist environment and may be picked up when walking in rural or suburban yards, woods, in long grass and scrublands. They are often found on dogs, cats, deer, or livestock and may jump to a human host when given the opportunity. Some ticks attach themselves and go unnoticed for several hours; others can cause pain, bruising and even severe irritation. Ticks can carry Lyme disease. Certain ticks are known to be carriers of viral encephalitis. Ticks can be extremely harmful, particularly to the very young or the very old. In rare instances, they emit a dangerous toxin that can ultimately result in paralysis and death.

* Inspect your children and yourself daily when any outdoor activity takes place. **Never pull a tick loose.** If you discover an attached tick, cover it in **T36-C5**. The tick should soon "let go," and you will be able to remove it easily with tweezers. Cover your hands to prevent disease contamination. Smash the tick thoroughly and flush. After you remove the tick, clean the site with **Antibacterial Liquid Soap**. Then dry thoroughly and apply **T36-C5**, **Mela-Gel**, **Triple Antibiotic Ointment,** or **CortiCare Anti Itch Creme**. Cover with a bandage for 24 hours. Repeat these applications at least several times per hour, or as often as necessary. If fever or any other conditions develop, contact your health care provider.

TINEA
See Fungal Infections

---

*Please consult your health care provider before starting any course of supplementation or treatment, particularly if you are pregnant or currently under medical care. Make sure you carefully read and understand all product packaging prior to use.

TINEA PEDIS

See Athlete's Foot

TINNITUS

Sufferers of this condition hear unexplained noises such as buzzing, ringing, roaring, whistling, or hissing. It can be in one or both ears. Tinnitus can be a symptom of almost any disorder of, or around, the ear. It may be caused by low-grade infections, anemia, trauma to the head, obstructions such as earwax, Eustachian tube obstruction, allergies, hardening of the acoustic arteries, tumors, toxicity from chemicals such as carbon monoxide, heavy metal poisoning, many drug reactions, and alcohol. See your health care provider.

* If an organic cause cannot be identified, decongestion is the next best approach. If congestion exists, use ***CounterAct Night-Time Cold, Allergy, Sinus Medicine*** as directed. See the section on *Sinus Congestion* in this book.

TMJ

See Temporomandibular Joint Dysfunction

TOENAIL

See Ingrown Toenail

TONGUE

See Glossitis

TONSILLITIS

Tonsillitis is an acute inflammation of the tonsillar lymph tissue in the throat, usually due to a streptococcal bacteria or virus. Epidemics of viral tonsillitis occur in the military or during summer camp. Symptoms in older children and adults include a sore throat upon swallowing, and congested Eustachian tubes. Young children will not complain of a sore throat, but will refuse to eat. High fever, headaches, and general fatigue are common. The enlarged and often reddened tonsils can be seen on either side of the back of the throat. Repeated treatments with antibiotics tend to produce resistant strains of bacteria. See the sections on *Air Purification, Disinfectants* and *Sore Throat* in this book.

* Improperly treated tonsillitis can lead to strep throat, rheumatic heart disease, and a chronically compromised immune system. Seek professional help.

Begin taking ***Activate Immune Complex*** at the first sign of tonsillitis to strengthen the immune system. For viral tonsillitis, drink ***G'Day Melaleuca Tea*** every hour. Apply ***T36-C5*** directly on the tonsils. You may use a Q-tip. Use ***CounterAct Cough Relief Medicine*** as directed if coughing, itching or discomfort is present. Gargle with ***Breath-Away***

Mouthwash 3 times each day. A positive culture is needed to confirm bacterial tonsillitis. See your health care provider. Until a definitive diagnosis is made, apply *T36-C5* to the tonsils each hour.

TOOTHACHE

Dental problems are more easily prevented than treated at home. A sensitive tooth, due to root exposure, thin enamel, or cavities can begin aching from things such as sweets, hot or cold foods, or an uneven bite plane. See the section on *Abscesses* in this book.

* For prevention, brush with **Denti-Care Classic Tooth Polish** or **Denti-Care Fluoride Tooth Gel** and use **Breath-Away Mouthwash** after every meal. Use **Exceed Dental Floss** at least once each day and chew **Insta-Fresh Gum** frequently. Apply *T36-C5* directly to the sensitive tooth and surrounding gum to achieve immediate relief, and see your dentist to determine the cause of your pain. Have regular checkups with your dentist to maximize the general health of your teeth.

ULCERATIVE COLITIS

See Colitis

ULCERS

See Canker Sores, Gastric Ulcers, Nasal Ulcers, Tropical Ulcers, and Varicose Ulcers.

ULCERS, VARICOSE

Open sores may form on the lower leg when the veins are not functioning properly. They are usually painless and are often a result of varicose veins. They frequently become infected and are very slow to heal. Elderly people and diabetics are particularly prone to this condition due to poor circulation.

* Wash the area carefully with **Antibacterial Liquid Soap** and then cover the affected area with a surgical pad saturated in a 1:3 solution of *T36-C5* and olive oil.

ULCERS, TROPICAL

Tropical ulcers (also known as nega sores) usually occur in hot, humid climates. A large painless sore develops, often on the feet or legs. This is usually associated with a bacterial infection, poor nutrition or environmental factors.

*As a preventive measure massage the legs daily with **Renew Intensive Skin Therapy**. To treat the ulcer, bathe the sore gently with **Antibacterial Liquid Soap** and water. Cover the area with **Triple Antibiotic Ointment** or a surgical paid saturated in a 1:3 solution of *T36-C5* and olive oil. See the section on *Leg Ulcers* in this book.

URETHRITIS

Urethritis is a bacterial infection of the urethra, which usually precedes an attack of cystitis. A sign of cystitis is the need to urinate frequently, accompanied by a painful burning sensation while urinating and sometimes feeling feverish. The urine may look cloudy.

* Proper hygiene is an important preventive measure. Women should wipe from the front to the back, and men should clean thoroughly after urination. Swabbing the opening of the urethra after urination with a cotton ball soaked in a solution of 1 cup of distilled water and 5 drops of *T36-C5* can be very helpful. Drink *G'Day Melaleuca Herbal Tea* frequently throughout the day.

Frequent bathing with Melaleuca oil as a general disinfectant is a good preventive measure. Prepare a bath with 8-12 drops of *T36-C5* and soak for 5-10 minutes. See the section on *Cystitis* in this book.

URINARY TRACT INFECTIONS

Almost any normal skin organism is capable of living in the nutrient rich, moist, and dark environment found in the lower urinary tract. Women are more prone to UTIs because of the constantly moist environment of the urethral opening and its close proximity to the anus. If improperly treated, UTIs can progress to bladder infections (cystitis) or kidney infections (nephritis). Fewer than half of the women with UTIs have any symptoms of the illness. Tight-fitting clothes, prescription drug reactions, synthetic undergarments, warm weather, inadequate toilet hygiene, or a generally weakened immune system can lead to bacterial or yeast infections in the urinary tract. Drinking enough water can usually prevent or overcome many of these shortcomings.

* The best treatment is prevention. Use cotton undergarments. Dry your body well after showering or bathing. Drink enough water and drink 4 to 12 cups of *G'Day Melaleuca Tea* each day. Wipe from the front to the back when using the toilet. Take *The Vitality Pak*, *Cell-Wise*, *ProVex* and/or *ProVex-Plus* as directed. Douche as needed with *Nature's Cleanse*. Contact your health care provider for further advice.

URTICARIA

See Hives

VAGINAL CLEANSING

Vaginal cleansing is cleansing of the vagina usually by means of a douche.

* Use *Nature's Cleanse* as directed. If that is not available, you might try using a mixture of 8-10 drops of *T36-C5* in one pint of distilled water.

Vaginal cleansing can also be accomplished by soaking for approximately 20 minutes in a warm bath to which 10 drops of *T36-C5* has been added.

---

*Please consult your health care provider before starting any course of supplementation or treatment, particularly if you are pregnant or currently under medical care. Make sure you carefully read and understand all product packaging prior to use.

VAGINAL INFECTIONS

See Thrush, Vaginitis and Yeast Infections

VAGINITIS

Bacteria and yeasts can infect the nutrient-rich vaginal lining causing painful swelling, foul odor, colored discharge, and reduced libido.

* For acute infections, use **Nature's Cleanse Feminine Douche** morning and evening for 3 to 5 days. For recurrences or chronic infections, douche each night. Bathe instead of showering each night, soaking for 30 minutes in a solution of 1 ounce of **Sol-U-Mel** and 1 ounce of **Renew Bath Oil**. Avoid sugar. Drink 2 to 6 cups of **G'Day Melaleuca Tea** each day and 2 to 3 quarts of water per day, along with taking **The Vitality Pak**, **Cell-Wise**, **ProVex** and/or **ProVex-Plus** as directed. This will help to build resistance to infections.

VARICOSE ULCERS

See Ulcers, Varicose

VARICOSE VEINS

Enlarged veins in the lower legs are common among civilized people because of standing and walking on flat, hard surfaces all day. Chronic constipation and pregnancy also tend to cause circulation backup in the legs, which leads to varicose veins. Occasionally there is leg pain or discomfort, but usually not. Valves in veins normally prevent blood from flowing backward or pooling. Sedentary lifestyles destroy this check-valve effect and lead to pooling. Varicose veins and hemorrhoids are often found together.

Toe action, like walking barefoot on a sandy beach, assists the pumping of blood back to the heart and keeps leg veins and their check-valves healthy. A clinical examination for venous circulation often finds the beginnings of blood clots blocking this natural flow. Some scientists feel that most blood clots plugging brain (stroke) and heart (heart attack) arteries originate in the oxygen-depleted veins of the legs. See the section on *Constipation* in this book.

* Elderly people may require specialized care beyond these suggestions. The bioflavanoids in **ProVex**, **ProVex-Plus** and **ProVexCV** have been known to greatly reduce the unsightly appearance of varicose veins, so take them daily. Do not wear tight-fitting belts or girdles. Wear support hose ONLY when walking or standing for prolonged periods of time. Wearing them while sitting or driving can cause more circulation problems than it helps. Walk barefoot for 10 minutes each morning in the dew or on a sandy beach. **Sole to Soul Revitalizing Foot Scrub** and **Sole to Soul Revitalizing Foot Lotion** can also be used to cleanse and stimulate improved circulation.

Maintain healthy, regular bowel movements. You should not have to strain when making a stool. Drink 2 to 6 cups of **G'Day Melaleuca Tea** each day. Take one or two *FiberWise* bars or drinks each day. They are excellent ways to increase dietary fiber and promote regularity and bowel mobility.

VERUCCA PLANTARIS
See Plantar Wart

VERUCCAE
See Warts

VIRAL ENCEPHALITIS
See Ticks

VIRAL SKIN INFECTION
See Dry Skin

VIRUS
See Influenza, Mononucleosis

WALKING
Walking is a wonderful exercise that can burn fat and improve your health. It is easily the most popular form of exercise for all ages. It is the only exercise in which the rate of participation does not decline in the middle and later years. Walking burns approximately the same amount of calories per mile as does running. It should be an important part of every wellness regimen.

* Make the effort to find good walking shoes that fit properly. Treat your feet well. Pamper them with *Sole to Soul Revitalizing Foot Scrub* to stimulate circulation and make them come alive with *Sole to Soul Revitalizing Foot Lotion.* Freshen them throughout the day with *Reviving Foot Spray*.

If an injury should occur, carefully clean it with *Antibacterial Liquid Soap* and, after drying, apply *T36-C5*. This should be followed with *Mela-Gel* or *Renew Intensive Skin Therapy*.

WARTS
Common warts, also known as verruca, are non-cancerous tumors caused by pathoviruses. Under microscopic examination, the flat plates of the epidermis are seen to be tilted at ninety degrees, growing outward instead of lying flat with the skin surface. Otherwise, the skin cells appear normal. Viral warts most frequently grow on the hands or fingers of children. Warts on the elbows, knees, face, and isolated sites elsewhere on the body are less common. They appear most frequently on sites subject to injury. The appearance and size depends upon the location and on the degree of irritation they are subjected to. They can be round or irregular, and are usually firm and dry. Color varies from

---

light gray, yellow, and brown, to grayish black. Size varies from ⅛ to ½ inch. They may come and go in the same individual in a haphazard way. Infections with the virus may appear as single or multiple growths and develop by spreading from one side of the body to the other. Complete regression is common, with or without treatment. Warts can persist for years and may reoccur at the same or different sites.

Plantar warts are common on the sole of the foot. When they are flattened by pressure, they are surrounded by cornified tissue and may be very tender. They can be distinguished from corns and calluses by their tendency to pinpoint bleeding when the surface is shaved away. Filiform warts are long, narrow growths usually seen on the eyelids, face, neck, or lips. Flat warts are smooth, flat yellow brown lesions seen more commonly in children and young adults, most often on the face. Warts of unusual shape, which resemble cauliflower or other structures, are most frequent on the head and neck, especially the scalp and in the bearded regions. Around the moist genital area, they are often called venereal warts and may or may not resemble warts in other parts of the body.

* For isolated common warts, apply *T36-C5* each morning and night faithfully for up to 3 weeks. If the wart is thick and dry, shave the excess away before applying *T36-C5*. **Sole to Soul Revitalizing Foot Scrub** and **Sole to Soul Revitalizing Foot Lotion** can also be used to cleanse and stimulate improved circulation. For body warts, bathe in a hot tub with 1 ounce of **Sol-U-Mel** and 1 ounce of **Renew Bath Oil** for 30 minutes. Apply *T36-C5* or **Mela-Gel** afterwards. Some warts require the added strength of *T40-C3* to disappear.

An alternate solution is to simply use **Renew Intensive Skin Therapy** to remove the skin warts. It may be a slower process, but it can be just as effective. Remember, a few types of warts do not respond to Melaleuca oil. Also see the section on *Plantar Warts* in this book.

WASP STINGS
See Bee and Wasp Stings

WEIGHT
See Obesity

WOUNDS
See Cuts, Abrasions, Skin Wounds

YEAST INFECTIONS
Yeast such as Candida albicans are naturally occurring in every human and do not tend to activate the body's immune defenses except in overgrowth situations. They are naturally kept from growing out of control by neighboring friendly bacteria that secrete anti-yeast chemicals. Broad-spectrum antibiotics given for other conditions

---

innocently destroy these friendly bacteria. When these friendly bacteria leave the body unprotected, yeasts can have a picnic on the nutrient-rich protein found on the skin and sugar-enriched mucous membranes. Once yeast infections get started, they must be dealt with in an aggressive way for best results.

Yeast infections are a generalized term that includes a variety of challenges including vaginal infection, inflammation, and irritation. Parasites, viruses, fungi, or bacteria can cause infections. Inflammation and irritation may be attributable to chemicals in tampons, bubble bath and tissue paper. Sometimes excessive use of harsh soap will cause vaginitis.

Clothing contributes to yeast infections, particularly in those containing synthetic fibers such as polyester and nylon. Synthetic clothing retains moisture and encourages yeast growth. Bacteria can remain in synthetic fibers even after washing.

While yeast infections are common complaints by women, they are not limited to just females. Jock itch is a form of yeast infection as well. Symptoms include pain, itching, spotting, odor, irritation and discharge. Recurrent or chronic infections will develop in those who are diabetic, and in those taking birth control pills or antibiotics. Symptoms can be alleviated for many; however, the majority will not be cured by traditional treatments prescribed.

This is contagious; therefore, intimate partners should treat it together and should pay attention to the danger of becoming re-infected.

** Use **Nature's Cleanse** according to the directions. Melaleuca alternifolia oil is the only antiseptic capable of eliminating each of the major types of vaginal yeast infections while exhibiting virtually no toxicity to vaginal tissue.

Drink **G'Day Melaleuca Tea** and take **The Vitality Pak**, **Cell-Wise**, and **ProVex**, **ProVex-Plus**, or **ProVexCV** with each meal. Avoid sugar, yeast, or mold-processed foods. Apply **T36-C5**, **Mela-Gel**, **Triple Antibiotic Ointment**, or **Renew Intensive Skin Therapy** to affected areas other than the vagina.

Wash your clothes in **MelaPower Laundry Detergent** and add one to two capfuls of **Sol-U-Mel** to each wash load. This will leave clothes as close to adverse organism-free as possible.

See the sections on *Air Purification, Body Odor, Dental Decay, Diaper Rash, Emphysema, Jock Itch, Mucous, Paronychia, Thrush, Urinary Tract Infections,* and *Vaginitis* in this book.

ZONA

Zona is also called shingles and is the same virus as chicken pox—herpes zoster. This virus affects the sensory nerves, and causes clusters of blisters to appear, often in the form of a band around the torso. The condition can be accompanied by severe pain, usually before the rash appears, and there may be fever. See the sections on *Shingles* and *Chicken Pox* in this book.

*Wash the affected area with ***Antibacterial Liquid Soap***. Pat dry and liberally apply ***T36-C5*** or ***T40-C3***. (***T40-C3*** is a rarer form of Melaleuca oil and is sometimes less offensive.) Allow the oil sufficient time to soak into the skin. After the rash has fully developed, usually within 2 or 3 days, soak in 1 oz. of ***Sol-U-Mel*** and 1 oz. of ***Renew Bath Oil*** in a tub of warm water for 15 minutes to help with the itching. After soaking, pat dry and reapply the ***T36-C5***. When the oil has started to be absorbed into the skin or is drying, apply either ***Mela-Gel*** or ***Renew Intensive Skin Therapy***. Repeat the process several times a day. Drinking one to four cups of ***G'Day Melaleuca Tea*** each day may also be helpful.

CHAPTER THIRTEEN

HEALTHY HOME SOLUTIONS

AIR FRESHENER

To make a fresh smelling and safe air freshener, combine 2 to 3 capfuls of *Sol-U-Mel* with 8 ounces of water in a spray bottle.

ANT KILLER

Spray concentrated *Pre-Spot Plus* on areas where ants congregate. Be aware of the surface of these areas when using *Pre-Spot Plus* as it can take the finish off of some wooden floors.

An alternate idea is to combine 1 ounce of *MelaMagic* and 1 ounce of *Sol-U-Mel* in a 16-ounce bottle filled with water. This works particularly well with large black ants.

Another simple solution is *Tough & Tender.* It will kill ants.

See the section under *Wasps, Yellow Jackets, Ants and Ticks* in this book.

ANT PREVENTION

If you prefer to just prevent ants, simply spray the most likely areas with 2 ounces of *Sol-U-Guard* combined with 16 ounces of water.

APPLIANCES

Unplug all electrical appliances before cleaning them. Use 1 teaspoon of *Tough & Tender* and 1 capful of *Sol-U-Mel* combined in a 32-ounce spray bottle filled with water to clean your kitchen appliances. Spray your appliance and allow it to sit for a moment before wiping.

For heavier cleaning, add 4 ounces of *MelaMagic* and 1 capful of *Sol-U-Mel* to a gallon of water. This is also an excellent grease cutter.

AUTOMOBILES

For dusting the inside, spray a solution of 5 drops of *Tough & Tender* in 16 ounces of water on a cloth. Wipe the area thoroughly. For the windows, spray on *Clear Power* (diluted to ½ the strength suggested on the bottle) and wipe them with a soft cloth or cheap paper towels.

Rustic Touch cleans vinyl and leather. It is also great for cleaning the dash of your car. **NOTE:** Spray it on a cloth to apply. If you spray it directly on the dash, you will get it on the inside of your windshield.

Make sure you read and understand all product packaging prior to use.

For cleaning the outside of the car, fill a bucket with warm water and add 10 drops of *Tough & Tender*. Apply with a cloth or spray bottle, and rinse with clean water.

To clean under the hood of your car, mix 1 capful of *Sol-U-Mel* and 2 ounces of *MelaMagic* in a 16-ounce spray bottle and fill with water. After spraying it on, let sit for 10 minutes and hose off the dirt and grime.

Add 4 to 5 drops of *Tough & Tender* to every 4 ounces of water in your windshield washer. It works amazingly well. (Make sure you use non-freezing washer fluid in the winter.)

BABY WIPES

Combine 1 teaspoon of *Sol-U-Mel* OR 1 capful of *Nature's Cleanse* with 1 capful of *Renew Bath Oil*, ¼ teaspoon of *Tough & Tender* and 2 cupfuls of water to make very effective and cost-efficient baby or travel wipes. Cut a roll of paper towels in half and remove the cardboard roll so that you can begin pulling the towels from the center. Place the towels in a plastic container and saturate with this solution. Replace the lid and cut a "star" in the center. You can then pull the towels through the lid.

An alternate solution would be to cut a roll of 1 ply (cloth like) Viva paper towels in half and place ½ of the roll into a 3 quart Rubbermaid Servin' Saver bowl with a lid. Add 2 cups of water, 1-2 tablespoons of *Koala Pals Kid's Shampoo* and 2 tablespoons of grapeseed oil (or baby oil). If you experience problems with mold developing, add 1-2 drops of *T36-C5* to the mixture. Cover and let them soak for 10 minutes or so before using. Remove center cardboard core and pull wipes from center and tear off.

Another recipe for baby wipes would be to use white Bounty paper towels (because they are stronger), and cut the roll in half. Take out the cardboard core. Mix in a large bowl—2½ cups of warm water, 1½ teaspoons of *Tough & Tender*, ½ teaspoon of *Sol-U-Mel*, and 1 capful of *Renew Bath Oil*. Stir and then put the ragged edge of the paper towels into the water first. Let this sit until all the water is soaked up. Put the towels into a large plastic container with a lid. Pull from the middle. This also makes wonderful hand and face wipes. Only half of a roll of towels is used, so make 2 bowls at once.

BALLPOINT PEN

Sol-U-Mel is very effective at removing ballpoint pen and many other difficult to remove items. Put a little *Sol-U-Mel* on the area and let it soak for a few minutes and then dab it with water.

BARBECUE GRILLS

Soak your bar-be-cue grill in a solution of 2 tablespoons of *MelaMagic* in ½ gallon of water. Clean it with a brush. For the outside of the grill, use 1 tablespoon of *Tough & Tender* and 16 ounces of water in a spray bottle and scrub with a soft brush. For baked on areas, use 1 ounce of *MelaMagic* combined with 8 ounces of water. Let it soak for a few minutes before scrubbing and rinsing.

BATHROOM – CEILINGS

Mix 1 teaspoon of *Tough & Tender* with 16 ounces of water in a spray bottle and apply to the ceiling. Wipe it with a damp cloth. For really dirty or greasy ceilings, use 1 tablespoon of *MelaMagic* with 16 ounces of water in a spray bottle.

BATHROOM – COUNTER

Add 3 ounces of *Sol-U-Mel* to water in a 16-ounce spray bottle. Spray on the counter and let it sit for a few minutes. Wipe it with a damp cloth. This will kill any germs that may be on your counter.

PreSpot works great on laminated countertops for tough stains. Spray it on and let it soak for a few minutes before wiping.

BATHROOM – DISINFECTING

Sol-U-Guard kills bathroom bacteria. Add 5 to 6 ounces of *Sol-U-Guard* to a gallon of water for very effective cleaning and disinfecting. It has been suggested that for a particularly challenging job, you may need to use 8 to 16 ounces of *Sol-U-Guard* for a gallon of water.

BATHROOM – FLOOR

Combine 2 tablespoons of *MelaMagic* and 1 capful of *Sol-U-Mel* in 16 ounces of water. Keep this in a spray bottle or mix it in a bucket. Spray or wipe it on the floor and mop thoroughly.

BATHROOM – HARD WATER SPOTS

Two tablespoons of *Sol-U-Mel* and 2 tablespoons of *Tub & Tile* mixed in a quart of water and sprayed on hard water spots will clean and shine, but also will wipe out fungus, mold and mildew. **Never** use *Tub & Tile* on genuine marble surfaces.

BATHROOM – MIRRORS

Use *Clear Power* (diluted to ½ the strength suggested on the bottle). Wipe the mirror with the *Clear Power* and **cheap** paper towels. It works great and at a very reasonable price.

BATHROOMS – MOLD AND MILDEW

Add 5 to 6 ounces of *Sol-U-Guard* and 1 to 2 capfuls of *Sol-U-Mel* to a gallon of water for an effective mold and mildew control formula. Spray on and scrub with a brush to eliminate the mold and mildew growth.

An alternate choice would be to apply *Tub & Tile* full strength. Spray it on and let it stand a few minutes before rinsing. This is also excellent when cleaning mold and mildew off bathroom shower curtains.

Make sure you read and understand all product packaging prior to use.

BATHROOM – ODORS

Use 3 ounces of **Sol-U-Mel** in 16 ounces of water to eliminate odors of all kinds.

BATHROOM – SHOWER CURTAIN

Combine 1 capful of **Sol-U-Mel** and 1 ounce of **MelaMagic** in a 16-ounce spray bottle of water and thoroughly spray the shower curtain. Allow some time for the cleaning combination to work and then use the shower to rinse off the mixture before wiping off the remaining grime.

BATHROOM – SHOWER STALL

Combine 1 ounce of **Tub & Tile** and 1 capful of **Sol-U-Mel** in a 16-ounce bottle filled with water and spray on the shower stall. Wipe thoroughly with a damp sponge.

For an extra-challenging shower stall, increase the mixture to 1 capful of **Sol-U-Mel** and 1 ounce of **Tub & Tile** in 6 to 7 ounces of water. **Do not** use **Tub & Tile** on marble.

Of course, this is an alternate solution to using the **No Work Daily Shower Cleaner**. With **No Work** you can keep your shower sparkling clean with a daily 15-second spray. Its dual action breaks up soap scum and hard water deposits and leaves behind a fresh smell.

By the way, the **Gold** and **Platinum Bar** are excellent for cleaning the shower door.

BATHROOM – SINK

Mix 4 tablespoons of **Tub & Tile** and 1 capful of **Sol-U-Mel** with 16 ounces of water in a spray bottle. Spray the sink and wipe it with a damp cloth. For rust stains or mineral deposits, use **Tub & Tile** full strength. You may need to use a soft bristle brush on stubborn stains. Rinse the sink with water. By the way, the **Denti-Clean Extra-Whitening Toothpaste** is a wonderful enamel cleaner.

BATHROOM – TOILET

Pour 4 tablespoons of **Tub & Tile** in the toilet. Let this sit for a few minutes, and then clean the area with a toilet brush.

If you have a lot of buildup, turn the water off on your toilet and let it drain. Pour in 2 ounces of **Tub & Tile** and let it sit for a few minutes before scrubbing with a toilet brush. In extreme cases, you might try 1 ounce of **Sol-U-Guard** in 16 ounces of water and repeat the procedure.

BATHROOM – UNDER THE COUNTER

Mix 5 drops of **Tough & Tender** with ½ capful of **Sol-U-Mel** and 16 ounces of water in a spray bottle. Clean thoroughly with a soft cloth or brush. The addition of **Sol-U-Mel** to the **Tough & Tender** mixture will take care of any mold or mildew problem under the counter.

Make sure you read and understand all product packaging prior to use.

BATHROOM – WALLS

Mix 1 teaspoon of *Tough & Tender* with 16 ounces of water in a spray bottle and apply this mixture to the walls. Wipe with a damp cloth.

BATHROOM – WIPES

Use the recipe for the Bounty paper towel baby wipes (in this book) and instead of making two batches of baby wipes, use half of the recipe for bathroom wipes. Buy the Bounty "select a size," pull them apart and fold them. Make the baby wipes as directed. In the second batch, however, add 1½ teaspoons of *Sol-U-Guard* to the mixture. This is wonderful for quick bathroom clean-ups.

BATHTUB

Mix 3 ounces of *Tub & Tile* with water in a 16-ounce spray bottle. Spray on the tub and let it sit for about 2 minutes. Wipe with a damp cloth. For rust spots, apply straight *Tub & Tile* to the area. Wait until the rust dissolves and then wipe with a damp cloth. For hard water or mineral deposits, use full strength *Tub & Tile* with a soft scrub brush. Initially there may be strong fumes due to the quantity of build up being dissolved, so run the fan or open a window. This problem should disappear very soon if *Tub & Tile* is used on a regular basis.

To maintain a cleaner tub, keep a bottle of *No Work* close by and spray the tub each time it is used.

For the chrome, try *Clear Power*. It is very effective.

BLEACH SUBSTITUTE

Use *MelaBrite Color-Safe Whitener & Brightener*. You may want to use ¼ cup in a white load for extra whitening as opposed to just ⅛ cup in a regular load.

BLINDS

Liberally spray the slats of your blinds with 1 tablespoon of *Tub & Tile* in a 16-ounce spray bottle filled with water. Rinse well and repeat the process on the reverse side of the slats. NOTE: Do not use *Tub & Tile* on wood blinds. Wood blinds should be cleaned with *Rustic Touch*.

An alternate solution would be to mix 5 drops of *Tough & Tender* with ½ capful of *Sol-U-Mel* and 16 ounces of water. Close the blinds and spray on the solution. Wipe them with a soft cloth.

BLOOD STAINS – CLOTHING

Blood is a very challenging stain to remove, but here are a couple of ideas to try. Spray the stained fabric with full strength *Pre-Spot Plus*. Let it sit for a few minutes and then rub out the stain with cold water. Repeat the procedure with *Pre-Spot Plus* if necessary. Wash the fabric with *MelaPower Laundry Detergent* and 1 to 2 capfuls of *Sol-U-Mel*, if possible.

Antibacterial Liquid Soap rubbed into any fresh red stain seems to work very well. This applies to blood as well as catsup, spaghetti sauce, and bar-be-cue sauce. Then wash as usual.

BOATS

The bottom of your aluminum fishing boat can be readied for a new season with a mixture of 1 ounce of **MelaMagic** with 8 ounces of water and 1 capful of **Sol-U-Mel**. Restore the interior with diluted **MelaMagic** or **Tough & Tender.**

Out of **MelaMagic**? Try 1 ounce of **Tub & Tile** combined with 3 ounces of water and 1 capful of **Sol-U-Mel**. Let this soak and then hose the boat with 1 tablespoon of **Tough & Tender** mixed in a gallon of water.

Try cleaning your fiberglass boat with diluted **Sol-U-Mel**. It will even work on the seats.

Any wood areas of the boat can be beautifully restored with **Rustic Touch**. (**Do not** use **Tub & Tile** on wood surfaces.)

BREAD BOX

If you spray the bread drawer or box with **Tough & Tender,** your bread will not mold as fast.

BROILER

After baking or broiling anything, run some water on the broiler pan and add a couple of squirts of concentrated **Tough & Tender**. If it is particularly bad, add 1 part of **Lemon Brite** mixed with 8 parts of water for a spray. Of course, **MelaMagic** is the magic grease cutter and will work effectively on built up grease.

BUG SPRAY

A safe and non-toxic bug spray can be made from a combination of ¼ cup of **Sol-U-Mel**, 5 drops of **T36-C5**, 1 teaspoon of **Tough & Tender**, and 14 ounces of water. It costs a fraction of commercial sprays and there have been some suggestions that home bug sprays may increase the risk of Parkinson's disease. Why take the chance?

BUMPER STICKER REMOVAL

Old bumper stickers should disappear by applying concentrated **Sol-U-Mel**. Let soak for a few minutes. It may take a couple of applications before the glue is dissolved.

CANDLE WAX STAIN

To remove wax stains from linens or carpeting, press a warm iron over a paper towel on the spot. Continue to iron until the wax melts and is absorbed into the paper towel. Then clean the area with ½ teaspoon of **Tough & Tender** in 16 ounces of water.

CAR CLEANING

See Automobiles

CARPET CLEANER – MACHINE MIX

Check the color fastness of your carpet before using any cleaning product.

For a safe and effective cleaning solution, combine ½ cupful of *MelaPower* with ¼ cupful of *MelaMagic* and 2 capfuls of *Sol-U-Mel* in 3 gallons of water.

One capful of *Sol-U-Mel* and 1 capful of *Tough & Tender* also make an excellent carpet cleaning machine solution. If you have soft water, reduce the amount of ingredients by at least 50%.

An alternate choice would be to mix ¼ cup of *PreSpot Plus*, ½ cup of *MelaMagic* and 1 tablespoon of *Sol-U-Mel*. Pour this solution into the tray of the carpet cleaner. This works beautifully.

NOTE: Rinse your carpets well after steam cleaning or shampooing, as any remaining product will attract dirt.

CARPET – DEODORIZATION

Mix 1½ capfuls of *Sol-U-Mel* with water in a 16-ounce spray bottle. Spray on the carpet and let it set for 5 minutes. Clean the carpet with a scrub brush and blot the area with a damp cloth.

CARPET – SPOTS

Clean spots on your carpet with 1 teaspoon of *Tough & Tender* and 1 capful of *Sol-U-Mel* blended in a 16-ounce spray bottle filled with water. If the spot is greasy, try 1 ounce of *MelaMagic* combined with 7 to 8 ounces of water.

An alternate choice might be to mix 2 tablespoons of *PreSpot Plus* with ½ capful of *Sol-U-Mel* and 16 ounces of water in a spray bottle. Apply the solution to the soiled area. Let it set for 5 minutes and then clean it with a soft brush. Blot the spot with a damp cloth until it is clean.

For extremely difficult spots, try concentrated *Pre-Spot Plus*. It may need to soak for a couple of hours before you rinse with warm water, but it usually does a good job and will not discolor the carpet.

CARPET – VACUUMING

Lightly spray the carpet with diluted *Sol-U-Mel* for the most effective vacuuming.

If you use a sweeper that runs in water, add 1 teaspoon of *Sol-U-Mel* to the water and it will refresh the air in your home while it cleans.

CEILINGS

For a very effective general cleaning disinfectant, mix 1 teaspoon of

Tough & Tender in a 16-ounce spray bottle of water or add 1 tablespoon of *Tough & Tender* to a gallon bucket of water. If you need a stronger mixture, add 1 capful of *Sol-U-Mel* to either the spray or the bucket.

CEILING FAN

Mix 5 drops of *Tough & Tender* with 16 ounces of water in a spray bottle. Spray on the fan and wipe with a soft cloth. If the fan is wood, you may use the same technique followed by *Rustic Touch Furniture Care* or simply use the *Rustic Touch* for the complete cleaning job.

CHEWING GUM

Remove all the chewing gum possible before applying concentrated *Sol-U-Mel*. Rub fabric against fabric or use a soft brush to clean the area.

ALWAYS check the color fastness of any carpet or fabric **BEFORE** applying *Sol-U-Mel* or any cleaning product.

CHINA STAINS

China that is seriously stained may have to be soaked overnight before washing. For soaking, dissolve ¼ to ½ cupful of *Diamond Brite* in a gallon of hot water. Following the soaking, wash and dry as usual.

CHOCOLATE

Wet the chocolate spots with water and with a damp Q-tip, apply concentrated *Sol-U-Mel*. Allow it to soak for a few minutes and then rinse out the *Sol-U-Mel*. Wash with *MelaPower* and *MelaBrite* as soon as possible.

An alternate solution would be to spray *Pre-Spot Plus* on the chocolate and wash as soon as possible in *MelaPower* and *MelaBrite*.

CHROME

Clear Power is a wonderful product to use on chrome, or anything shiny. For best results mix it in distilled water and wipe with a soft cloth or cheap paper towels. Consider using ½ the amount indicated on the directions.

CLAY FLOWER POTS

To clean moss or algae, spray clay flowerpots with 1 teaspoon of *Sol-U-Mel* mixed with 16 ounces of water. Scrub them with a stiff brush or steel wool. Rinse with water and towel dry.

CLEANING BOOSTER

Offensive odors can be eliminated from your wash by adding 1 capful of *Sol-U-Mel* to each load. Bacteria causes odors and *Sol-U-Mel* eliminates bacteria while leaving clothes smelling fresh and clean. The same procedure is very effective if you have mildewed clothes, such as the ones you leave in the washer while on vacation.

Make sure you read and understand all product packaging prior to use.

COFFEE STAINS

Coffee stains on kitchen counters or tables can easily be removed by applying concentrated *Tub & Tile*. Rinse with a clean sponge before wiping dry. Formica or fiberglass counter tops should be rinsed immediately. Do not allow the *Tub & Tile* to dry on this surface before rinsing and wiping.

CONCRETE PATIOS

For general cleaning, mix 1 tablespoon of *MelaMagic* in ½ gallon of warm water. Dump a small puddle of this solution on the floor and scrub with a brush. Spray the floor with water to rinse.

COPPER

Have your tried the penny test to see what *Tub & Tile* does to copper? Dip a copper penny in a capful of *Tub & Tile* and watch it clean that dirty, tarnished old penny in seconds. It will do the same for your copper pots and frying pans. Spray or wipe *Tub & Tile* on the copper and wipe the grit and black tarnish away. In most cases it is not even necessary to use it concentrated.

COUNTERTOPS

Use 1 teaspoon of *Tough & Tender* in a 16-ounce spray bottle filled with water to spray countertop surfaces. Wait several moments before wiping with a damp cloth or clean sponge. If you have cleaned fish or chicken on the countertop, clean with *Antibacterial Liquid Soap*. Apply a small amount on a sponge and wipe the counter before rinsing. This will not only eliminate the smell, but will disinfect as well. If you have dark Formica countertops, using *Rustic Touch* after cleaning makes them look like new. Use *Pre-Spot Plus!* to effectively remove juice stains from countertops.

CRAYON

To clean crayon marks off of walls, use concentrated *Sol-U-Mel*. Gently try a small amount on the crayon mark, as this may also remove what is under the crayon mark—such as the paint.

An alternate solution would be to mix 5 drops of *Tough & Tender* with 16 ounces of water. If you need more cleaning strength, use 1 tablespoon of *MelaMagic* with ½ capful of *Sol-U-Mel*.

For clothing, spray the affected area with full strength *Pre-Spot Plus!* Let it sit for a few minutes. Scrub the mark to loosen the crayon from the fabric. If the spot still exist, repeat the procedure. When the crayon has been removed, wash the clothing with *MelaPower Laundry Detergent*.

CUTTING BOARD

It is very important to keep your cutting board clean and bacteria free. Washing it with a combination of 1 part of *Tough & Tender* and 1 part of *Sol-U-Mel* blended with 5 parts of water in a spray bottle will do the job. Allow it to sit for a few moments before rinsing and wiping dry.

Make sure you read and understand all product packaging prior to use.

DESKS

For dusting, nothing works better than *Rustic Touch*. If you do not have that available, try ½ teaspoon of *Tough & Tender* and a drop or two of *Sol-U-Mel* in a 16-ounce spray bottle filled with water. For ink stains, apply full strength *Tub & Tile* or *Sol-U-Mel* to the ink spot. Repeat if necessary. (**NOTE:** Do not put full strength *Tub & Tile* or *Sol-U-Mel* directly onto a wood surface.)

DIAPERS

Most people use disposable diapers now, but for those who still prefer to use cloth ones, odor is sometimes a challenge. Be sure to use a pail with a lid for soiled diapers. Cover the diapers with a combination of water and 1 capful of *Sol-U-Mel*, 3 tablespoons of *MelaPower* and 3 tablespoons of *MelaBrite*. Soak them overnight before washing with ⅛ of a cup of *MelaPower* (1 pump) and 1 to 2 capfuls of *Sol-U-Mel*. For whiter diapers, add ⅛-¼ cup of *MelaBrite* as well.

DIRT – CLOTHING

Ground in dirt stains can be effectively taken care of by applying full strength *MelaPower Laundry Detergent* before adding the garment to the regular wash load. Wash as usual using *MelaPower* and *MelaBrite*.

An alternate choice would be to spray the dirty area with full strength *PreSpot Plus*. Let it sit for a few minutes and then launder in *MelaPower Laundry Detergent*.

DISINFECTANT

Combine 1 part of *Sol-U-Mel* with 5 parts of water in a spray bottle. This is a much safer and far more cost effective disinfectant spray than you will find anywhere else. This is a very good item to carry with you when you travel and stay in rooms where all kinds of toxic chemicals have been used.

Remember to carry *Clear Defense* with you everywhere. It can be used in restaurants, public restrooms and simply after handling doorknobs and shaking hands.

DISHES – DISHWASHER WASHING

When you first begin to use *Diamond Brite* in your dishwasher, run at least one empty cycle with 2 to 4 ounces of *MelaMagic* and the regular amount of *Diamond Brite*. This will clean out any residue or buildup from the commercial soaps previously used. Then, use the *Diamond Brite* as directed.

Clear Power is a very good replacement for the rinse cycle products. Add straight *Clear Power* to the dispenser and check for really sparkling glasses. If you do not have a dispenser in your dishwasher, mix ⅙ of a bottle of *Clear Power* with 20 ounces of water and spray the dishes down before you close the door.

You can also use *Tough & Tender* in the rinse dispenser and perhaps even *Tub & Tile* once a month or so. Whichever you choose to use, it will be much more economical than the store brands.

An alternate choice would be to use diluted *MelaMagic* in the rinse dispenser. Also, if you are using *Clear Power* and the dishes are extra greasy, spray them with *MelaMagic,* or if they are just tough dirty dishes, spray *Tough & Tender* directly on them.

Every 12-15 loads run *Tub & Tile* in your dishwasher to clean it out. The temperature of your dishwasher and the chemicals in your water will all affect the cleaning effectiveness. The amount of the products you use will sometimes have to be adjusted due to these two variables.

DISHES – HAND WASHING

Use 5 to 7 drops of *Lemon Brite* in a sink full of water. For baked-on food, fill a container with hot water to which 2 or 3 drops of *Lemon Brite* have been added. Let the dishes soak for ½ hour and then wash as usual.

DISHES – STAINS

Soak stained dishes or china in a bucket or sink of hot water containing ⅓ cup of *Diamond Brite*. Let them soak for 1 hour. If stains have not dissolved, soak them overnight.

DRIVEWAYS

Combine 1 part of *MelaMagic* with 8 parts of water and 1 to 2 capfuls of *Sol-U-Mel* and spray on any fresh grease stain. Hose the driveway with water.

DUST MITES

Sol-U-Mel, when diluted according to directions and sprayed in the air, will kill all airborne germs and viruses and will deodorize at the same time. When sprayed on upholstery, it will suffocate dust mites. Be sure to spray your mattress periodically even if you don't flip it any more.

DUSTING

Always dust before you vacuum so that the dust particles can be picked up by the vacuum cleaner. Keep your air conditioner and heater clean and well serviced so that the amount of dust and bacteria particles floating throughout your home is limited.

Using *Rustic Touch* will condition your wood furniture and woodwork, while it cleans dust and wax buildup and leaves behind a mirror shine. The cleaned surfaces stay non-magnetic and seem to repel dust and dirt for a longer period of time. Use it on natural and artificial wood furniture, laminated surfaces, vinyl, leather and paneling.

On all other surfaces, mix 5 drops of *Tough & Tender* with 16 ounces of water in a spray bottle. Spray on a cloth and wipe away the dust.

Make sure you read and understand all product packaging prior to use.

ENAMEL

The *Classic Tooth Polish* is a wonderful enamel polish. Save your old tooth polish tubes and slice them open when you are ready to polish your enamel. There is usually enough residue to do the job and it is very economical.

FABRIC DYE STAINS

Spray the affected areas with *PreSpot Plus*. Let it sit for about 1 minute and then soak in a container with ⅛ cup of *MelaPower* (1 pump) in a gallon of water for 30 minutes. If the stain is not completely gone, reapply *PreSpot Plus* and wash in the washing machine as usual.

FINE WASHABLES

To launder wool, nylon, or other fine fabrics, add 1 teaspoon of *Tough & Tender* to a basin of cold water. Gently wash and rinse your fine washables.

FINGERNAIL POLISH

Sol-U-Mel is very effective at removing fingernail polish and many other challenging substances. Put a little *Sol-U-Mel* on the area and let it soak for a few minutes and then wipe it with water.

FIRE ANTS

Spray the ants with *PreSpot Plus*. It is very effective. For fire ant pain, splash the area with *Sol-U-Mel*.

For a foolproof way to kill fire ants consider this: After you have mopped the floor with *Tough & Tender* and/or *MelaMagic,* or you have washed the car with *Tough & Tender*, add a 5 or 6 drops of *Lemon Brite* and stir. Pour half of the bucket on the fire ant bed. After about 30 minutes pour the other half on the bed.

If you are really mad about the fire ants, like when they have invaded your flower beds, mix the following in a two gallon bucket of water: 1 capful of *Tough & Tender*, 1 capful of *MelaMagic*, 1 capful of *Sol-U-Mel*, 1 capful of *Tub & Tile* and always 10 drops of *Lemon Brite*. Sir and pour half of the bucket on the fire ant bed. Wait 30 minutes and pour on the other half. This kills them "dead" and they won't come back. Plus, that will be the greenest part of your lawn!

FIREPLACE

For the fireplace glass, use *Clear Power* (diluted to ½ of the strength suggested on the bottle). Wipe with a soft cloth or cheap paper towels.

For the outside of the fireplace, use 2 tablespoons of *MelaMagic* with 16 ounces of water. Spray on the soiled area and scrub with a brush.

FIRST AID KIT – HOME AND CAR

T36-C5, Clear Defense, Renew Intensive Skin Therapy, Triple Antibiotic Ointment, Mela-Gel, Sun-Shades Waterproof Sunblock, CounterAct Extra Strength Pain Reliever, Antibacterial Liquid Soap, scissors, tweezers, Band-Aids, gauze, and a very small container of water (for washing wounds).

FLOORS – LINOLEUM AND CERAMIC

For mopping, use ½ cup of *MelaMagic* in a gallon of water. For a quick clean up, make a spray by mixing 1 part of *MelaMagic* to 8 parts of water.

An alternate choice would be to use 6 ounces of *Sol-U-Guard* in a gallon of water.

FLOORS – HARDWOOD

Use 1 tablespoon of *Tough & Tender* in a gallon of water to clean your hardwood floors. Be sure to dry the floors carefully.

FLOORS – SCUFFMARKS

Rub scuffmarks with *Antibacterial Liquid Soap* or *Sol-U-Mel*. If working on wooden floors check a small area first to be sure that they have been properly sealed.

FLY CONTROL

Spray fly-prone areas daily for one week with a combination of 1 teaspoon of *Tough & Tender* and 1 capful of *Renew Bath Oil* in a 16-ounce spray bottle filled with water. After the first week, spraying only 2 to 3 times each week should control the flies. Spray your porches, decks, and yards after each rainstorm. Wearing *Sun-Shades 15* or *30* as a repellent is very effective in areas where you have deer flies.

FREEZER

To clean spills, use 5 drops of *Tough & Tender* with 16 ounces of water in a spray bottle. Spray on and wipe clean with a cloth. To kill mold or mildew, mix 1 capful of *Sol-U-Mel* with 16 ounces of water in a spray bottle. Spray on and let set for 5 minutes. Wipe with a soft cloth.

FRUIT JUICE SPOTS – CLOTHING

Spray the area with full strength *PreSpot Plus*. Let it set for a few minutes, and then launder with *MelaPower Launder Detergent* as usual.

FRUIT AND VEGETABLE WASH

Place fruits or vegetables in a bowl of water containing 2-4 drops of *Tough & Tender*. Let them sit for about 5 minutes and then rinse carefully.

An alternate solution would be to mix ½ teaspoon of *Tough & Tender* with ½ teaspoon of **Sol-U-Mel** with 16 ounces of water in a spray bottle. Spray your fruits and vegetables and rinse well. The **Sol-U-Mel** will dissolve the wax on the fruit. Even if you peel vegetables and fruits, they should be rinsed thoroughly before you eat them. Discard all the outer layers of leafy vegetables such as lettuce and cabbage, before you rinse and eat them. Remove rinds of fruits before serving them and peel all rooted vegetables.

FURNITURE

For spot cleaning, use 1 tablespoon of **PreSpot Plus** with 16 ounces of water. (You may want to test for color fastness on a hidden area.) For wood, leather or vinyl, use **Rustic Touch Furniture Care** as directed.

FURNITURE – OUTDOOR

Outdoor furniture can easily be cleaned by spraying with 1 teaspoon of **Tough & Tender** and 1 capful of **Sol-U-Mel** combined in a 16-ounce bottle of water. This will loosen the dirt so that they can easily be wiped with a sponge or rag and rinsed with the garden hose.

GARAGE FLOOR

On a sealed garage floor, use 1 part of **MelaMagic**, 8 parts of water and 1 to 2 capfuls of **Sol-U-Mel**. Spray this mixture on fresh grease stains, scrub with a brush and rinse with a garden hose.

GARBAGE CANS

Pour ¼ to ½ cup of **MelaMagic** and 1 to 2 capfuls of **Sol-U-Mel** into the garbage can. Fill the can ¼ full with hot water and scrub the sides with a soft brush. Pour the mixture out and rinse with water. To prevent odor, clean them frequently.

An alternate solution would be to use **Sol-U-Guard** as directed for extra strength disinfecting power.

GAS SPILLS

Soak a cloth in **MelaMagic**. Wipe up the spill. You may also try adding some **Sol-U-Mel** to the cloth to eliminate the odor.

GLASS

Use **Clear Power** as directed on the label. Terry towels, old cloths or very cheap paper towels are excellent for wiping windows after spraying. (Try using the **Clear Power** diluted to ½ of the strength suggested on the bottle.) For best results use distilled water with the **Clear Power**.

GLASS TABLETOPS

Clean with **Clear Power** (diluted to ½ of the strength suggested on the bottle). Apply a mixture of ½ teaspoon of **MelaSoft** and 1 quart of water. Spray or wipe on the glass top. Dry with a cloth towel. This will keep the lint off.

Make sure you read and understand all product packaging prior to use.

GRAPE JUICE STAINS – CLOTHING

Grape juice stains need to be sprayed immediately with *Pre-Spot Plus*. Let soak and then wash as usual with *MelaPower*.

GRASS STAINS – CLOTHING

Spray *Pre-Spot Plus* or *MelaPower* on the grass stain. Let it sit for a few minutes and then soak in a bucket of warm water containing 2 tablespoons of *MelaPower Laundry Detergent*, for several hours.

Tough & Tender works well on grass stains as well.

GREASE – CLOTHING

Spray grease stains on clothing before laundering with *Pre-Spot Plus* and rub gently. Launder as usual with *MelaPower* and *MelaBrite*.

If you are dealing with major grease or extremely stubborn grease, mix a solution of 2 tablespoons of *MelaPower Laundry Detergent* and 1 capful of *Sol-U-Mel* with 2 gallons of warm water. Put the clothing in this solution and let it soak for a few hours. If the grease spots are not dissolved, apply a squirt of *Antibacterial Liquid Soap*. Rub it in with your finger or a soft brush. Let this stand for a few minutes before rinsing with warm water.

You can also add *MelaMagic* directly to the water in the washing machine. It is very effective against grease.

GREASE SPILLS

Pour full strength *MelaMagic* on the grease spot and let it set for 15 minutes. Then wipe it up.

GREASE SPOTS – RUGS AND CARPETING

Rub a small amount of *Antibacterial Liquid Soap* into the spots on your rugs or carpeting for a quick cleanup. Rinse and blot the stain with a dry cloth.

GREASY HANDS

Using *The Gold* or *Platinum Bar* or *Antibacterial Liquid Soap* works well. You might also try a little bit of *MelaMagic*. Rub your hands together and then rinse with water.

GUM

Pour full strength *Sol-U-Mel* on the affected area. Let it set for a minute or so. Rub to loosen the gum, and then wash in *MelaPower Laundry Detergent* as usual.

To effectively clean sticky, gummy surfaces, apply full strength *Sol-U-Mel*. If the sticky area is on wood, carefully check a small area to be sure the wood has been sealed before applying too much *Sol-U-Mel*.

HAIR – STATIC ELECTRICITY

When you are challenged with static hair, spray some diluted *MelaSoft* on your hairbrush or comb. It works wonders to calm a bad hair day.

HARD WATER SPOTS

For heavy duty cleaning of hard water spots, rub the area with concentrated *Tub & Tile*. Rinse and wipe dry. **Do not use *Tub & Tile* on marble surfaces.**

HOT TUBS

No Melaleuca products, including *T36-C5*, *Renew Bath Oil*, or *Sol-U-Mel*, should be used in an operating hot tub or permanent Jacuzzi tub. Melaleuca alternifolia oil is not compatible with the filtration system in those sophisticated environments.

To clean an empty hot tub, use concentrated *MelaMagic* and it may require a lot of elbow grease, but it will work.

HOUSE – EXTERIOR CLEANING

Mix 2 ounces of *MelaMagic* with 16 ounces of water, or a ratio of 2 parts of *MelaMagic* to 8 parts of water. Apply this solution by either spraying or wiping on the surface of the house. Scrub with a brush and rinse with water.

HUMIDIFIER

Placing 1 to 2 tablespoons of *Sol-U-Mel* in your humidifier's water chamber will not only clean it but will fill your home with fresh, healthy air as well. It has also been suggested that a few drops of *T36-C5* added to the humidifier will add to the freshness.

HUMIDIFIER, ELECTRONIC

If your home has a central heating system with a built in humidifier, stir in 10-15 drops of *T36-C5* for every 8 ounce cup of water resting in the tray. Repeat at least once a month or as frequently as needed. This will not only freshen your home, but will prevent mold and other air impurities.

INK STAINS – CLOTHING AND SURFACES

Spray *Pre-Spot Plus* on ink stains and rub with your finger or a soft brush. Let it sit for a few minutes and then rinse with warm water. If it is a stubborn stain, repeat the procedure or soak the spot overnight.

An alternate solution is to use *Tub & Tile* or *Sol-U-Mel* directly on the spot. *Sol-U-Mel* is especially effective if the fabric has been in the dryer before being treated. It may also be used on "dry clean only" fabrics.

Be sure to check all fabrics for colorfastness before applying any product.

Make sure you read and understand all product packaging prior to use.

For ink on surfaces, try rubbing the area with a combination of 1 ounce of *MelaMagic* and 1 capful of *Sol-U-Mel* mixed in 8 ounces of water. The ink should be easily removed unless the surface has not been sealed.

INSECT REPELLENT

Roaches are the dread of all of us. Try grabbing your diluted bottle of *Sol-U-Guard* and giving them a quick spray. They will die within a couple of seconds and you still don't have to worry about having insecticide in your home.

To rid your home of other creatures such as beetles, crickets and termites, try treating them with 10 to 12 drops of *T36-C5*, 1 capful of *Sol-U-Mel* and 1 teaspoon of *Sol-U-Guard* in a 16-ounce spray bottle filled with water.

The "ultimate" mosquito, black fly, and no see'em spray consist of 4 ounces of *Sol-U-Mel*, 4 ounces of *Renew Bath Oil*, and 5 ounces of *Moisturizing Hand Creme*. Spread on exposed body skin or over the entire body. Keep in mind, shampooing with *Naturals Melaleuca Oil* or *Herbal Shampoos* and using *Sun-Shades Sun Block* also affords insect repellent protection.

Also note that *Tub & Tile* will kill wasps and *Pre-Spot Plus* and *Tough & Tender* will kill ants.

INSECT REPELLENT – BABIES AND CHILDREN

Blend 3 ounces of *Sol-U-Mel* into 16 ounces of water and lightly spray this on the baby and children's skin, clothes and carrier.

INSECT REPELLENT – ADULTS

An excellent insect repellent for adults is made by combining 5 ounces of *Moisturizing Hand Creme* with 4 ounces of *Renew Bath Oil* and 4 ounces of *Sol-U-Mel*. For best results, put this solution on all exposed skin a couple of times each hour.

Some prefer to simply use 1 teaspoon of *Moisturizing Hand Creme* with 5 drops of *T36-C5*.

For a general outdoor spray, blend 2 capfuls of *Sol-U-Mel* with 10-12 drops of *T36-C5* in a 16-ounce spray bottled filled with water. Or, just use 1 tablespoon of *Sol-U-Mel* and 16 ounces of water.

Different body types respond to different insect repellent formulas. Don't be afraid to experiment and find your own solution and then pass it on. Some people have said that even taking the Melaleuca vitamins has stopped mosquito bites.

Here is another formula: Combine 2 ounces of *Renew Bath Oil*, 2 ounces of *Sol-U-Mel*, 1 ounce of *Tough & Tender*, 20+ drops of *T36-C5* with 6 to 12 ounces of water. Apply this frequently with a spray bottle.

INSECT REPELLENT – OUTSIDE AIR

Mix 2 tablespoons of *Sol-U-Mel* and 16 ounces of water. Spray it into the area where people are present.

An alternative would be to blend 2 ounces of *Sol-U-Mel* with 5 drops of *T36-C5* and 1 teaspoon of *Tough & Tender* in 16 ounces of water. Spray this mixture around doors, on screens, or trees and garbage cans, etc.

Spray *Tough & Tender* around outdoor lights to keep insects from flying around the lights.

Place a bucket full of water and *Tough & Tender* very close to a light on your patio and leave it all night. You will be amazed how many bugs you will collect in one night. (Use just enough *Tough & Tender* to make some suds.)

INSECT REPELLENT – PLANTS

Use ½ teaspoon of *Tough & Tender* in a 16-ounce spray bottle filed with water. Spray on any plants that have pests.

JEWELRY

Dip most of your fine jewelry into concentrated *Tub & Tile*. (Do not use on soft stones, pearls, or silver.) Rinse well before allowing it to dry. Using *Tough & Tender* on a toothbrush works well, too. Gently scrub the article and rinse carefully. Scrubbing with the *Melaleuca Denti-Clean* is also very effective. Simply scrub the jewelry with an old toothbrush and rinse as usual. Most ordinary jewelry worn throughout the day can be kept clean by immersing hands in the various cleaning solutions suggested in these pages. Even washing your hands with *Antibacterial Liquid Soap* will keep your everyday jewelry sparkling. It does not leave the usual soap residue.

An alternate solution would be to remove the solution from a jar of jewelry cleaner and replace it with ½ teaspoon of *Lemon Brite* and enough water to fill the jar. Let the jewelry soak for a few minutes, then rinse and dry carefully.

KITCHEN – ALL PURPOSE CLEANER

For a general, all-purpose kitchen cleaner, add 1 tsp. of *Tough & Tender* and 1 capful of *Sol-U-Mel* to a 16-ounce spray bottle filled with water.

KITCHEN – CABINET

To clean the outside of the cabinet, mix 1 tablespoon of *MelaMagic* with 16-ounces of water in a spray bottle. Spray the cabinet and wipe it clean with a cloth. For the inside of the cabinet, add 5 drops of *Tough & Tender* to 16 ounces of water in a spray bottle. Spray the cabinet and wipe it with a dry cloth.

KITCHEN – CEILING AND WALLS

Mix 2 tablespoons of *MelaMagic* in a bucket of hot water. Use a cloth to wash down the ceiling and walls with this solution. Let them air dry.

Make sure you read and understand all product packaging prior to use.

KITCHEN – COPPER

Mix 2 ounces of *Tub & Tile* with 16 ounces of water in a spray bottle and spray it on any copper pieces. Wipe it with a clean cloth.

KITCHEN – COUNTERS

Use a 16-ounce bottle of water and add 5 to 7 drops of *Tough & Tender.* Spray on the counters and use a clean damp sponge to clean. Either allow the counters to air-dry or rinse with a kitchen cloth and dry. For removing stubborn stains, use *Sol-U-Mel* full strength.

PreSpot works great on laminated countertops for tough stains. Spray it on and let it soak for a few minutes before wiping.

KITCHEN – DISHWASHER

To clean the outside of the dishwasher, use 5 drops of *Tough & Tender* in 16 ounces of water in a spray bottle. Spray on the dishwasher and wipe it with a cloth. Fill only ½ of one of the auto-load cups of your dishwasher with *Diamond Brite* to clean your dishes. To clean the inside of the dishwasher, run one full wash cycle with *Diamond Brite* and no dishes. **NOTE:** When you first start using Melaleuca products, the dishwasher and the washing machine should be run empty with Melaleuca products several times to clean out the residue of the more toxic previously-used products.

KITCHEN – FLOORS

Mix 1 tablespoon of *MelaMagic* with a bucket full of hot water. Mop the floor and let it air dry.

KITCHEN – ODORS

Use 3 ounces of *Sol-U-Mel* with 16 ounces of water to eliminate odors of all kinds.

KITCHEN – OVEN

Use concentrated *Tough & Tender* to clean your oven. It can be applied with a cloth or a sponge. Let it sit for a few minutes before wiping and drying. If you feel that it needs a little extra boost, add 1 capful of *Sol-U-Mel* to the *Tough & Tender* before cleaning.

Some prefer to simply use 2 ounces of *Sol-U-Mel* combined with 16 ounces of water in a spray bottle. This will work well on more heavily soiled areas. You may need to use a gentle cleaning pad as well. Once the oven is clean, be sure to rinse it well before using.

For the grilled-on spots, mix a combination of *Diamond Brite* and *MelaMagic* or use straight *MelaMagic*. Apply this to these very difficult spots and allow soaking as long as possible before rinsing and wiping dry. If scrubbing is necessary, use a soft scrubbing pad.

An alternate choice would be to use 4 tablespoons of *MelaMagic* and 1 capful of *Sol-U-Mel* with 16 ounces of water in the spray bottle. Apply to the oven and let it set for 5 minutes. Wipe it with a damp cloth.

Make sure you read and understand all product packaging prior to use.

KITCHEN – SINK

For general cleaning, put a few drops of **Tough & Tender** in the sink and scrub with a soft brush. To whiten or shine a sink, spray it with **Sol-U-Mel** and sprinkle it with a little bit of salt. Scrub it and watch it sparkle!

Use concentrated **Tub & Tile** or **Diamond Brite** to clean the scuffmarks off enamel sinks. Scrub the stains gently and then rinse. Repeat as necessary. You will be amazed! You may also want to try the **Classic Tooth Polish**. It is wonderful enamel cleaner.

KITCHEN – STOVE

For minor stove clean ups, use 5 drops of **Tough & Tender** with 16 ounces of water in a spray bottle. Apply and let it sit for a few minutes before you wipe and dry the area.

For major clean ups, apply concentrated **MelaMagic** with a spray bottle or soft cloth. Let it sit for a few minutes and then use a soft scrubbing pad to lift off the grime. Wipe with a damp cloth.

KITCHEN – VENTILATION HOOD

Clean all the ventilation hood surfaces with concentrated **MelaMagic**. Apply it with a damp sponge or cloth. Allow it to sit for a few minutes and then wipe with a clean damp cloth or paper towel.

An alternate solution would be to clean with a mixture of 2 teaspoons of **Tough & Tender** mixed with 1 capful of **Sol-U-Mel** in a 16-ounce spray bottle of water. Spray and wipe the area for a sparkling clean.

LABELS

When the countertop gets stained from price stickers or bread bags, spray concentrated **Tub & Tile** on the area and wait 15 minutes or more before rinsing off.

When you run across a label on a product that does not want to come off or, at least, wants to leave a sticky surface, try wiping with a small amount of **Sol-U-Mel** on a soft rag.

LAUNDRY

Believe it or not, 1 pump (⅛ cup) of **MelaPower** is sufficient for an average wash load. If you have a water softener, you may be able to use even less! ⅛ of a cup of **MelaBrite** will brighten your load considerably. In all-white loads you may want to use ¼ of a cup for extra whitening. The **MelaSoft** can be added to the wash load or to the dryer; which ever is easier for you. It can be used as easily as placing it on a soft cloth and throwing it in the dryer with the wet clothes. As small amount as one large or two small capfuls will work quite well.

If you are washing clothes that have mildew or any other type of odor, add 1 capful of **Sol-U-Mel** to your normal wash load. It is very effective. Some even recommend adding **Sol-U-Mel** to every load for the additional germ protection.

Make sure you read and understand all product packaging prior to use.

LAUNDRY STAINS

Use *Pre-Spot Plus!* It will take out almost all stains. Some stains will require concentrated *Pre-Spot Plus*. However, many lighter stains will disappear with a 50% concentration just as well.

For challenging stains, allow the *Pre-Spot Plus* to soak into the cloth before putting it in the washer. Sometimes it helps to scratch the stain or rub fabric on fabric. If the stain is still visible, repeat the process a time or two. Some find that it is even more effective if you moisten the garment first and then spray *Pre-Spot* on the moistened garment and let it set for a little while before washing.

If you temporarily run out of *Pre-Spot Plus*, use full strength *Tough & Tender* on the fabric stain. After applying with a damp cloth, allow it to remain for a few minutes before rinsing.

If you have tried everything else and simply can't get a stain out of a white fabric, use *Melaleuca's Denti-Clean Extra-Whitening Toothpaste*. It is amazing on everything from polyester to cotton and even some delicate fabrics.

For removing red stains such as catsup, spaghetti sauce or blood, try rubbing the area with *Antibacterial Liquid Soap*. It works wonders!

If you are away from home, *Hot* or *Cool Shot Mouth & Throat Spray* is the best as an instant spot and stain remover. Spray the spot with *Hot* or *Cool Shot* and then rub with a fingernail before rinsing with cold water. It's magic!

LAWN FURNITURE

Mix 1 teaspoon of *Tough & Tender* with 16 ounces of water in a spray bottle. Spray this solution on the furniture and wipe it with a cloth.

LAWN MOWERS

To remove dirt and grease marks from your lawn mower, mix a solution of 1 tablespoon of *MelaMagic* with ½ gallon on water. Spray or wipe the solution on your mower and allow it to sit for a few minutes before rinsing. Repeat if necessary.

LEATHER CLEANER

Rustic Touch cleans vinyl and leather. It is also great for cleaning the dash of your car. **NOTE:** Spray it on a cloth to apply. If you spray it directly on the dash, you will get it on the inside of your windshield.

Rustic Touch is also very effective for waterproofing leather boots.

An alternate choice would be to use a 1:2 solution of *Antibacterial Liquid Soap* and water. It is very effective for removing dirt and scuffmarks from leather.

LEATHER SOFTENER

Try rubbing *Moisturizing Hand Creme* into stiff, old leather. It works like magic.

Make sure you read and understand all product packaging prior to use.

LIPSTICK – CLOTHING

Spray *Pre-Spot Plus* on a lipstick stain and let it set for a few minutes. If this does not work, soak the clothing for a few hours in a 2-gallon bucket of cold water containing 2 tablespoons of *MelaPower Laundry Detergent*. Rinse with cool water. Add 1 to 2 capfuls of *Sol-U-Mel* to your regular wash and launder as usual.

Try using *Sol-U-Mel* as a pre-spot treatment on "dry clean only" fabrics.

MACHINE PARTS

Mix 2 tablespoons of *MelaMagic* and 16 ounces of water in a spray bottle. Spray on the part and let it soak. Wipe it with a damp cloth. If the part is grimy, soak it in the above solution and then scrape off as much of the build up as possible. Remove the remainder with a stiff brush (natural, wire, or brass) that is kept wet with the cleaning solution. For small parts, clean with a rag soaked in either full strength *MelaMagic* or in the above solution.

MAGIC MARKER

Concentrated *Sol-U-Mel* can be used to remove permanent marker stains, but you must be very careful that the surface to be cleaned has been sealed. *Sol-U-Mel* can remove a surface's finish.

MICROWAVE

Mix 5 drops of *Tough & Tender* with 16 ounces of water in a spray bottle. Apply to the microwave and wipe it with a damp cloth.

MIRRORS

Regularly use *Clear Power* to clean your mirrors. If *Clear Power* is unavailable, try adding 2 to 3 drops of *Tough & Tender* to a 16-ounce spray bottle filled with water. Just spray it on and wipe with a soft cloth or cheap paper towels.

MOSQUITO SPRAY

Looking for an excellent mosquito spray that will not harm your family? Try combining 1 teaspoon of *Tough & Tender* with 1 capful of *Sol-U-Mel* and 1 capful of *Renew Bath Oil* in a 16-ounce spray bottle filled with water. This is safe not only for your clothes and the outdoor area in general, but you can spray it directly on your skin.

MOLD AND MILDEW

In some areas of the country mildew and mold are prevalent due to the humid environment. When the mold count is high, spray your home with diluted *Sol-U-Mel*. It can help prevent those "morning headaches."

An alternate solution is to place *T36-C5* in an open container in your bedroom at night. Even a drop or two on your pillow will help.

See the section on *Bathroom – Mold & Mildew* in this book.

NON-MAGNETIC SURFACES

To repel the dust and keep television and computer screens clean and static free, wipe them with a damp cloth and concentrated *Tough & Tender*.

ODORS

Use diluted *Sol-U-Mel* to eliminate odors of all kinds, including pet odors, smoke, and other strong odors. Spray in the air or on surfaces. In the laundry, add 1 to 2 capfuls of undiluted *Sol-U-Mel* to eliminate odors and boost the cleaning strength of *MelaPower*.

OIL – CLOTHING

Spray *PreSpot* on oily spots on your clothing and let it dry before washing. It will even remove motor oil.

OVENS

See Kitchen – Oven and Toster Oven

PAINT

Spray *PreSpot Plus* on paint spots or splatters. Rub with your finger or a soft brush. Let it set for a few minutes and then rinse in warm water. This method works very well for most paint stains, but you must remember that some paints are there to stay.

PAINT – ACRYLIC

Spray acrylic paint spots with *Pre-Spot Plus*. Give the paint time to dissolve and then rub the area with your fingernail or a brush. Rinse with cold water and repeat if necessary.

PAINT – OIL AND WATER BASED

Apply *Pre-Spot Plus* to any paint stain. Wait a few minutes to allow it to soak in before rubbing cloth against cloth. If any paint remains after you rinse the garment, repeat the process before washing with *MelaPower* and *MelaBrite*.

PANELING

Clean old looking paneling by wiping with a cloth dampened with *Tough & Tender*. Wipe on and dry with a clean cloth. Then enhance the look of the wood by wiping with *Rustic Touch*. It has a tremendous renewing ability.

PET ODORS

See Odors

PET STAINS

Sol-U-Mel is great for removing pet stains from the carpet.

Make sure you read and understand all product packaging prior to use.

PIANO KEYS

With a soft cloth dampened with a little *Tough & Tender*, carefully wipe the piano keys and then thoroughly dry.

Amazingly enough, some people will stick tape on their piano keys, or even worse, write the names of the notes on the keys with marker pens. *Sol-U-Mel* seems to be the best cleaner for removing not only the tape and the pen marks, but also for cleaning the age-old dirt off the fronts of the keys. **Be careful, however, with the black keys.** If they are painted wood instead of natural wood or plastic, *Sol-U-Mel* will remove the black paint. Either isolate the white keys while cleaning them, or do a small test on the black keys before applying the *Sol-U-Mel*.

PLANTS

Add 1 tablespoon of *Tough & Tender* to 16 ounces of water in a spray bottle. (Or, you may use *Sol-U-Mel* diluted as directed.) Spray on the roses to kill aphids and other undesirables. *Tough & Tender* can even be effective against webworms and a great deal safer than the normally recommended webworm spray. See the *Healthy Garden* chapter in this book for additional gardening applications for Melaleuca products.

PLASTIC

Use *Rustic Touch* to clean your plastic sunglasses. It is also an excellent way to clean plastic covers.

POTS AND PANS

Use *Tub & Tile* to clean stainless steel pots and pans, especially when they have been boiled dry or have baked-on grime on them. It seems to eat away at the black mess and make it much easier to restore to their original condition.

Tub & Tile is also very effective when cleaning copper pans.

REFRIGERATOR

Mix 5 drops of *Tough & Tender* with ½ capful of *Sol-U-Mel* in a 16-ounce spray bottle of water. Spray the inside and outside of the refrigerator with this solution and dry with a soft cloth.

RUST

To remove rust stains from clothes, soak the area in concentrated *Tub & Tile*. When the rust spots have faded, wash as usual with *MelaPower* and *MelaBrite*.

Rust spots can be removed from a number of other surfaces by using *Tub & Tile* as well. **Just remember not to use it on genuine marble.**

SAW BLADES

To clean resin buildup from saw blades, shaper bits, or router bits, apply *MelaMagic* full strength. Wipe them with a damp cloth. Soaking or scrubbing with a soft bristled brush may be necessary. Dry thoroughly and coat with a thin film of light oil (3-in-1, WD 40, vegetable oil, etc.) to guard against rusting.

SCUFFMARKS
See Floors - Scuffmarks

SHOES
To remove scuffmarks from shoes, spray them with **Rustic Touch**. What a difference it will make in your "professional" shoe-polishing job.

SINKS
See Bathroom - Sink or Kitchen - Sink

SILVER CLEANER
Classic Tooth Polish is excellent silver cleaner. Apply with a soft cloth and then rinse and dry. The shine will last much longer and is considerably safer than toxic silver polishes. (Save your empty tubes and when it is time to polish the silver, slice them open and you will find enough of the **Tooth Polish** residue to do quite a cleaning job. It is very economical, too!)

Diamond Brite can be substituted if **Tooth Polish** is not available.

SOFTENER – CLOTHING
Add 1 or 2 capfuls of **MelaSoft** to the final rinse for an average load of laundry.

An alternate choice would be to put one large or two small capfuls of **MelaSoft** on a soft cloth and toss it in with the wet clothes in the dryer. Every few loads put the cloth in the wash. It will have the same effect on the newly washed clothes and clean the rag at the same time.

SPILLS
To clean up spills, wet a cloth or paper towel with a mixture of 1 teaspoon of **Tough & Tender** combined with 16 ounces of water. Also, spray the stain and begin to blot from the outside edge in. After the stain is removed, rinse and soak up all the moisture from the article. (If you use paper towels, use cheap paper towels. Expensive towels have added softeners and the good Melaleuca products will release these ingredients and sometimes leave streaks.)

Hot or **Cold Shot** will take out spaghetti or coffee stains when you are out to dinner and don't have your **PreSpot** with you. Simply spray the spot and let it dry. Then scratch off the stain.

STARCH, SPRAY
Try **Revive** for a spray starch. It works wonders.

Another solution would be to use diluted **Tough & Tender**. It doesn't make your clothes stiff like starch, but certainly helps with the ironing.

Make sure you read and understand all product packaging prior to use.

STATIC CLING

If you have a garment that tends to have static cling, lightly spray *MelaSoft* to the underside. This will alleviate the static and allow the material to fall naturally.

Revive is also very effective for static cling. Dilute it by 50% and it works just as well.

STOVE

See Kitchen – Stove

TAR

Soak a cloth with *Sol-U-Mel* and wipe the affected area. This should dissolve the tar right away.

When you find tar on your clothes, apply concentrated *Sol-U-Mel* with a toothbrush and you will find that the tar will roll right off.

For tar on your car, try *Pre-Spot Plus*. It is also very effective in taking tar off without hurting the finish on cars.

TICKS

See Wasps, Yellow Jackets, Ants and Ticks

TILE

Mix 5 drops of *Tough & Tender* with 16 ounces of water in a spray bottle. Spray on the tile and dry.

TOASTER OVEN

Use either the *Clear Power* as directed or 5 drops of *Tough & Tender* with 16 ounces of water in a spray bottle. Spray on the toaster oven and dry with a soft cloth.

TOILET

See Bathroom – Toilet

TOYS

Frequently treat washable toys to a good soaking in a sink or tub of water with 1 capful of *Sol-U-Mel* and 1 teaspoon of *Tough & Tender* added. After the toys have soaked, rinse them well and dry carefully.

Toys that cannot be soaked can be sprayed with the same combination of *Sol-U-Mel* and *Tough & Tender* in 16 ounces of water and then dried carefully.

Machine washable stuffed animals, dolls, and blankets should be washed as usual with *MelaPower* (1 pump) and 1 capful of *Sol-U-Mel*.

TREE PITCH

Spray affected areas with *Advanced Expressions Styling Spray* (hair spray). Let it sit for about one minute. Wash the area with *Melaleuca Antibacterial Liquid Soap* and water.

TUBS

See Bathtub

UPHOLSTERY

Always check the manufacturer's cleaning instructions before cleaning upholstery or upholstered furniture.

If you choose to do self-cleaning, try ½ capful of *Sol-U-Mel* and 1 capful of *Tough & Tender* in a 16-ounce spray bottle filled with water. Apply this solution with a soft rag. A soft, but firm, brush may have to be used on the arm areas. Do not soak the fabric, as you do not want to get moisture in the backing or filling. After cleaning, rinse and dry thoroughly as any remaining product could attract dirt.

VEGETABLE WASH

See Fruit and Vegetable Wash

VINYL

See Leather Cleaner

WALLPAPER STRIPPER

Tough & Tender is a very effective wallpaper stripper.

WALLS

For a very effective general cleaning disinfectant, mix 1 teaspoon of *Tough & Tender* in a 16-ounce spray bottle of water or add 1 tablespoon of *Tough & Tender* to a gallon bucket of water. If you need a stronger mixture, add 1 capful of *Sol-U-Mel* to either the spray or the bucket.

WASHER

Before running your first load of wash using *MelaPower Laundry Detergent*, it is best to run the washer empty with ¼ cup of *MelaPower Laundry Detergent* (2 pumps) to clean out the chemical residue. Then run your normal wash load using ⅛ cup of *MelaPower Laundry Detergent* (or 1 pump). To whiten your laundry load, add *MelaBrite* as directed. Add 1 capful of *Sol-U-Mel* to deodorize the clothing.

WASHING, HAND

Adding a few drops of *T36-C5* to your water when you are washing items by hand is an excellent way to disinfect your clothes. It will also kill dust mites, which are known to be responsible for a number of allergic reactions.

WASPS, YELLOW JACKETS, ANTS AND TICKS

Diluted *Tough & Tender* and/or diluted *Tub & Tile* are very effective against wasps, yellow jackets and ants.

When it comes to ticks, it is much more effective to put a drop or two of *T36-C5* directly on the tick and wait a moment for it to back out.

Make sure you read and understand all product packaging prior to use.

If, after a treatment or two, it has not released on its own, gently pull the tick out with tweezers. Do not pull the tick out with your bare hands as Lyme disease and Rocky Mountain Spotted Fever can be the result of handling ticks with your bare hands.

WATER STAINS ON WOOD

Rub *Moisturizing Hand Creme* into the water stain. Let it set for a while, then buff it with a soft cloth.

WINDOWS

Use *Clear Power* on the glass as directed. Clean with cheap paper towels. The Melaleuca products are effective enough to bring out the additives in the more expensive paper towels which can leave streaks. They can also release the ink on the newsprint from the old-time popular newspaper-cleaning trick. Old towels and cloths can leave lint. Cheap paper towels are by far the most effective when cleaning windows.

Also try using *Clear Power* diluted to ½ the strength recommended on the bottle. For most uses this is sufficient and even more economical.

WINDOW SCREENS

Mix 1 tbsp. of *Tough & Tender* with 1 gallon of warm water. Dip the screen into this solution and scrub it clean with a soft brush. Let it air dry.

WINDSHIELD WASH

In the summer, use a combination of diluted *Tough & Tender* and *Clear Power* to replace the windshield wash in your vehicles. (Make sure to use nonfreezing washer fluid in the winter.)

WRINKLES

When schedules have been too busy and you are just too tired to fold those freshly washed clothes, never fear, *Revive* is here! Just spray and shake the clothes and hang them or lay them over a chair until they dry. Not only will the wrinkles come out, but they will smell fresh, too. Some suggest diluting it by half. It seems to work just as well.

WOOD FLOORS

See Floors – Hardwood

WOOD FURNITURE

To clean dirt from wood furniture, mix 1 teaspoon of *Tough & Tender* and 1 gallon of water. Apply this solution with a rag or sponge. Carefully towel dry the furniture. For heavy stains, use 1 tablespoon of *Sol-U-Mel* and 1 gallon of water. Finish cleaning with *Rustic Tough Furniture Care* and a soft rag.

YELLOW JACKETS

See Wasps, Yellow Jackets, Ants, and Ticks

Make sure you read and understand all product packaging prior to use.

CHAPTER FOURTEEN

HEALTHY CATS & DOGS

PRECAUTIONS

If you are like most people, your pets are very special to you. It is important to you to take the best care of them that you can. If you have not already done so, removing all of the grocery store brand cleaning and personal care products from your home is probably the easiest thing you can do to prolong the good health of your pets. Animals are more sensitive to toxic chemical vapors than we are because they are much lower to the ground where the vapors accumulate.

When using Melaleuca, or any other products, be sure to follow the package directions carefully. When using T36-C5 or T40-C3 on your pets, apply a diluted solution to a small area for 48 hours to check for sensitivity. If no reaction occurs, it should be safe. See *Dilution Formulas* below.

Always consult your veterinarian before starting any course of supplementation or treatment for your pet. Every effort has been made to ensure that the information contained in this book is complete and accurate. However, neither the publisher nor the author is engaged in rendering professional advice or services to the individual reader. The ideas, procedures and suggestions contained in this book are not intended as a substitute for consulting with your veterinarian. Neither the author nor the publisher shall be liable for any loss, injury, or damage allegedly arising from any information or suggestion in this book.

GENERAL INFORMATION

The hair and skin of most animals should not be overly washed with harsh detergents or shampoos. Cats and dogs can develop sensitivity and produce dry skin as a result of overwashing. Preventive care during seasonal infestation with fleas, ticks, mites and other insects can be accomplished by proper nutritional support to the animal. Dogs appear to have a particularly high requirement for extra calcium and magnesium. Cats appear to require additional B-complex, often in the form of brewers yeast. Both dogs and cats appear to fare very well when treated with *Sol-U-Mel, Renew Bath Oil,* and *T36-C5*. Optimum nutritional support should be provided based on the individual animal. Your natural veterinarian should be consulted if you are uncertain as to what your pet may need.

RECOMMENDED T36-C5 DILUTION FORMULAS

Large Dog: Mix 10 drops of *T36-C5* in 1 teaspoon of olive, coconut or grapeseed oil. This is a 10% solution. Apply 2-4 times each day.

Medium to Small Dog: Mix 5-10 drops of *T36-C5* to every teaspoon of olive, coconut or grapeseed oil and apply 2-4 times per day.

Cat: Mix 5-10 drops of *T36-C5* in 1 teaspoon of olive, coconut or grapeseed oil and apply 2-4 times each day.

If your pet is light haired (white, gray, etc.) there is an increased risk of reaction when using T36-C5. Keep the dilution percentage to a minimum.

ANIMAL FIRST AID KIT

For outings with animals, always carry *T36-C5, Triple Antibiotic Ointment, Sol-U-Mel, Mela-Gel, Antibacterial Liquid Soap* and *Renew Intensive Skin Therapy*, gauze, tape, tweezers, scissors, and water (in a small container for cleaning). One general rule of thumb: Use *T40-C3* on serious infections and *T36-C5* on less serious conditions.

ANTISEPTIC

T36-C5 is a natural antiseptic for your pet. Bathe wounds, bites, scratches, etc. with a dilution of 2 drops of *T36-C5* mixed with 3 drops of olive, coconut, or grapeseed oil. Add to a small bowl of warm water and apply with cotton wool. Dab it onto the wound 2 times each day to help stop an infection. For larger wounds or wounds that are slow to heal, seek advice from a vet.

As an antiseptic, use a 2% dilution of *T36-C5* and olive, coconut or grapeseed oil for small birds up to hens. A 3% dilution is appropriate for small dogs and cats, while up to a 5% dilution can be used for larger dogs. A 5% dilution is also suggested for horses and cattle.

CAR ACCIDENT

A vet must see car accident victims. Either call a vet to the scene or transport your pet very carefully as soon as possible. Small dogs and cats can be wrapped in a blanket and put into a large box to make traveling easier.

FLEAS

Even if you have never owned a pet, if you have moved into a new home in the last 18 months, it is possible that you have fleas. To rid your home of fleas, mites and dust mites, shampoo carpets, upholstery and soft furnishing with *T36-C5* in the water reservoir. If using an electric shampooer, add *T36-C5* to the washing water (1½ tsp. to 32 oz.).

Skirting boards should be washed with a strong solution. Remember the cracks and crevices. Let water drip into them. Wipe all kitchen cupboards regularly.

Do not forget to treat the car as well.

*See the precautions at the beginning of this chapter.

CATS & DOGS

Also see the section on *Cats* in this chapter.
Also see the section on *Dogs* in this chapter.

CATS & DOGS – ABSCESSES

* Abscesses are painful, pus-filled sacks of infection which can occur in or on any surface of the body. Clean the area with **Antibacterial Liquid Soap** and water. Apply **T36-C5** to the abscess. To encourage drainage and drive the **T36-C5** into the wound, apply hot, moist packs over the area. When draining, keep the area clean and apply **T36-C5**, followed by **Mela-Gel** or **Triple Antibiotic Ointment** 2 to 3 times per day until the redness disappears and the wound is adequately covered with a scab.

Abscesses will usually drain; however, if the area drains but does not heal, it may indicate foreign matter in the wound.

CATS & DOGS – ABSCESSES IN THE MOUTH

See Cats & Dogs - Dental Problems

CATS & DOGS – ALLERGIES, CHRONIC

* Giving a large pet 2 **ProVex-Plus** per day and a small pet 1 **ProVex-Plus** per day will help with their chronic allergies. Give the capsules to your pet wrapped in a piece of cheese or in the center of a piece of hotdog. Or open the capsules and mix them with your pet's food.

CATS & DOGS – ANIMAL BITES

See Antiseptic

CATS & DOGS – ARTHRITIS

* Combine 2-3 drops of **T36-C5** with 1 teaspoon of sweet almond or corn oil and massage the arthritic area. If you follow with a heating pad, be sure that the setting is on low to prevent burning. See also the section on *Dogs – Arthritis* in this chapter.

CATS & DOGS – BATHING

* Try bathing your cat or dog in **Tough & Tender**. It will make their coats shine, and even if they spend a lot of time outdoors, they will not have fleas.

CATS & DOGS – BEDDING

* Wash bedding every 2-4 weeks in **MelaPower Laundry Detergent** and **MelaBrite**. In the winter you may find it very helpful to have two beds for your pet so that you can have one available while the other is being washed. While the bed is being washed, wipe the area where the bed is normally located with a diluted solution of **Tough & Tender**. If you

*See the precautions at the beginning of this chapter.

want to deodorize the area as well or want a little stronger disinfectant, add *Sol-U-Mel* to your cleaning solution.

CATS & DOGS – BLANKETS

* Wash your pet blankets in *MelaPower* and *MelaBrite*. A single teaspoon of *T36-C5* or a capful of *Sol-U-Mel* can be added to boost the cleaning and deodorizing power.

CATS & DOGS – BITES AND CUTS

* Clean well with water and *Antibacterial Liquid Soap.* To prevent infection, apply *Triple Antibiotic Ointment* or *Mela-Gel* 2 to 3 times per day until redness disappears and the wound is adequately covered with a scab. See the *Antiseptic* section in this book.

CATS & DOGS – BRONCHITIS, CHRONIC

* *ProVex-Plus* is excellent for dealing with chronic problems. Give two per day for a large animal and 1 per day for a small animal. *Activate* is a very effective way to boost the immune system for an animal with a chronic infection. Give the capsules to your pet wrapped in a piece of cheese or in the center of a piece of hotdog. Or open the capsules and mix them with your pet's food.

CATS & DOGS – COAT CONDITIONER

* In between bathing your pet, keep its coat healthy and pest free by mixing 1 drop of *T36-C5* in ⅛ cup of oil. Store this mixture in a bottle and sprinkle a few drops all over the coat, especially around the neck area. Comb through the fur.

An alternate choice would be to sprinkle a few drops onto a sponge and rub over the pet's coat. Always avoid the eye area.

CATS & DOGS – DENTAL PROBLEMS

* Combine 1 tablespoon of glycerin and 9-10 drops of *T36-C5* in a spray bottle. Shake well. When the mixture is cloudy the oil is evenly dispersed. If an oily film appears on top, it is not fully dissolved and you may need to add a little more glycerin to the mixture. Add ½ cup of water to this mixture. Shake the bottle vigorously before each use. Spray the mouth several times each day. Once a week, dip a toothbrush into this mixture and brush your pet's teeth. This reduces the amount of bacteria in the mouth and helps to prevent abscesses, foul breath, gum disease and excessive salivation.

An alternate solution is to mix 5 drops of *T36-C5* into ¼ cup of water in a spray bottle and spray the area several times each day.

CATS & DOGS – DERMATITIS

* Skin conditions like rashes, flaky skin, redness or itchiness should be treated to prevent secondary infections and reduce any stinging or

---

*See the precautions at the beginning of this chapter.

itching. You may need to keep the pet in a clean cage or pet carrier to prevent a contagious condition from spreading to others. Cut the hair around the affected area and wash with **Antibacterial Liquid Soap**. Pat the area dry. Apply **Renew Intensive Skin Therapy**, **Triple Antibiotic Ointment**, or **Pain-A-Trate** 2 to 3 times each day until the condition improves. See your natural veterinarian if the problem persists.

CATS & DOGS – EARS

* Dogs and cats are often prone to ear infections, sometimes caused by parasites. When treating the ears, use a dropper and massage the ears after medicating them. Be careful of the animal shaking its head. Do not put the dropper inside the ear. Apply a slightly warmed mixture of the following, twice each day if possible, until alleviated. Swab excess with cotton wool.

Cat/Small Dog: 1 drop of **T36-C5** with 2 teaspoons of olive oil, apply a few drops of this mixture to each ear as directed above.

Med/Lg Dog: Mix 1 drop of **T36-C5** with 1-2 teaspoons of olive oil, apply a few drops of the mixture to each ear.

For ear mites or to clean ears of either cats or dogs, apply 1 or 2 drops of **T36-C5** to a cotton swab and wipe the inside of the ear as needed.

CATS & DOGS – ECZEMA

* For cats and small dogs, apply a mixture of 2 drops of **T36-C5** and 1 tsp. of coconut oil to the infected area twice a day. Dab it on with cotton wool. For larger dogs, apply 2-4 drops of **T36-C5** combined with 1 tsp. of coconut oil to the infected area with cotton wool twice each day.

CATS & DOGS – EPILEPSY

* **ProVex-Plus** has been used to successfully prevent seizures. Give 2 capsules per day, overlapped with the regular seizure medication, for one week. Then try weaning the animal off of the seizure medication gradually. Give the capsules to your pet wrapped in a piece of cheese or in the center of a piece of hotdog. Or open the capsules and mix them with your pet's food.

CATS & DOGS – EXCESSIVE SALIVATION

See Cats & Dogs - Dental Problems

CATS & DOGS – FEEDING BOWLS

* Place 1 drop of **Tough & Tender** in each feeding bowl. Fill it with hot water and clean thoroughly. Rinse well before reusing.

Washing the water bucket with **Sol-U-Guard** once a week will ensure that it does not instantly become green with mold.

Wipe the area around the bowls with ½ teaspoon of **T36-C5** and a cup of hot water blended with a squirt of **Antibacterial Liquid Soap** or **Lemon Brite**. Dry the area with a paper towel.

*See the precautions at the beginning of this chapter.

CATS & DOGS – FLEAS

* For general flea protection, wash all bedding in the washing machine with 1 capful of **Sol-U-Mel** and ⅛ cup of **MelaPower Laundry Detergent** (1 pump). Add 2 ounces of **Sol-U-Mel** to 16 ounces of water and apply to the areas where your cat or dog sleeps or rests during the day and evening. Wash your cat or dog with **Naturals Melaleuca Oil Shampoo** or **Antibacterial Liquid Soap**. If the fleas are severe add a capful of **Sol-U-Mel** to the bath water. It is best to wash your pet outside so the fleas won't jump off in your house.

It is very important that your pets be carefully treated for fleas, as cats and dogs can become infected with tape and/or round worms from fleas.

You might also consider adding garlic and brewers yeast to your pet's diet. Fleas hate the taste.

CATS & DOGS – FOUL BREATH

See Cats & Dogs - Dental Problems

CATS & DOGS – FRACTURES

* Using **ProVex-Plus** at the ratio of 2 per day for a large pet and 1 per day for a small pet, will speed the healing rate of fractures. Give the capsules to your pet wrapped in a piece of cheese or in the center of a piece of hotdog. Or open the capsules and mix them with your pet's food.

CATS & DOGS – FUR CARE

* Comb your pet's fur daily, especially on longhaired breeds. If matted, try wetting the matted hair with a mixture of 1 drop of **T36-C5** and ½ teaspoon of oil. Rub it in and try to ease the matted fur a little at a time from the top of the matt with a comb.

If you do have to cut the patch of fur off, try cutting down vertically instead of horizontally and ease with the comb again. Cutting this way makes less of a bald patch. If the skin is nicked, bathe the wound with an antiseptic to prevent infection. See the *Antiseptic* section in this book.

CATS & DOGS – GUM DISEASE

See Cats & Dogs - Dental Problems

CATS & DOGS – HEART PROBLEMS

* **ProVex-Plus** is excellent for dealing with chronic problems. Give two per day for a large animal and 1 per day for a small animal. **Activate** is a very effective way to boost the immune system for an animal with a chronic infection. Give the capsules to your pet wrapped in a piece of cheese or in the center of a piece of hotdog. Or open the capsules and mix them with your pet's food.

---

*See the precautions at the beginning of this chapter.

CATS & DOGS — HOT SPOTS

  * Hot spots and abrasions on the body respond well to *T36-C5* applied frequently to reduce the pain, prevent infection, and promote healing. *Mela-Gel* can be applied if drying or scaling results.

  Triple Antibiotic Ointment prevents the animals from chewing on the hot spots and making them worse. It is very healing, too.

CATS & DOGS — INFECTIONS OF THE SKIN

  See Abscesses, Eczema, Bathing, Coat Conditioner and Fleas

CATS & DOGS — INSECT BITES AND STINGS

  * Carefully remove the stinger by scraping out with thumbnail or flat card. Be careful not to agitate the sac of poison. Apply *T36-C5* with a cotton swab to soothe the pain and neutralize the venom. If your pet is stung in the mouth apply bicarbonate of soda and ice and consult a vet as soon as possible. If your pet is stung in the mouth by a wasp, dab with vinegar and ice to avert swelling, and consult your vet as soon as possible.

  If your animal shows any signs of abnormal swelling, wheezing, coughing, sneezing, panting or anything that you are worried about, consult your vet immediately. Your pet may be having an allergic reaction to the sting.

  Keep insects off your pet by mixing 15 to 20 drops of *T36-C5* with 1 cup of water OR use diluted *Sol-U-Mel*. Place in a spray bottle and shake well to mix the oil and water before each application. Spray your pet before he/she goes outside.

  See the *Antiseptic* section in this book.

CATS & DOGS — ITCHING

  See Eczema, Bathing, Coat Conditioner and Fleas

CATS & DOGS — JOINT AND MUSCULAR DISORDERS

  * Combine 1 teaspoon of almond or corn oil with 3 drops of *T36-C5* and massage into the affected area. If you choose to cover with a heating pad, use it only on the lowest temperature to prevent burning. Giving a large pet 2 *ProVex-Plus* per day and a small pet 1 *ProVex-Plus* per day may help reduce pain and inflammation and speed healing. Give the capsules to your pet wrapped in a piece of cheese or in the center of a piece of hotdog. Or open the capsules and mix them with your pet's food.

CATS & DOGS — KENNEL COUGH

  * Giving a large pet 2 *ProVex-Plus* per day and a small pet 1 *ProVex-Plus* per day can help kennel cough. Give the capsules to your pet wrapped in a piece of cheese or in the center of a piece of hotdog. Or open the capsules and mix them with your pet's food.

*See the precautions at the beginning of this chapter.

CATS & DOGS –
KIDNEY PROBLEMS, CHRONIC

* **ProVex-Plus** is excellent for dealing with chronic problems. Give two per day for a large animal and 1 per day for a small animal. **Activate** is a very effective way to boost the immune system for an animal with a chronic infection. Give the capsules to your pet wrapped in a piece of cheese or in the center of a piece of hotdog. Or open the capsules and mix them with your pet's food.

CATS & DOGS – LEECHES

* If you live by marshy ground, your dog or cat could pick up a leech. Dab the leech with **T36-C5** until it falls off. Treat the wound as suggested in the *Antiseptic* section of this book.

CATS & DOGS – LICE

* Isolate your pet to keep the lice from spreading. Wash thoroughly with **Antibacterial Liquid Soap**. Mix 15 to 20 drops of **T36-C5** with 1 cup of water. Place in a spray bottle and shake well to mix the oil and water before each application. Spray the pet liberally with this mixture. Brush it in well to soften and dislodge the nits (the eggs of the lice). Let this stand for at least 10 minutes. Pat the animal dry with paper towels and dispose of the towels. Dab pure **T36-C5** with a cotton ball to stubborn areas. Repeat daily until all signs of the lice are gone. Add 2 ounces of **Sol-U-Mel** to 16 ounces of water, and apply to areas where your cat or dog sleeps or rests during the day and evening.

See the sections on *Bedding, Bathing, Coat Conditioner,* and *Kennel Hygiene* in this book.

CATS & DOGS – MOUTH INFECTION

See Abscesses and Insect Bites and Stings

CATS & DOGS – MOUTH ULCER

* A mouth ulcer is caused by a minor viral infection and is usually located on or under the tongue or on the inside of the pet's cheek. Combine 3-12 drops (depending on the size of the animal) of **T36-C5** with 1 cup of water in a spray bottle and shake vigorously. Spray the area as needed until it heals. The oil will not only heal but will help with the pain as well.

CATS & DOGS – NAIL (CLAW) INFECTION

* Apply 10 drops of **T36-C5** blended with 1 teaspoon of oil to any claw/nail that appears to be infected. Treat twice each day for seven days. Try to discourage your pet from licking the area. If the infection persists or gets worse, see your vet.

See the section on *Dogs – Nail (Claw) Care* in this book.

*See the precautions at the beginning of this chapter.

CATS & DOGS – OIL (DIESEL)
See Tar

CATS & DOGS – PARASITES
See Fleas, Ticks, Bathing, Kennel Hygiene (Dogs), and Lice

CATS & DOGS – PAW ABRASIONS

* A dog's and cat's paws can become cracked and infected. Bathe the paws in antiseptic solution (See the *Antiseptic* section in this book.) and apply a few drops of the following mixture: 1-2 drops of *T36-C5* blended with ½ cup of almond oil. Store this mixture in a dark glass bottle and apply it to the paws 2-3 times each day. If your pet will wear little socks, it will assist in the healing and help to keep the area clean.

An alternate solution is to treat paw abrasions with **Mela-Gel** or **Triple Antibiotic Ointment.** Apply twice daily as long as needed.

See the sections on *Nail (Claw) Infections, Nail (Claw) Care* and *Splinters* in this book.

CATS & DOGS – RASHES
See Eczema and Lice

CATS & DOGS – RINGWORM

* Bathe the infected area with **Naturals Melaleuca Oil Shampoo** as often as possible. Clipping the hair away from the affected area makes it easier to treat. Twice daily apply *T36-C5* directly on the lesion for one week or longer. Be patient, ringworm can take a while to heal.

Disinfect the bedding, pet carriers, kennels, scissors, grooming tools and the treatment area, as ringworm is easily transmitted. Add 1 tablespoon of *T36-C5* to 1 quart of water and use as a disinfectant.

CATS & DOGS – SCENT MASKING
See Soiling

CATS & DOGS – SERIOUS INJURIES

* Pets with serious injuries may heal more rapidly when they get the proper nutrition.

Some veterinarians are noticing a dramatic decrease in healing times when dogs are given **ProVex-Plus**. For larger breeds, give two capsules per day. For smaller breeds, give one capsule per day. Give the capsules to your pet wrapped in a piece of cheese or in the center of a piece of hotdog. Or open the capsules and mix them with your pet's food.

CATS & DOGS – SOILING

* To clean an area, mask the smell and so prevent re-soiling, clean the matter from the area, and blot liquids with a paper towel. Wash with a solution of 1½ cups of hot water and a squirt of **Lemon Brite**. For

---

*See the precautions at the beginning of this chapter.

seriously soiled areas, you may need to add 20 to 30 drops of *T36-C5* and/or 1 capful of *Sol-U-Mel* to increase sanitation and deodorizing. Patch test before applying to the area and, if safe, clean and blot dry.

CATS & DOGS – SORE MUSCLES
See Cats & Dogs – Sprains

CATS & DOGS – SPLINTERS
* If your pet picks up a splinter or thorn, remove with a pair of tweezers and apply 1 drop of *T36-C5* twice each day until the area is healed. See the *Antiseptic* section in this book.

CATS & DOGS – SPRAINS
* Add 3 drops of *T36-C5* to 1 teaspoon of sweet almond or corn oil and shake well. Massage the mixture into the sprained area and apply a heating pad. Be very sure that the heating pad is on the lowest temperature to prevent burning.

CATS & DOGS – STAINS
* Mix 2 capfuls of *Sol-U-Mel* in a 16-ounce spray bottle of water. Saturate the stain and then blot it with a white towel until all the residue and odor is gone.

CATS & DOGS – SUNBURN
* Apply *Renew Intensive Skin Therapy* or *Mela-Gel* to the area 2 to 3 times each day. Keep the pet out of the sun as much as possible.

An alternate solution is to apply equal parts of *T36-C5* and vitamin E oil to the sunburned area. Keep it moist. Apply it in the evening and keep your pet out of the sun.

CATS & DOGS – SURGERY
* *Antibacterial Liquid Soap* should be used on any animal that is being prepared for surgery. Follow this by using *T36-C5* just inside the skin before closing, to cut down on infection.

CATS & DOGS – TAR
* If your pet is covered in tar, mix 1 tablespoon of *Tough & Tender*, 1 teaspoon of salt, and 2 drops of *T36-C5* and rub into the tar. Rinse with warm water and shampoo with *Naturals Melaleuca Oil Shampoo*. Repeat the process if necessary. See the section on *Cats & Dogs – Bathing* in this book.

CATS & DOGS – THORNS
See Splinters and Antiseptic

---

*See the precautions at the beginning of this chapter.

CATS & DOGS – TICKS

* To remove embedded ticks, apply a drop of *T36-C5* on the site of the skin puncture. In a few minutes, the tick will usually let go and back out. Reapply if necessary. If it does not release, gently remove with tweezers.

After washing your pet (see the sections on *Bathing* in this book), make a mixture of 10:1 of water and *T36-C5* and put it on your pet's coat. Allow it to dry naturally. This will not only beautify the pet's coat but will help to prevent fleas and ticks. **Make sure that the animal gets no oil on the eyes.**

NOTE: When pulling ticks off your cats and dogs, always have a barrier between your hand and the tick itself. Lyme disease and Rocky Mountain Spotted Fever can be transmitted.

CATS & DOGS – TOYS

* Wash your pet's toys often. Soft toys can be washed in a solution of hot water and *Antibacterial Liquid Soap*. Two or three drops of *T36-C5* could be added if the toys are particularly dirty. Rinse and dry thoroughly.

Wipe plastic and rubber toys with the same solution.

CATS & DOGS – VACCINATIONS

* To prevent infection: For dogs, apply *T36-C5* with a cotton ball to the affected area 2-3 times each day.

For cats and small pets, mix 18 drops of *T36-C5* into 1 teaspoon of sweet almond or corn oil and apply to the affected area 2-3 times each day. Mix well before each use.

CATS & DOGS – WARTS

* Warts are small, usually hard, tumor growths on the skin. A virus causes them. Moisture helps them to live. To soothe the pain of bleeding or itching, apply 1-2 drops of *T36-C5* directly to the warts. Keep the area dry. Watch your pet for adverse reactions. If one occurs stop the treatment immediately. Be patient; it can take weeks for the warts to disappear. Certain types of warts do not respond to Melaleuca oil.

CATS & DOGS – WATER BOWLS

* Add one cup of *G'Day Melaleuca Herbal Tea* to your pet's water bowl each day. They need to detoxify too.

Also see the section on *Cats* in this chapter.
Also see the section on *Dogs* in this chapter.

*See the precautions at the beginning of this chapter.

CATS

See also the section on *Cats & Dogs* in this chapter.

CATS – CHRONIC URINARY PROBLEMS

* *ProVex-Plus* is excellent for dealing with chronic problems. Give two per day for a large animal and 1 per day for a small animal. *Activate* is a very effective way to boost the immune system for an animal with a chronic infection. Give the capsules to your cat wrapped in a piece of cheese or in the center of a piece of hotdog. Or open the capsules and mix them with your cat's food.

CATS – DE-CLAWING

* Rather than suturing or gluing the area where the claw has been removed, simply apply a drop of *T36-C5* and bandage.

CATS – DEWCLAWS

* Damaged dewclaws should be treated as a wound. If your pet is persistently damaging the dewclaws, seek the advice of a vet.
See the *Antiseptic* and *Nail (Claw) Infection* sections in this book.

CATS – DIARRHEA

* Use a combination of *Sol-U-Mel* and *Tough & Tender* to spray on the spots and then wipe with a damp cloth. If you do not already have a spray mixture ready, just pour *Sol-U-Mel* on the spots and then spray with *Tough & Tender*. The cleaning effect will be the same.

CATS – FIGHT SCRATCHES

* Catfight scratches heal nicely with *Mela-Gel* after bathing with *Antibacterial Liquid Soap*. Keep in mind that cat scratches are very serious to humans as many disease-causing germs are found on cat claws. Caution should be taken when cleaning cat litter boxes. For preventing the spread of germs through the skin, use *Clear Defense* to sanitize and kill germs on your hands without the need for soap and water.

CATS – FLEAS

* Put some *T36-C5* on your cat if it begins to scratch for fleas. It will instantly quiet the cat, and the licking of its itching and sore places will spread the oil all over its body. Not only will this heal the sore, stop the scratching, and kill the fleas, but also it will give your cat the most beautiful coat you have ever seen. A bonus — the fleas will disappear from the house, too.

CATS – LITTER TRAY

* Apply 1-2 drops of *T36-C5* diluted with oil into corners of the cat litter tray to deodorize. Apply only a small amount at first for your cat to get accustomed to it.

When changing the litter box, it is often advisable to put an opened supermarket carrier bag, as a liner, onto the base of the tray. Tuck the edges under the tray (or a couple of pages from a newspaper folded to fit) and fill with cat litter. This can then be scooped up and disposed of when the litter is very soiled. Wipe out the litter tray with a piece of dampened paper towel soaked in a solution of ¼ cup of hot water, **Antibacterial Liquid Soap** and 20 drops of **T36-C5** before putting the liner down.

CATS – RINGWORM

* Ringworm usually appears as a ring-shaped sore. It is caused by a fungus and is contagious, so keep the pet isolated until the treatment is successful. Cut hair away from the affected area and wash thoroughly with **Antibacterial Liquid Soap**. Apply **T36-C5** directly to the area with a cotton ball 2 or 3 times a day. Be aware of any signs of sensitivity. Some breeds react to the pure oil, in which case applying **Dermatin**, **Mela-Gel** or **Triple Antibiotic Ointment** is effective. It may take a week or more to clear up this condition.

CATS – SPRAYING

* Spraying is a natural habit for tomcats. They are marking their territory. Neutering the cat usually stops this annoying habit, but when a cat feels insecure by the addition of another pet, even another family member, changing houses, etc., your tomcat could revert to his old ways again.

Make your cat as secure as you can with lots of reassurance. Mask the area he sprays with a solution of 1 cup of hot water combined with a squirt of **Antibacterial Liquid Soap** and 20+ drops of **T36-C5**.

If all else fails and your tomcat is still spraying inside the home, purchase a plastic spray bottle from a garden center. Fill the bottle with warm water and 1 drop of **T36-C5**, and blend well. When (and only when) you actually catch him spraying inside the house, give him 2-3 short bursts of water to his tail (always avoid spraying head and eyes) and put him outside. Within a few days he should get the message and stop spraying indoors.

To clean those sprayed spots, pour **Sol-U-Mel** on them and then spray with **Tough & Tender**. Wipe the area with a damp cloth. (The two products can also be used blended together into a spray.)

CATS – VOMIT

* **PreSpot Plus** seems to be the chosen product to clean "kitty puke" from carpets.

Also see the section on *Cats & Dogs* in this chapter.
Also see the section on *Dogs* in this chapter.

*See the precautions at the beginning of this chapter.

DOGS

See also the section on *Cats & Dogs* in this chapter.

DOGS – ABSCESSES

* Pets often get into fights. It is a natural territorial trait. When the skin is punctured by a tooth or claw, infection can set in and an abscess is most likely the result. At the first sign of a puncture wound or abscess, dab with an appropriate solution of *T36-C5* (see *Dilution Instructions* in this book) and try to keep the pet from licking the area treated for at least 30 minutes after application. When the abscess bursts, allow it to drain and keep applying *T36-C5* for 7 days.

If the abscess is large, if it is situated in the mouth, shows no sign of improvement or the animal is in obvious distress, consult a vet as soon as possible. If the abscess appears to be hard or becomes hard, consult a vet; it may not be an abscess.

DOGS – ALLERGIES

* Just as in humans, allergies in dogs may be treated with *ProVex* or *ProVex-Plus*. For larger breeds, give two capsules per day for the first month and then reduce to one capsule per day. Give smaller breeds one capsule per day and then reduce to one capsule every other day after the first month. Give the capsules to your dog wrapped in a piece of cheese or in the center of a piece of hotdog.

An alternate choice for allergies or coughs would be to apply 1 or 2 drops of *T36-C5* on a cotton swab and wipe the inside of the nostrils as needed.

DOGS – ARTHRITIS

* Painful inflammation of the joints usually causes a dog to limp. Some veterinarians are having excellent results using *ProVex-Plus* for arthritis in dogs. For large breeds, give two capsules per day for the first month and then reduce to one capsule per day. Give smaller breeds one capsule per day and then reduce to one capsule every other day after the first month. One veterinarian claims to have successfully treated 15 to 20 dogs with either hip dysplasia, or some other serious form of arthritis, using this treatment. Give the capsules to your dog wrapped in a piece of cheese or in the center of a piece of hotdog.

It has also been suggested that dogs with arthritis be given one *Replenex* each day. *ProVex* works in connective tissues and *Replenex* works in the joint. Both are great for arthritis.

DOGS – BATHING

* Bathe your dogs monthly to avoid infestation by fleas. *Naturals Melaleuca Oil Shampoo* does a wonderful job on a dog's coat. Not only will the dog's coat be very shiny, but it will also help to repel fleas. Five drops of *T36-C5* can be added to the warm bath if you feel that you need

*See the precautions at the beginning of this chapter.

a stronger solution. Lather your pet, and allow the shampoo to stay on the coat for 5 minutes before rinsing.

Sol-U-Mel is a great dip after shampooing your dog. It will also deodorize the pet.

An alternate solution is to bathe your dogs in **Antibacterial Liquid Soap**. It is very effective, especially if they have been itching.

Tough & Tender does the very same thing for your pet as pet shampoo except with **Tough & Tender** you have the benefit of **T36-C5**, which will kill fleas and heal sores.

DOGS – CUTS AND SCRATCHES

* *Sol-U-Mel* is excellent for cleaning cuts on your dog. Just sponge it on the open wound to clean it.

DOGS – DEODORANT

See Bathing and Soiling

DOGS – DRY SKIN

* Dry skin is usually a sign of either improper nutrition or the use of harsh chemicals in certain shampoos being applied. See the *Dogs – Bathing* section in this book.

For shorthaired dogs, **Renew Intensive Skin Therapy** can be used to relieve itchy, dry skin. If the itchy skin continues, consult your vet to select the proper diet for your dog.

DOGS – FLEAS

* Use your fingertip to place **T36-C5** behind the ears of your dog, under the chin and at the base of the tail. It is very effective at preventing fleas.

To repel fleas and ticks for your dogs, combine 2 tablespoons of *Sol-U-Mel*, 2 tablespoons of **Tough & Tender** and 4 drops of **T36-C5** in 16 ounces of water in a spray bottle. Shake well and spray on the dog's coat.

An alternate solution would be to make a mixture of ⅓ **Naturals Melaleuca Oil Shampoo**, ⅓ **Sol-U-Mel** and ⅓ water. This thins out the shampoo, enabling you to get it on the whole dog evenly. It will kill every flea on the dog. (Do not get it in the dog's eyes.)

Spraying *Sol-U-Mel* in the yard is an excellent way to kill bugs, fleas and ticks.

If you have fleas in your carpet, add ½ teaspoon of **MelaPower** and 2 capfuls of *Sol-U-Mel* to the carpet shampooer when you fill it with water. Shampoo all the carpet and upholstery. This will deodorize at the same time that it kills your fleas.

DOGS – HIP DYSPLASIA

* Hip dysplasia is usually caused by congenital arthritis in the hip joint. Two **ProVex-Plus** taken daily for one month by a large dog seems

*See the precautions at the beginning of this chapter.

to help. At the end of the first month, cut the dose to one per day. Continue this dose, as it is a natural anti-inflammatory. The severity of the condition will help determine the amount to use.

For a small dog, start with one per day for the first month and then one every other day after that. Give the capsules to your dog wrapped in a piece of cheese or in the center of a piece of hotdog.

DOGS – HOT SPOTS

* When *T36-C5* is applied frequently, "hot spots" and body abrasions should respond well. *T36-C5* will reduce pain and prevent infection while promoting healing. Use *Mela-Gel* if drying or scaling results.

Triple Antibiotic Ointment prevents the dog from chewing on the hot spots and making them worse. It is also very healing.

DOGS – ITCHING

* Make a container of towelettes by soaking paper towels in *Nature's Cleanse*. Use them when your dog seems to be scratching in one spot or shows signs of developing a sore. It tames the itch and keeps the pet smelling clean as well.

DOGS – KENNEL HYGIENE

* If you have to keep your dog in a kennel, wash it down every few weeks during late spring and summer. (Be sure it is not damp during the winter.) Use a squirt of *Antibacterial Liquid Soap* or *Lemon Brite* with 32 ounces of hot water and 1½ teaspoons of *T36-C5*.

DOGS – LICE

* *Naturals Melaleuca Oil Shampoo* is very effective for getting rid of lice. It will also condition the dog's hair coats and makes hair mats easily removable. It is anti-static, which means dust does not collect as readily, and it will prevent any skin fungus.

DOGS – MANGE

* Isolate your dog to keep the condition from spreading to other animals. Wash the dog thoroughly with *Antibacterial Liquid Soap*. Mix 15 to 20 drops of *T36-C5* with 1 cup of water. Place this mixture in a spray bottle and shake it well to mix the oil and water before each application. Spray the dog liberally with this mixture. Brush it in well. Let it stand for at least 10 minutes. Pat the dog dry with paper towels and dispose of the towels. Dab pure *T36-C5* with a cotton ball on stubborn areas. Repeat daily until the condition subsides. Add 1 ounce of *Sol-U-Mel* to 16 ounces of water, and apply to the areas where your dog sleeps or rests during the day and evening.

In addition, remember that proper nutrition is essential. See the section on *Eczema* in this book.

*See the precautions at the beginning of this chapter.

DOGS – NAIL (CLAW) CARE

* Cutting dogs' claws/nails usually needs to be done by a professional with a special claw/nail clipper.

Before your appointment, soak the claws in a mixture of 5 drops of *T36-C5* and 2 teaspoons of oil. Do this for two days before and two days after they have been clipped to help prevent splitting and infection.

DOGS – PAW ABRASIONS

* *Mela-Gel* or *Renew Intensive Skin Therapy* can be used to treat paw abrasions. Since dogs do not like the smell or the taste of Melaleuca oil, they are unlikely to lick it. Applications should be repeated several times each day as needed.

DOGS – SKUNK ODORS

* When your dog has a run in with the wrong kind of animal, run a large outdoor tub full of water and wash him/her with *Antibacterial Liquid Soap*. Repeat if necessary. (The next bath will probably need to be yours!)

It has also been suggested that your dog be immediately washed in *Naturals Melaleuca Oil Shampoo*. It works very well on skunk odor.

NOTE: If a skunk has sprayed your pet, act immediately to eliminate the odor. The longer it stays on the pet, the more difficult it is to remove. Immediately rinse the pet with cool water. (Warm water only amplifies the odor.) Then wash and rinse as suggested above.

DOGS – TICKS

* When you find a tick on your dog, apply *T36-C5* directly on the tick and it will let go within a few minutes. This prevents pulling ticks off and leaving an infected area. See the *Dogs – Fleas* section in this book.

A formula for tick spray would be to combine 2 tablespoons of *Sol-U-Mel*, 2 tablespoons of *Tough & Tender* and 4 drops of *T36-C5* in a 16-ounce spray bottle and fill with water. Be sure to brush the coat backwards as you spray to keep off fleas and ticks. Spray every 7 to 10 days depending on the severity of the tick season. (You can also use this for nature-loving, woods-roaming kids, but you should probably spray them more often than every 7 to 10 days!)

DOGS – WORMER

* Show dogs tend to have stomach problems as a result of using too much worm medicine. Try saving the used *G'Day Melaleuca Herbal Tea* bags, and mix one in with your dog's food.

*See the precautions at the beginning of this chapter.

CHAPTER FIFTEEN
HEALTHY HORSES

PRECAUTIONS

Always consult your veterinarian before starting any course of supplementation or treatment for your animal. Every effort has been made to ensure that the information contained in this book is complete and accurate. However, neither the publisher nor the author is engaged in rendering professional advice or services to the individual reader. The ideas, procedures and suggestions contained in this book are not intended as a substitute for consulting with your veterinarian. Neither the author nor the publisher shall be liable for any loss, injury, or damage allegedly arising from any information or suggestion in this book.

HORSE LOVERS – PLEASE READ!

We sincerely hope you'll find the tips in this section helpful with your horse(s). If you should find an application for Melaleuca products that works well for you that is not already in this book, please tell us about it. If we publish your suggestion, we'll send you a free copy of the book it's published in. Send your suggestion to the address in the front of this book, or by email to uses@rmbarry.com.

We would also be very interested to know how these suggestions work for you. We greatly appreciate your input.

Many thanks to all the horse owners, farmers, ranchers, and veterinarians who contributed to this chapter. You epitomize the spirit of "enhancing lives." We sincerely hope and expect your contributions will help horse lovers all over North America, Australia, and eventually, the world.

HORSES – ABSCESSES

* For a hoof abscess, wash thoroughly with *Antibacterial Liquid Soap* and then soak the area with *T36-C5*. Wrap the hoof after treating it so that it will remain as clean as possible. Repeat this process three times each day even after the abscess has drained, for a full ten days. If the condition does not improve within twenty-four hours, contact your vet.

An alternate solution would be to put a capful of *Sol-U-Mel* in about a quart of warm water and soak the abscessed foot.

HORSES – ALL PURPOSE SPRAY MIXTURE

* Combine 16 ounces of *Sol-U-Mel* and 4 ounces of *Tough & Tender* in a 1-gallon bucket of water. (Use distilled water if possible.) Blend thoroughly and use this as a spray for challenging areas.

HORSES – ARTHRITIS

* *Replenex* is very effective for arthritic conditions in horses as well as other animals. Check with your veterinarian for the proper dosage.

HORSES – BARBED WIRE CUTS

* Combine 2 ounces of *Sol-U-Mel* with 1½ teaspoons of *Tough & Tender* and 10 drops of *T36-C5* in a 16-ounce spray bottle with water. Treat the cut with this mixture twice each day. It is amazing how little scarring there will be.

HORSES – BATHING

See Horses – Washing

HORSES – CLEANING

* Clean buckets and water troughs used for your horses with *Sol-U-Guard*. *Tough & Tender* can also be used for cleaning the containers for your horse's water. After cleaning, a few capfuls of *Sol-U-Mel* can be added to the water trough when you fill it to kill the bacteria.

Clean bits and leather with *Tough & Tender*, and shine the bits with *Tub & Tile.*

Wash the saddle pads with *MelaPower* after each use. Don't use *MelaSoft*, as it is better that the pads remain absorbent. The winter blankets can also be washed in *MelaPower*.

Use *Moisturizing Hand Creme*, with approximately 5 drops of *T36-C5* added to it, to soften any leather and make it pliable again. Use it on leather riding gloves (when you are finished using them, leave them on your hands and put this mixture on just like you would put it on your hands). They will stay soft and last much longer. It is also very effective on dry bridles.

Another suggestion is to condition the leather with *Rustic Touch* after it has been cleaned with *Tough & Tender* or *Antibacterial Liquid Soap*. (It can also be used to condition vinyl—like the interior of your old truck!)

Moisturizing Hand Creme can be used instead of *Rustic Touch* to condition leather after cleaning and your hands will love it, too!

Tough & Tender can be used to clean tack, and it can be used in a power sprayer to clean the barn or house. Some spray it on the walls to repel flies. It is perfect to wash the horse trailer that has sat around all winter and has mildew.

See also *Horses – Washing* in this book.

---

*See the precautions at the beginning of this chapter.

HORSES – CUTS, SCRAPES AND BURNS

* On any cut, scrape or burn use the *Horses - All Purpose Spray Mixture* on the injured area twice a day until it is healed. Cuts, scrapes, and burns can be serious if left untreated. *T36-C5* is very effective when used on almost any injury as is the *Mela-Gel* and the *Triple Antibiotic Ointment.*

A quick way to clean an open wound is to sponge on *Sol-U-Mel*. It is a very effective cleanser.

Mela-Gel is also very effective for cuts on horses. *Antibacterial Foot Spray* can also be used to spray on small wounds.

HORSES – CROSS-FIRING WOUNDS

See Horses - Over Reaching

HORSES – DERMATITIS

* Dermatitis is usually seen on horses that have not received proper care. Place your horse in a dry, clean, isolated, area or stall and bath thoroughly. (See the section on *Horses - Washing* in this book.) Apply *Renew Intensive Skin Therapy*, or *Triple Antibiotic Ointment* 2-3 times each day until the condition improves. *T36-C5* can also be applied to certain conditions with a cotton ball.

Provide your horse with plenty of fresh, clean water and proper food and contact your vet if the condition does not improve in a reasonable amount of time.

HORSES – DRY CRACKED HOOVES

* A mixture of 1 ounce of *Sol-U-Mel* blended into 32 ounces of water in spray bottle is a very effective spray for dry hooves. Spray the hoof walls and soles.

HORSES – EARS

* Horses are often prone to ear infections, sometimes caused by parasites. When applying to the ears, use a dropper and massage it in. Be careful of the animal shaking its head. Do not put the dropper inside the ear. Combine 1 drop of *T36-C5* and 1 teaspoon of olive oil and apply a few drops to each ear. Wipe away the excess. Repeat twice each day if possible until alleviated. If the infection persists, see a vet.

HORSES – FLY CONTROL IN STALL AREAS

* For fly control in the stall areas, spray the area liberally with a 16-ounce spray bottle of water mixed with 1 teaspoon of *Tough & Tender* and 2 ounces of *Sol-U-Mel*. Carefully protect the horse's eyes and face from any type of spray. Apply liberally early in the day. This solution may be sprayed on the horse's body to repel flies.

It has also been suggested to try blending 2 tablespoons of *Tough & Tender* with 2 capfuls of *Renew Bath Oil*, ½ capful of *Sol-U-Mel*, and 5-10 drops of **T36-C5** in 32 ounces of water in a spray bottle. This is a strong mixture for the worst part of fly season and in the fall as the bug population decreases, the **Sol-U-Mel** and **T36-C5** can be decreased. This works on face flies, both flies and horse flies, as well as black houseflies.

Some mix ¼ cup of **Tough & Tender** with 2 oz. of **Sol-U-Mel**, and 2 oz. of **Renew Bath Oil** in a gallon of water. This spray is more effective the more you use it. It seems that the oil accumulates over time so you need to have some patience in the spring. You have to start off spraying more often. This mixture can also be used to repel bugs on you.

Combining **Moisturizing Hand Creme** with 5 drops of **T36-C5** makes a very effective mixture for preventing small black flies on horses' ears and muzzles. (It is great for your arms, face and neck as well.)

It has also been suggested to mix a little of the **Melaleuca Sun-Shades** into the fly spray mixture. Some think that it works even better that way. The **Sun-Shades** have also been used directly on the horse's face to keep the flies and mosquitoes off of them.

HORSES – FLY BITES

* Apply **T36-C5** directly to the area of the bite. Repeat application every two hours until swelling and itching disappear. Cover the oil with **Mela-Gel**, **Triple Antibiotic Ointment** or any type of moisturizer to prevent dryness.

Antibacterial Foot Spray can be very helpful to stop itching from bites.

HORSES – FOOT ROT

* Spray the hoof(s) twice each day with the *Horses - All Purpose Spray Mixture*. If the feet are severely affected, clean and trim the hoof(s).

HORSES – FUNGUS

* Horses with white feet will get dew poisoning or a fungus on their white feet or on their noses at certain times of the year. Dry the horse's legs when they come in and apply **Dermatin** or **Triple Antibiotic Ointment** or **Mela-Gel**.

HORSES – GALLS

See Horses - Saddle Sores

HORSES – GIRTH ITCH

* Fill a 16-ounce spray bottle with water and 2 teaspoons of **Nature's Cleanse**. **Spray** this on areas that are affected by girth itch and other fungicidal or pesticidal skin irritations. No rinsing is necessary. Two applications will usually completely clear up serious problems.

Antibacterial Foot Spray can be very helpful to stop itching from fungal conditions.

*See the precautions at the beginning of this chapter.

HORSES – GNATS

* *Triple Antibiotic Ointment* used on the horse's ears will keep the gnats away for a day or so. *Mela-Gel* used the same way will keep them away for 3 or 4 days. Also, it will heal any bites in the ears. Put a dollop on the end of your thumb and run it up the inside of the ear and on the underside in the tender area where the gnats bite.

HORSES – GREASY HEEL

* Clean the affected area with *Antibacterial Liquid Soap* and warm water. Spray twice a day with a mixture of ¼ teaspoon of *T36-C5* and ½ cup of water. If the area cracks, apply *Mela-Gel* or *Triple Antibiotic Ointment*. If the area oozes, keep it as dry as possible by treating it only with the oil mixture. After it dries, dust the area with pure cornstarch. This is a very sensitive area and if you encounter challenges with the treatment, try spraying the mixture on the horse's leg or soaking it in a bucket. Covering it with a cotton sock can help, too. Be sure to change it twice a day.

HORSES – GROIN INJURY

* Horses can easily get injured on fences, especially if they get spooked. Generally an injury will have to be sutured and the recommended treatment is to inject the area with betadine solution three times a day for perhaps months. Try using *Sol-U-Mel* in water in place of the betadine. You will be amazed how quickly the area will heal.

HORSES – HOOF ROT

* Mix 8 ounces of **Sol-U-Mel**, 1½ teaspoons of *Tough & Tender* and 1½ quarts of water. Clean the foot with the solution and then wrap it with gauze soaked in the solution. Remove the bandage after four days and if the foot still needs treatment, start spraying the solution on the unwrapped foot two times each day until the foot is healed.

HORSES – INSECTS

* Mix ⅓ of the small bottle of *T36-C5* with 32 ounces of water in a spray bottle. It is a very effective insect repellent and costs approximately $2 per bottle as opposed to $7-$10 for insect spray from the discount tack stores. (Shake before applying.)

Triple Antibiotic Ointment, *Mela-Gel* and *T36-C5* should be used for tick bites and other insect bites.

Horses have been known to be allergic to mosquito saliva. In such cases, giving the horse a saturation dose of *ProVex* and then cutting back until the maintenance dose is determined, has been very effective. Even more economical is to give the horse *ProVexCV* to manage the condition.

*See the precautions at the beginning of this chapter.

HORSES – LEG MANGE

* This condition can be contagious and therefore the horse should be isolated and all space and equipment should be disinfected after the condition is cleared up. This includes destroying or burning any straw or shavings that have been in contact with the infected horse. See the section on *Horses – Cleaning* in this book.

Clean the area thoroughly with *Antibacterial Liquid Soap* and warm water. Then saturate a cotton ball with *T36-C5* and treat the affected area. Repeat twice a day until the condition clears. Gloves should be worn for protection.

An alternate treatment is to soak a leg wrap in *T36-C5* and wrap the leg. Change the bandage 1-2 times each day.

Leg mange can also be treated by spraying the affected area with 1 tablespoon of *T36-C5* mixed with ½ cup of water. Spray the affected area and the surrounding area to prevent spreading of the mange.

HORSES – LICE

* Use *Naturals Melaleuca Oil Shampoo* to get rid of lice and discourage ticks. It also softens mane and tail hair, encourages growth and prevents tangles. It is anti-static, which means dust does not collect as readily. In addition, it helps prevent any skin fungus.

HORSES – MANGE

* The horse should be isolated in a clean, dry stall and the affected areas should be washed thoroughly with *Antibacterial Liquid Soap* and warm water. Apply *T36-C5* with a cotton ball and allowed to dry. Treat your horse twice a day with 7-10 days or until signs of the mites are gone. To prevent recontamination, disinfect the stall as well as all brushes, tools and other equipment that were used while caring for the horse. (See the section on *Horses – Cleaning* in this book.)

HORSES – MUSCLE SORENESS

* Dr. Wang said that if a horse will eat the *Access Bar* (broken up into small pieces) that it would not hurt them and could help prevent lactic acid build up in their muscles just like it does for us. They would probably need a couple of bars at a time.

HORSES – NAIL PUNCTURE WOUNDS

WARNING: If the nail is still in the horse's foot, do not remove it until a veterinarian has decided whether or not to x-ray.

* The position of the nail near the bone must be determined to predict the outcome of this injury. Horses have very poor circulation in the frog of their feet. Sometimes surgery may be needed. Otherwise, begin soaking the foot in a mixture of 2 capfuls of *Sol-U-Mel* and 1 capful of *Antibacterial Liquid Soap* in 2 quarts of warm water for 30 minutes morning and evening. After soaking, apply *T36-C5*, then *Mela-Gel* and

*See the precautions at the beginning of this chapter.

cover the area with gauze. Repeat for 3 weeks even if the horse walks without a limp before that time.

HORSES – NEWBORN FOAL

* The umbilical cord of newborn animals must be treated shortly after the animal's birth to prevent infection. Treat the umbilical cord with **T36-C5** and it will dry up in a few days with no signs of infection. The ability of the Melaleuca oil to penetrate and kill harmful bacteria without irritating sensitive tissues is ideal for this purpose.

HORSES – ODOR CONTROL

* Blending 1 ounce of **Sol-U-Mel** into a 32-ounce spray bottle of water is a very effective mixture for stall odor control. Spray on any wet urine spots in the stall and it will immediately take the odor away.

HORSES – OVER REACHING

* These wounds can be very painful and tend to be very sensitive. You may want to spray the wound first with a mixture of **T36-C5** and water to take out the initial pain before cleaning. Wait a few moments and then clean the wound thoroughly with Antibacterial Liquid Soap and warm water. Treat again with **T36-C5**, **Mela-Gel** or **Triple Antibiotic Ointment.** Put a cotton sock over the foot and secure. This will allow the area to breathe while protecting it. Repeat the treatment daily until the foot heals.

HORSES – PRESSURE SORES

See Horses - Saddle Sores

HORSES – QUITTOR

* Clean the hoof wall thoroughly with **Antibacterial Liquid Soap** and warm water, allow to dry. Apply **Mela-Gel** or **Triple Antibiotic Ointment**. This is a very sensitive situation and straight **T36-C5** is not recommended, although some prefer to spray the area with a mixture of ¼ teaspoon of **T36-C5** and ½ cup of water. A vet should see serious or neglected conditions.

HORSES – RINGWORM

* Spray the affected area with the *Horses - All Purpose Spray Mixture* as needed to heal.

It has also been suggested that **T36-C5** is good for treating small areas of ringworm or any fungal challenges.

Your horse should be isolated, as ringworm is a very contagious fungus. This condition can be challenging to heal so don't give up. After the horse is clean of any signs of ringworm, disinfect the stall, halter, buckets and any grooming tools that were used during treatment. (See the section on *Horses - Cleaning* in this book)

*See the precautions at the beginning of this chapter.

HORSES – SADDLE SORES

* These types of sores are usually caused by ill-fitted equipment or by abuse. Combine 15-20 drops of *T36-C5* with ¼ cup of water and dab on the area with a cotton ball. *Renew Intensive Skin Therapy*, *Mela-Gel* or *Triple Antibiotic Ointment* can also be used to help heal these sores. Allow the sores to heal and correct the cause to prevent scarring.

HORSES – SARCOID WART

* A type of wart called a sarcoid sometimes appears on young colts. It apparently is pretty common in colts and many times they will outgrow them. The common suggestion is to use iodine on them. Try *T36-C5* instead, and see how quickly they will heal and not return.

HORSES – SHEATH CLEANING

* *Antibacterial Liquid Soap* is great for sheath cleaning. It melts the smegma, as it is a natural solvent and very gentle. It is also good for washing manes and tails to stop itching.

An alternate choice is to combine ¼ teaspoon *T36-C5* with 1 cup of sunflower seed oil and use in a squirt bottle.

HORSES – SORES ON MOUTH CORNERS

* Apply *T36-C5* to the sore areas followed by *Renew Intensive Skin Therapy*.

HORSES – SUMMER SORES

See Horses - Fly Bites

HORSES – SUNBURNED NOSES

* If your horse has white markings on their faces, the pink skin at the bottom of their face and on their nose and lips doesn't grow hair in the summer and can be extremely sensitive to sunburn. Rub the *Sun-Shades* 15 or 30 on their faces each morning to prevent sunburn. It is also good for healing sunburn.

Using *Sun-Shades* on darker horses such as black or liver chestnuts, will keep them from fading in the summer. It will also keep the flies off and can even be mixed into a fly spray mixture. (See the on *Horses - Fly Control in Stall Areas* section in this book.)

HORSES – SWEET ITCH

* For large areas, make up a large (150 ml) dark glass labeled bottle of 1-2 teaspoons of *T36-C5* and approximately ½ cup of coconut oil. Apply to the infected area with cotton wool. Try a 5% dilution initially. If there is not improvement in the itching try up to 10%, if there is no adverse reaction. If the condition persists, see your vet if you haven't already.

HORSES – TICKS

* To remove ticks, place several drops of *T36-C5* onto each tick and wait a moment or two. The tick will usually begin to back out and can be encouraged by gently pulling with a pair of tweezers. **NOTE: Be sure to cover your hands when handling the tick as Lyme disease and Rocky Mountain tick fever can be contracted from such handlings.**

HORSES – THRUSH

* Two teaspoons of *Nature's Cleanse* combined with 16 ounces of water is a very effective treatment for minor thrush. In more severe cases, increase the *Nature's Cleanse* to 3 teaspoons with the 16 ounces of water. In 48 hours there should be no sign of thrush. To prevent the return of dry hoof walls and heels, spray with this mixture when the hoof is trimmed or cleaned. This will instantly deodorize the smell of thrush.

Others use 1 tablespoon of *Nature's Cleanse* and 1 tablespoon of *Renew Bath Oil* in one pint of water. Spray on the hoof walls and sole. Minor thrush and dry hoof walls and heels will usually be cured in a single application.

Try blending 2 tablespoons of *Tough & Tender*, 2 capfuls of *Renew Bath Oil*, ½ capful of *Sol-U-Mel* and 5-10 drops of *T36-C5* in 32 ounces of water in a spray bottle and spraying on the hoof sole and around the frog to kill thrush.

An alternate solution would be to blend 1 ounce of *Sol-U-Mel* in 32 ounces of water in a spray bottle and spray on the entire hoof to treat thrush.

It has also been suggested that 4 ounces of *Sol-U-Mel*, 1½ teaspoons of *Tough & Tender*, 10 drops of *T36-C5* mixed together in a 16-ounce spray bottle with water, works very well for thrush. Spray generously 2-3 times each day and leave the area open to the air.

Some horseshoers say that *Antibacterial Foot Spray* is the best product ever to clear up thrush and other foot problems.

To prevent the thrush condition that occurs on the bottom of the horse's feet, have the shoer put *Sol-U-Guard* on when he take off the old shoes.

HORSES – TIMBER WOLF ATTACKS

* Combine 4 ounces of *Sol-U-Mel*, 1½ teaspoons of *Tough & Tender*, 10 drops of *T36-C5* with water in a 16-ounce spray bottle. Spray the injured area generously 2-3 times each day. Leave the wound open to the air. (One rancher saved a horse that had been treated for four months with Combiotic and the vet had recommended that it be put down. The horse not only recovered when treated with this combination, but later had a foal.)

---

*See the precautions at the beginning of this chapter.

HORSES – TRIMMING

* If the farrier trims your horse too short, it can become lame. Put 8-10 drops of *T36-C5* in a dish and mix with enough *Mela-Gel* to be able to apply to all four feet. Put this mixture on the sole and hoof wall of each foot with a toothbrush. You should notice a difference within ½ hour. Continue this treatment morning and night for about a week and a half. The mixture takes away a lot of the pain and promotes healing.

HORSES – WARTS

* Although most warts clear up on their own, some do bleed. Putting *T36-C5* on the wart will not only aid in the healing, but will help with the discomfort as well. This may need to be applied for several weeks. If the wart is bleeding, coating it with *Mela-Gel* or *Triple Antibiotic Ointment* will help.

See the section on *Horses – Sarcoid Wart* in this book.

HORSES – WASHING

* Use *Naturals Herbal Shampoo* to wash your horse's coat. The Herbal Shampoo has a conditioner in it so it will make it easy to get tangles out of the mane and tail. It will also decrease flaking and dry skin. This can be followed with a rinse of *Sol-U-Mel* and *Renew Bath Oil* to keep the coat healthy and shiny. This is also good for cleaning gummy spots on the legs.

An alternate choice would be to bathe the horse in *Tough & Tender*.

Koala Pals Conditioning Shampoo can be used on the face, as it is gentle and won't burn their eyes.

A mixture of *Tough & Tender* and *Sol-U-Mel* with water in a spray bottle is an excellent spray on the oily dirty dock of a tail that hasn't been washed in a while. Just spray on liberally and rub in. Wait a few minutes and then wash the tail with *Naturals Herbal Shampoo*. It cuts right through the dirt and you won't have to work so hard to get it clean and shiny.

Antibacterial Liquid Soap can also be used on the dock of the tail to cut through the greasy buildup and clear up any skin problems in that area. Try it on the mane as well.

Use *Renew Bath Oil* on their faces, legs and groin area for showing (instead of Vaseline). It will also help to repel bugs.

CHAPTER SIXTEEN

HEALTHY FARM ANIMALS

PRECAUTIONS

Always consult your veterinarian before starting any course of supplementation or treatment for your animal. Every effort has been made to ensure that the information contained in this book is complete and accurate. However, neither the publisher nor the author is engaged in rendering professional advice or services to the individual reader. The ideas, procedures and suggestions contained in this book are not intended as a substitute for consulting with your veterinarian. Neither the author nor the publisher shall be liable for any loss, injury, or damage allegedly arising from any information or suggestion in this book.

FARMERS – PLEASE READ!

We sincerely hope you'll find the tips in this section helpful in your farming operation. If you should find an application for Melaleuca products that works well for you that is not already in this book, please tell us about it. You'll be helping hundreds of farmers and ranchers who use this guide regularly. If we publish your suggestion, we'll send you a free copy of the book it's published in. Send your suggestion to the address in the front of this book, or by email to uses@rmbarry.com.

We would also be very interested to know how these suggestions work for you. Let us know, and tell us if (and how) you were able to save money in your operation by using Melaleuca products. We greatly appreciate your input.

Many thanks to all the farmers, ranchers, and veterinarians who contributed to this chapter. You epitomize the spirit of "enhancing lives." We sincerely hope and expect your contributions will help farmers and ranchers all over North America, Australia, and eventually, the world.

GENERAL INFORMATION

ANT KILLER

Spray concentrated *PreSpot Plus* on all ant prone areas. Or add a little *T36-C5* to your regular *Sol-U-Mel* and spray the ants. It may take 2-3 days, but by the 4th day they will be gone and won't come back. This formula will also control flies, mosquitoes and paper wasps.

ANT PREVENTATIVE

Combine 2 ounces of *Sol-U-Guard* with 8 ounces of water and spray all areas where ants tend to congregate.

FLY CONTROL

For very effective fly control, combine 1 teaspoon of *Tough & Tender* with 1 capful of *Renew Bath Oil* in 16 ounces of water. Spray your animals and the animal areas daily for 7 to 10 days. Follow this with a weekly spray until the fly problem is under control. **DO NOT** spray this or any mixture directly into an animal's face or eyes.

Some prefer to combine 1 teaspoon of *Tough & Tender* with 1 teaspoon of *Renew Bath Oil* and 10 drops of *T36-C5* in 16 ounces of water.

An alternate choice might be to use 2 capfuls of *Sol-U-Mel* and 10 drops of *T36-C5* added to a 16-ounce spray bottle filled with water. Spray all barn and stall confinement areas several times each week.

Another choice would be to combine 2 ounces of *Sol-U-Mel* with 16 ounces of water. Spray directly on the animal.

For personal use, any of the above combinations will work or you might try combining 4 ounces of *Moisturizing Hand Lotion* with 4 ounces of *Renew Bath Oil* and 4 ounces of *Sol-U-Mel*. It works great for camping as well as for farm work.

By the way, these will also work as mosquito repellents.

MOSQUITO REPELLENT

For mosquito protection, liberally apply *Sun-Shades 15* or *30* to all exposed body areas. For additional recipes for insect control, see the section on *Fly Control* in this book.

PRESSURE WASHING

Use *MelaMagic* in your pressure washer. Dilute as directed and add *Sol-U-Mel* to boost the cleaning power of the mixture.

CLEANING GREASY EQUIPMENT

Since *MelaMagic* is a grease cutter, it is generally accepted as the product of choice for cleaning farm equipment. However, some have found that concentrated *PreSpot Plus* makes it easier to remove the grease and grime.

WOUND SPRAY

Mix 2 capfuls of *Renew Bath Oil*, 3 capfuls of *Sol-U-Mel*, 2 capfuls of *Nature's Cleanse*, 5 drops of *Antibacterial Liquid Soap* and 1 quart of water. Use twice daily on superficial cuts and abrasions. This is **NOT** for deep cuts or puncture wounds.

---

*See the precautions at the beginning of this chapter.

CATTLE

CATTLE – ABSCESSES
* Scrub the hoof well with **Antibacterial Liquid Soap** and water. Rinse and, using a dropper, put several drops of **T36-C5** directly on the affected area. Confine the animal to a clean area during treatment.

CATTLE – BLOATING
* Add 4 tablespoons of **Tough & Tender** to a pint of water and give it orally to an adult cow. It will break down the surface tension and allow the gas to pass.

CATTLE – CASTRATION
* Follow the remedies and recipes listed just below under *Cattle – Cut, Scrapes, and Burns* for healing the cut site following castration.

CATTLE – CUTS, SCRAPES AND BURNS
* Treat an injured area twice daily with a combination of 16 ounces of **Sol-U-Mel** and 4 ounces of **Tough & Tender** in a gallon bucket of water. Continue using until the area has healed. Cuts, scrapes, and burns can be serious if left untreated. If a more severely injured animal will allow you in close enough to treat it, apply **Mela-Gel** or **Tripe Antibiotic Ointment** to the injury as well. **T36-C5** is also very effective when used on injuries. For cement burns, apply a liberal amount of **T36-C5**, followed by **Pain-A-Trate**, particularly if there is swelling. As with other injuries, continue treating until the injury has healed.

CATTLE – DEHORNING INFECTIONS
* For dehorning infections, flush the infected areas with a syringe filled with a mixture of 2-4 tablespoons of **Tough & Tender** and 2 capfuls of **Sol-U-Mel** blended in a gallon of water. After flushing, allow to dry and apply **T36-C5** to the infected area. Repeat daily as necessary.

CATTLE – HOOF ROT
* Clean the hoof thoroughly with **Antibacterial Liquid Soap** and water. Then simply use ½ cup of **Tough & Tender** in a plastic or rubber booty tied or taped onto the leg. Inspect daily and repeat until the condition is cleared up.

CATTLE – PHOTOSENSITIZATION
See Cattle – Sunburn

CATTLE – MANGE
* This condition is contagious and caution should be used when treating the animals. They should be isolated and any articles used during the treatment should be destroyed or carefully disinfected after each use.

*See the precautions at the beginning of this chapter.

Bedding should be changed daily and disposed of so that no other farm or domestic animal can come into contact with it. Be sure to wear gloves at all times. See the section on *Calf – Pens – Mange* in this book.

Scrub the affected area thoroughly with **Antibacterial Liquid Soap** and water and rinse. Clip away any matted or unwanted hair and dab **T36-C5** on the affected area and the surrounding area with a cotton ball. Repeat this treatment once a day until the condition clears.

Using **Naturals Melaleuca Oil Shampoo** when bathing your cattle will help maintain good hygiene. **Sol-U-Guard** is an excellent disinfectant for any tools.

CATTLE – RINGWORM

* Since ringworm is contagious, the affected animal should be isolated and any articles used during treatment must either be disposed of or carefully disinfected. See the section on *Calf – Pens and Mange* in this book.

Scrub the affected area thoroughly with **Antibacterial Liquid Soap** and water and rinse. Once the area is dry, dab **T36-C5** onto the ringworm with a cotton ball. Repeat the treatment several times per week until the condition clears. Be patient as this is a very challenging condition to eliminate.

CATTLE – SUNBURN

* **T36-C5** is very soothing for the cattle that get sunburn and photosensitization. Mix ¼ teaspoon of **T36-C5** and ⅓ cup of water and spray the affected area. Be careful to avoid the eyes. Provide shade, if necessary, for severe cases and avoid excessive direct sunlight until the condition clears.

Photosensitization occurs worldwide and is most common in cattle and sheep. It seems to be triggered by ingestion of certain plants such as St. John's Wort.

CATTLE – THRUSH ON THE FEET

* Apply **Sol-U-Mel** or **T36-C5** directly on the affected area. Then use a clean, large cotton sock that has been soaked in four ounces of the all-purpose mixture combined with 12 ounces of water to form a good solution. (See the section on *Cow – All Purpose Spray Mixture* in this book.) Make sure the sock is thoroughly soaked. Then fit the sock over the affected foot and wrap with rubber or cotton straps to keep in place. Keep the foot wet with this solution and consider isolating the animal, as thrush can be extremely contagious.

*See the precautions at the beginning of this chapter.

CALVES

CALF – BIRTHS
* When a calf has a difficult birth place put 5 to 10 drops of *T36-C5* down each nostril, and 5 to 10 drops on the back of the tongue, as soon as it is born.

CALF – COUGHING
* Spray *Sol-U-Guard* into their bedding at least once a week and more often if needed. Dilute as instructed on the bottle.

CALF – MILK REPLACER TIPS
* Dissolve 3 *Vita-Bears Children's Vitamins* in a cup of milk and add it to the warm milk replacer. This will assure that the calves are receiving their needed vitamins and minerals.

When calves are switching from milk to milk replacer, add 1 oz. of *Nature's Cleanse* to the pail for the first two feedings and the calves should not have a problem with the switch.

CALF – PENS AND MANGE
* You should be able to keep mange under control by washing out the pens using a garden sprayer and then spraying down the bedding using a mixture of 1 ounce of *Sol-U-Guard* and 16 ounces of water. This should be done once a week.

CALF – PNEUMONIA
* When a calf develops pneumonia, put 5-10 drops of *T36-C5* in each nostril and 6 drops on the back of the tongue. Repeat daily for 7 to 10 days as needed.

CALF – NAVAL ILL
* Combine 2 ounces of *Sol-U-Mel*, 1½ teaspoons of *Tough & Tender* and 10 drops of *T36-C5* in a 16-ounce spray bottle of water. Use as a preventative in newborn calves. If the navel is swollen, change the 2 ounces of *Sol-U-Mel* to 4 ounces for the treatment.

(One rancher said that they have not lost a calf to navel ill since switching from iodine to this mixture.)

CALF – SCOURS
* For scours, orally administer, with a syringe, 1 ounce of *Nature's Cleanse* diluted in 4 ounces of water. The calf should be treated twice daily (morning and evening) until the bowel movement firms up. **Do not give *Nature's Cleanse* full strength!**

This can also be put in the milk if the calf is drinking. It usually takes

*See the precautions at the beginning of this chapter.

about 2 days of treatment.

(In 1991, one farmer spent $1,000 on medicine and lost 25 calves. In 1992 this same farmer spent $70 on four bottles of *Nature's Cleanse* and lost no calves.)

CALF – SCOURS – PREVENTION

* Combine ¼ cup of *Sol-U-Guard* in a 16-ounce spray bottle filled with water. Spray the bedding or wherever they sleep, weekly. This even works outside and in dirt floor barns that you cannot wash. Spray more often if you notice scouring stool in the bedding. Spray the scouring stool when you see the piles. When possible move the calves to clean ground.

Remember, it is also aromatic, so spray into the air and let it drift to the ground in the barn.

CALF – UNTHRIFTY

* Unthrifty can be dealt with effectively by enhancing the calf's nutrition. Add 3 dissolved *Vita-Bears Children's Vitamins* to the calf's milk both morning and night.

COWS

COW – ALL PURPOSE SPRAY MIXTURE

* Mix 16 ounces of *Sol-U-Mel* and 4 ounces of *Tough & Tender* in a 1-gallon bucket and fill with water. This can be used as an all purpose spray.

COW – CHAFED OR SORE TEATS

* Use the *Cow – All Purpose Spray Mixture*, listed in this book, 2 to 3 times daily until the sore or chafed teats have healed.

COW – COWPOX

* The incubation period for cowpox is from 4-7 days and there are several recognizable stages. *T36-C5* can be applied to the lesions at any stage and will help with the healing process as well as soothe the pain and sensitivity. This condition is contagious, so the animals need to be isolated. Using latex or rubber gloves clean the affected area with *Antibacterial Liquid Soap* and water. Rinse and thoroughly spray the area with a mixture of ¼ teaspoon of *T36-C5* and ½ cup of water. Some prefer to apply the oil directly on the lesions with a cotton ball. Be sure all tools and bedding are carefully disinfected. See the section on *Calf – Pens – Mange* in this book.

COW – INFECTION POSSIBILITY

* Combine 2 ounces of *Sol-U-Mel*, 1½ teaspoons of *Tough & Tender*

---

*See the precautions at the beginning of this chapter.

and 10 drops of *T36-C5* in a 16-ounce spray bottle filled with water. Use this mixture after dehorning, brisket tagging or anytime you see a threat of a possible infection.

COW – MASTITIS

* An infected quarter should be treated twice each day with a liberal application of liquid *Pain-A-Trate*. Continue this treatment as needed until the cow is free of infection. If mastitis is severe, apply a liberal amount of *T36-C5* before applying the liquid *Pain-A-Trate*.

When you have an outbreak of herd mastitis, mix 1 ounce of *Sol-U-Mel* with 10 ounces of water and use it as a teat dip.

It has even been suggested that for very serious cases 10 cc of *Sol-U-Mel* be injected directly up the teat canal, followed by massaging the quarter. **This procedure should be used with caution.** An injection of 3 cc of *Nature's Cleanse* and 20 cc of water generally works very well.

COW – PREDIP OR SPRAY

* To prepare a predip to clean the cows before milking, combine 4 ounces of *Antibacterial Liquid Soap*, 16 ounces of *Tough & Tender,* and 2 ounces of *Sol-U-Guard* or *Sol-U-Mel* in enough water to make 5 gallons. This is very cost effective compared to the usually recommended brands of dip.

COW – POST DIP

* Post dip should be used after milking to prevent infection (mastitis). Combine 2 gallons of Prop-glycol, 4 ounces of *Antibacterial Liquid Soap*, 16 ounces of *Tough & Tender*, and one tube of *Mate Shower Gel* with enough water to make 5 gallons. This is used to moisturize the teats. Shake before filling the dip containers. This is a high emollient dip for frost and sun protection. The Prop-glycol is the anti-freeze ingredient.

Use red food coloring in one of the dip containers to help identify the different dips.

COW – PROLAPSED UTERUS

* Combine 4 ounces of *Sol-U-Mel*, 1½ teaspoons of *Tough & Tender* and 10 drops of *T36-C5* in a 16-ounce spray bottle with water. Wash the uterus with this solution. Remove as much of the after birth as possible and spray liberally with this solution before putting back in the cow while she is on her feet. Once in, with your arm up her uterus, whip back and forth as hard as you can to straighten the uterus out. This mixture will not only take out the swelling but it will also prevent infection.

*See the precautions at the beginning of this chapter.

COW – RINGWORM
* Wash the area with *Antibacterial Liquid Soap* and then apply *T36-C5*, *Mela-Gel* or *Renew Intensive Skin Therapy*. See the section on *Cattle – Ringworm* in this book.

COW – TEAT CUTS
* Teat cuts and sore teats can quickly be treated with *Triple Antibiotic Ointment.*

COW – TEAT SPRAY
* Spray the teat and the teat end with a mixture of 1 ounce of *Sol-U-Mel* combined with 5 ounces of water. Rinse and repeat the treatment.

Another effective teat spray is to combine 1 ounce of *Sol-U-Guard*, 3 ounces of *Antibacterial Liquid Soap*, and 2 ounces of *Bath and Shower Gel i*n one gallon of water.

COW – UDDER EDEMA OR FRESH UDDER
* Use the *Cow – All Purpose Spray Mixture*, listed in this book, on the udder twice daily.

COW – UDDER SORES
* Use the *Cow – All Purpose Spray Mixture* listed in this book to liberally spray any sores that appear between the quarters, or between the udder and the leg area. Repeat at least twice a day until the sores have healed.

An alternate solution is to mix 2 teaspoons of *Sol-U-Mel* and 1½ teaspoons of *Tough & Tender* in 16 ounces of water. First clean and dry the sores. Then, spray the solution twice daily on the weeping lesions. Spraying on dried up sores isn't necessary.

COW – UDDER WASH
* For a very effective udder wash, combine 1 quart of *Tough & Tender* with 3 quarts of water. Use 2 ounces of this mixture with 1 capful of *Sol-U-Mel* in 5 to 10 gallons of water. Immediately prior to putting on the milkers, spray the udders with a mixture of 1 part of *Sol-U-Mel* combined with 5 parts of water.

(In a week's time, one farmer reduced his somatic cell count from 52,000 to 15,000. This was the lowest count in the county. Later, Federal Inspectors investigated for peroxide use and found nothing wrong in what he was doing.)

Some prefer to use 1 teaspoon of *Tough & Tender* to 2 gallons of water as an udder wash.

*See the precautions at the beginning of this chapter.

CHICKENS

CHICKEN – CANNIBALISM

* *T36-C5* is very effective for masking the scents that cause poultry cannibalism. Add 2-4 drops of *T36-C5* (depending on the size of the bird) to 4 drops of coconut oil and pour into a fine spray atomizer bottle with ½ cup of warm water, shake bottle well before each use and either spray directly onto the area (avoid the head completely) or mist a piece of gauze and dab the area. This is effective for stopping self-plucking and parasites. Wipe around the cages too and destroy the cleaning cloth.

CHICKEN – COCCIDIOSIS

* Spray the chicken bedding with 1 ounce of *Sol-U-Guard* mixed in a quart of water.

CHICKEN – DISEASE REDUCTION

* Adding 3 to 4 drops of *Sol-U-Mel* in the small drinking water reservoirs or 2 to 3 tablespoons of *Sol-U-Mel* in a 500-gallon reservoir, will reduce the incidence of disease.

CHICKEN – EGG ROOM SALMONELLA AND ASPERGILLUS

* Spray the egg room weekly using ½ ounce of *Sol-U-Guard* mixed in a quart of water.

CHICKEN HOUSE – FOGGING BARNS

* Use 1 ounce of *Sol-U-Mel* to every 5 ounces of water when fogging the barns.

CHICKEN HOUSE – SALMONELLA

* Use either 1-ounce of *Sol-U-Mel* or 1 ounce of *Sol-U-Guard* in a quart of water when spraying the chicken house to kill salmonella. This will also kill other types of bacteria.

CAUTION: Avoid direct contact with the birds when spraying.

GOATS

GOATS – ABSCESSES

* If an abscess has not erupted in an injured area, dab full-strength *T36-C5* on the site with a cotton ball or Q-tip. If it is draining, clean the area with *Antibacterial Liquid Soap* and water and after it dries, drop 1-2 drops of *T36-C5* on the site. Repeat the cleaning and treatment 1-2 times each day until the abscess is healed.

*See the precautions at the beginning of this chapter.

GOATS – CUTS, WOUNDS, BITES AND STINGS

* *T36-C5* can be used on most cuts, wounds, bites and stings. Once the area is cleaned with *Antibacterial Liquid Soap* and water, rinse and pat dry.

In most cases you can apply the oil directly on the affected area with a cotton ball or Q-tip. *Mela-Gel* and *Triple Antibiotic Ointment* are very effective treatments as well.

GOATS – ECZEMA

*Any disturbance affecting the skin is generally covered under the broad term, Eczema. The affected area should be thoroughly washed with *Antibacterial Liquid Soap* and water and patted dry. Clip away any excess hair and apply *T36-C5* with a cotton ball. Treat the condition daily until it clears. If it becomes stubborn or worsens, contact your vet.

GOATS – GOAT POX

* Goat pox in goats, unlike other farm animals, can become serious. A specific virus is responsible for this condition and it can become contagious. It is much like treating an abscess. First clean the area thoroughly with *Antibacterial Liquid Soap* and water. Saturate a cotton ball with *T36-C5* and dab in onto the area if it has not erupted. Using a dropper, place *T36-C6* onto the area after it has begun to drain. Be sure to wear gloves when treating this condition.

GOATS – HOOF CONDITIONS

* Remove your goat from a damp environment and wash the hoof thoroughly with *Antibacterial Liquid Soap* and water. Put ½ teaspoon of *T36-C5* and ½ cup of water in a spray bottle and spray the hoof well. Keep the goat in a clean environment and treat daily or every other day, depending on the severity of the condition.

GOATS – MANGE

* There are four types of mange that can affect goats, psoroptic mange, sarcoptic mange, demodectic mange and chorioptic mange. Psoroptic mange is much less severe than other types of mange, but if left untreated it may become infected. Sarcoptic mange is a more severe type, which untreated, can leave the skin leathery and wrinkled. Young kids are susceptible to this condition. Demodectic mange involves hair follicles and looks like small abscesses. Chorioptic mange is known as the "leg mange."

In all cases the goat should be isolated during treatment. Thoroughly clean the affected area with *Antibacterial Liquid Soap* and water. Rinse and clip away any matted or unwanted hair. Dab the affected area and the surrounding area with a cotton ball saturated with *T36-C5*. Repeat the treatment 1-2 times each day until the condition clears.

*See the precautions at the beginning of this chapter.

If you are working around the ears, clean them thoroughly and then wipe with one drop of *T36-C5* on a cotton ball. Do not drop *T36-C5* directly into the ear canal. As with any condition, if it gets worse, contact your vet.

GOATS – PHOTOSENSITIZATION
See Goats - Sunburn

GOATS – RINGWORM
* Ringworm is not as common in sheep and goats as it is in other species, but it they do get it, they must be isolated as it is very contagious. Clean the affected area with ***Antibacterial Liquid Soap*** and water. Pat dry and clip away any unwanted or matted hair. Dab the affected and surrounding areas with *T36-C5* on a cotton ball. Repeat the treatment once a day and be patient, as it is a challenging condition to clear up.

GOATS – SEEDY TOE
* The condition called seedy toe may cause your goat to become lame. Carefully clean the area with ***Antibacterial Liquid Soap*** and water and rinse well. Pat dry and, using a dropper, put *T36-C5* directly on the site. Protect the area from dirt by putting an old cotton sock over the foot. Repeat the treatment 1-2 times each day depending on the severity.

GOATS – SKIN CONDITIONS
* There are various skin conditions which goats are susceptible to, similar to those in cattle and sheep. They will vary in severity and many will respond to *T36-C5*. Regular shampooing with ***Naturals Melaleuca Oil Shampoo*** will help the goat remain in good condition and will help to prevent many skin conditions. See the areas of special skin conditions for goats listed in this book.

GOATS – SUNBURN
* Sunburn is more likely to be seen on goat breeds such as Saanen and Norwegian Dairy, although it can be seen on others as well. St. John's Wort seems to be triggering factor in photosensitization, as it appears to be associated with ingestion of certain plants. Photosensitization is most common in cattle and sheep but is does occur worldwide and can affect many species.

Keep your goat in a shaded area when being treated. Clip away any matted or unwanted hair and clean the area with ***Antibacterial Liquid Soap*** and water. Coat the affected area with *T36-C5*, ***Mela-Gel*** or ***Triple Antibiotic Ointment***. If the condition reoccurs, consider keeping your goat in a shaded area during the intense sunlight hours.

---

*See the precautions at the beginning of this chapter.

GOATS – WARTS

* A virus causes warts on the teats and although not usually serious, they are prone to bleeding. Applying *T36-C5* will aid in healing as well as soothe the pain and sensitivity. It may take several weeks to clear when applying the oil daily or every other day.

HOGS AND PIGS

HOGS – ABSCESSES

* At the acute or early stage of an abscess, the site is particularly sensitive to the touch. Saturate a cotton ball with *T36-C5* and dab it on the site several times each day. Continue the treatment, keeping the area clean, while it comes to a head and drains.

HOGS – BATHING

* Wash the hogs in *Antibacterial Liquid Soap* and it will not only clean them, it will heal their sores from scratching and keep their skin from drying out.

HOGS – CANDIDA

* Clean the site thoroughly with *Antibacterial Liquid Soap* and water. Pat the area dry with a paper towel and carefully dispose of the sued towels. Saturate a cotton ball with *T36-C5* and dab onto the site several times each day until the condition clears.

HOGS – COCCIDIOSIS

* Spray the bedding and pen with a dilution of 1 ounce of *Sol-U-Guard* and a quart of water. Isolate the animal from others until the condition subsides.

HOGS – CONFINEMENT – CLEANING

* Use a pressure washer to clean the walls and the ceilings of any confinement area with 32 ounces of *MelaMagic* blended into 24 gallons of water. Adding 3 to 4 tablespoons of *Sol-U-Mel* can boost the strength of this mixture. One spraying should eliminate mold re-growth.

(One hog farmer reduced his cost of cleaning his confinement area from $36 to $7 per cleaning by using this method.)

Another suggestion is to spray all the walls and ceilings with a mixture of 1 ounce of *Sol-U-Mel* in a quart bottle filled with water.

HOGS – CUTS, WOUNDS, BITES AND STINGS

* Always clean any cut, wound, bite or sting thoroughly with *Antibacterial Liquid Soap* and water. Rinse and dry carefully. Check to be sure that no foreign matter is imbedded in the injury and then treat

*See the precautions at the beginning of this chapter.

with a cotton ball and *T36-C5*. Repeat the treatment daily until a healthy scab is formed or until the bite or sting disappears.

HOGS – DISINFECTING UDDER AT FARROWING TIME
* Use 1 ounce of *Sol-U-Mel* combined with 20 ounces of water.

HOGS – FOGGING BARNS
* Use up to 1 ounce of *Sol-U-Mel* with 5 ounces of water when fogging the barns.

HOGS – LICE
* When the hogs get lice, wash them with *Antibacterial Liquid Soap* and then spray them with *Sol-U-Mel* and *Tough & Tender* mixed together in a spray bottle. If you will also spray the pens, you will usually get rid of the lice in one treatment.

HOGS – MASTITIS
* When the sows have mastitis or are holding their milk, apply *T36-C5* to the bag followed by **Pain-A-Trate**.

HOGS – PENS – MANGE
* Wash out the pen area with water. Then use 1-ounce of *Sol-U-Guard* combined with 30 ounces of water to spray the empty hog pens and their bedding. The bedding may need to be sprayed weekly to keep the mange under control.

HOGS – PHOTOSENSITIZATION
See Hogs – Sunburn

HOGS – PITYRIASIS ROSE
* This condition of unknown origin effects young pigs and particularly those of the Landrace breed. Wash the affected area with *Antibacterial Liquid Soap* and water and rinse well. Pat the area dry and with a cotton ball, apply *T36-C5* onto the area 1-2 times each day until the condition clears.

HOGS – RINGWORM
* This condition is contagious, so isolate your animal while treating for ringworms. Wash the area with *Antibacterial Liquid Soap* and water and rinse thoroughly. Pat the area dry and dispose of the used paper towels. Saturate a cotton ball with *T36-C5* and dab it on the site several times each day. Be patient as this is a challenging condition to treat. Be sure to wear gloves when treating ringworms and carefully dispose of or disinfect any items in contact with the animal during treatment.

*See the precautions at the beginning of this chapter.

HOGS – SALMONELLA IN BARNS

* Spray the barn area at least once a month with a solution of 1 ounce of *Sol-U-Guard* and 30 ounces of water to decrease the likelihood of salmonella.

HOGS – SOW WASH

* Spray the sow using a mixture of 1 teaspoon of *Tough & Tender* and 1 capful of *Sol-U-Mel* combined in a 16-ounce spray bottle filled with water. Spray the bedding using 1 ounce of *Sol-U-Guard* and 30 ounces of water.

HOGS – SUNBURN

* Animals exposed to intense sunlight may be affected by either sunburn and/or photosensitization. Occurring worldwide, photosensitization is more commonly seen in sheep and cattle and seems to occur at the onset of ingesting certain plants or grasses, such as St. John's Wort, rape and alfalfa. White breeds are more frequently affected.

Provide shade for your animal during periods of intense sunlight and during treatment. Bathe with *Antibacterial Liquid Soap* and water and rinse. Use a light coat of *Mela-Gel* or *Triple Antibiotic Ointment*. *Renew Intensive Skin Therapy* or *Sun-Shades Sunscreen* would also provide some healing and protection.

PIGLETS – FOOT ROT

* This condition affects pigs up to six months of age and if neglected can lead to septicemia. Clean the hoof carefully with *Antibacterial Liquid Soap* and water. Rinse and spray the entire hoof and around the coronary band thoroughly once a day with a mixture of ½ teaspoon of *T36-C5* and ½ cup of water. If possible, isolate the pig and keep it in a clean environment until the condition is eliminated.

PIGLETS – GREASY PIG DISEASE

* Rubbing your piglets every day with *Moisturizing Hand Lotion* will help to alleviate greasy pig disease. In more serious cases, you may have to apply it 2 or 3 times each day until the condition is clear.

An alternate solution would be to spray the pigs daily using a solution of one part of *Sol-U-Mel* and five parts of water.

PIGLETS – ITCH PROBLEMS

* Lightly spray or sprinkle the piglets with a water can using a mixture of 1 ounce of *Sol-U-Guard* and 50 ounces of water will help with an itch problem.

WARNING: Flaky skin may develop if the piglets are treated more than once a week.

---

*See the precautions at the beginning of this chapter.

PIGLETS – RESPIRATORY PROBLEMS

* Misting the farrowing pens daily with 1 ounce of *Sol-U-Mel* combined with 5 ounces of water will help to reduce the number of piglets with respiratory challenges.

SHEEP AND LAMBS

SHEEP – CUTS, WOUNDS, BITES AND STINGS

* Clean any injured area with *Antibacterial Liquid Soap* and water. Rinse and pat dry. Be sure that there are no foreign objects in the injured area that need to be removed. Saturate a cotton ball with *T36-C5* and squeeze out the excess. Dab the oil on the affected area and repeat 1-2 times each day until the condition clears.

SHEEP – FOOT ABSCESSES

* Foot abscesses are more likely to develop when the soil and pastures are wet. The animal needs to be removed from the damp environment and placed in a clean, dry area. Wash the foot thoroughly with *Antibacterial Liquid Soap* and water. Rinse and dry carefully and then apply a mixture of ½ teaspoon of *T36-C5* and ½ cup of water with a spray bottle. Spray the area thoroughly. Keep the wound clean and allow it to drain. Repeat the treatment 1-2 times each day until the condition is clear.

SHEEP – FOOT ROT

* This condition is very contagious under warm, moist conditions. Place the animal in a clean, dry environment during treatment. Wash the foot with *Antibacterial Liquid Soap* and water. Rinse and dry carefully. Spray the foot thoroughly with a mixture of ½ teaspoon of *T36-C5* blended with ½ cup of water. Repeat the treatment 1-2 times each day until the condition clears.

SHEEP – MANGE

* If your sheep appears to have any type of mange, shear and wash the animal with *Antibacterial Liquid Soap* and water. Rinse carefully and apply *T36-C5* directly to the site with a squeezed out cotton ball. This should be applied 2-3 times each day until the condition clears. The animal should be isolated during the treatment period.

SHEEP – ORF

* The infectious dermatitis that affects both sheep and goats is called Contagious Ecthyma (Orf). It is important that the animals be isolated until the condition is clear. Treat by putting 1 drop of *T36-C5* on a cotton ball and dabbing it onto the lesion of the lips and/or feet 1-2 times each day until a scab appears and falls off.

*See the precautions at the beginning of this chapter.

SHEEP – PHOTOSENSITIZATION

* Photosensitization is most common in cattle and sheep. The skin of lightly pigmented animals becomes inflamed from long-term exposure to ultraviolet rays. Thus the animal should be placed in the shade during treatment and until the condition is clear. Saturate a cotton ball with *T36-C5* and squeeze out the excess. Apply this directly to the affected area. It will not only promote healing but will help with the discomfort as well.

SHEEP – RINGWORM

* Ringworm is uncommon in sheep and goats, but it does occur. It is very contagious, therefore the animal must be isolated and any tools used during the treatment time must be carefully disinfected. *Sol-U* Mel is an excellent disinfectant for this purpose. Be sure to wear gloves when treating your sheep and be very patient, as this will take some time to clear.

Wash the affected area with **Antibacterial Liquid Soap** and water. Rinse and pat dry with paper towels. Carefully dispose of the used towels. Saturate a cotton ball with *T36-C5* and after squeezing out the excess, dab it directly on the ringworm site. Repeat this treatment 2-3 times each day until the condition clears.

SHEEP – SHEEP KED

* Sheep ked (sheep tick) can spread rapidly through a flock as this insect can spend its entire life on its host. After shearing, put ½ teaspoon of *T36-C5* into ½ cup of water and spray the animal thoroughly.

SHEEP – SHEEP POX

* Characterized by wide spread skin eruptions, Sheep Pox is a virus that is serious, and often fatal for sheep. *T36-C5* can help with the pain and irritation of the lesions, but a vet should be consulted immediately.

SHEEP – SKIN CONDITIONS

* Applying *T36-C5* directly on the site with a cotton ball can treat dermatitis or lumpy wool or strawberry foot rot. The infected animal should be isolated and the wool around the affected area sheared away. Treat the area 1-2 times each day until the condition is clear.

SHEEP – WARTS

* Warts are rare in sheep. However, if they do occur, they can be transmitted to other sheep. Treat them with a cotton ball saturated with *T36-C5*, squeezed out, and dabbed directly onto the affected area. Repeat the treatment 2-3 times each day until the condition clears. This treatment can take weeks.

*See the precautions at the beginning of this chapter.

LAMBS – MAGGOTS

* If your lamb gets blowfly larvae (maggots) in a wound, clean it with diluted *Sol-U-Mel* and pack the wound with *Triple Antibiotic Ointment*. The maggots will not be able to move out fast enough! It will also prevent reinfestation.

TURKEYS

TURKEY – DRINKING WATER

* Use 2 capfuls of *Sol-U-Mel* to 10 gallons of water for drinking. This same combination can be used to spray around the water tanks and feeders.

TURKEY HOUSE

* The empty turkey house should be misted weekly with a combination of 1 ounce of *Sol-U-Mel* and 5 ounces of water.

(One farmer used this in his turkey house and received the cleanest results ever on his pre-shipping blood tests.)

TURKEY HOUSE – SALMONELLA

* To prevent the growth of Salmonella in the turkeys and the spread of it to their eggs, spray the turkey house with 1 ounce of either *Sol-U-Mel* OR *Sol-U-Guard* combined with 30 ounces of water. This spray should kill most bacteria including salmonella. **Do not spray the birds.**

TURKEY LINE FLUSHING

* Flush all of the water lines using a mixture of 2 capfuls of *Sol-U-Mel* combined with 1 tablespoon of *Tough & Tender* and 5 gallons of water and let them soak overnight. Rinse them well with plain water before reusing.

*See the precautions at the beginning of this chapter.

CHAPTER SEVENTEEN
HEALTHY GARDEN SOLUTIONS

This is a beginning chapter in our book. It contains some exciting ideas shared by our readers. As you read it and think of other ways Melaleuca products have worked in your garden, please share them with us. You can send your suggestions to us at the address in the front of this book, or email us at uses@rmbarry.com.

Please use caution when using these suggestions in your garden. Thank you and happy gardening.

ANT KILLER

Spray concentrated **Pre-Spot Plus** on the areas where ants congregate. Be aware of the surface of these areas when using **Pre-Spot Plus** as it can take the finish off of some wooden floors.

An alternate idea is to combine 1 ounce of **MelaMagic** and 1 ounce of **Sol-U-Mel** in a 16-ounce bottle filled with water. This works particularly well with large black ants.

Another simple solution is **Tough & Tender.** It will kill ants.

ANTS, FIRE

Spray fire ants with **PreSpot Plus.** It is very effective. For fire ant pain, splash the area with **Sol-U-Mel.**

For a foolproof way to kill fire ants consider this: After you have mopped the floor with **Tough & Tender** and/or **MelaMagic** or you have washed the car with **Tough & Tender,** add a 5 or 6 drops of **Lemon Brite** and stir. Pour half of the bucket on the fire ant bed. After about 30 minutes pour the other half on the bed.

If you are really mad about the fire ants, like when they have invaded your flower beds, mix the following in a two gallon bucket of water: 1 capful of **Tough & Tender**, 1 capful of **MelaMagic**, 1 capful of **Sol-U-Mel**, 1 capful of **Tub & Tile** and always 10 drops of **Lemon Brite**. Sir and pour half of the bucket on the fire ant bed. Wait 30 minutes and pour on the other half. This kills them "dead" and they won't come back. Plus, that will be the greenest part of your lawn!

ANT PREVENTION

If you prefer to just prevent ants, simply spray the most likely areas with 2 ounces of *Sol-U-Guard* combined with 16 ounces of water.

APHIDS

Spray for aphids, spider mites and fungus on roses and other plants with a mixture of 2 teaspoons of *Nature's Cleanse* and 16 ounces of water. This can be sprayed on the plants daily if needed.

An alternate solution would be to use *Sol-U-Mel* to get rid of aphids on your roses. Mix it a little stronger than is recommended on the bottle.

It has also been suggested that a 3% solution of *Tough & Tender* is very effective for killing aphids and stopping the onset of mildew on rose bushes without damaging the plants.

See the section on *Rhubarb* in this book.

APPLE SPRAY

Spray apples in the orchard with one bottle of *Renew Bath Oil* mixed into 5 gallons of warm water.

ARMY WORMS

Mix ½ cup of *MelaMagic* in 2 gallons of water to spray for army worms. Spray the cocoon, nest and "whatever that webby thing is called." The web will dissolve and the worms shrivel up instantly. Spray any new evidence of the worms as soon as they appear. By the way, it will also stop ant invasions.

BAGWORMS

Spray the nest of bagworms with diluted *Lemon-Brite*. It may take a couple of heavy sprayings to do more than make them sick.

BUGS – YARD

Mix 1 cup of *Lemon Brite* dish liquid soap and 1 cup of already mixed *Breath-Away Mouthwash* into a 20 gallon hose-end sprayer and soak your lawn, garden beds and trees to the point that the fluid is running off. Bugs hate it! This will also remove dust, dirt and pollution from grass blades, making any lawn fertilizer work twice as well.

Tough & Tender diluted and used in a lawn sprayer unit makes an excellent bug spray.

Diluted *Sol-U-Mel* is very effective for crickets and crawling bugs.

CRAPE MYRTLES

Mix *Sol-U-Mel* in a spray bottle, as directed, and use to combat the fungus that grows on crepe myrtles.

DISINFECTANT

Occasionally you will need to disinfect your pruning sheers to keep mold spores from spreading. The *Anti-Bacterial Liquid Soap* will do an excellent job and clean your hands as well.

FERTILIZER

Tough & Tender diluted through a lawn sprayer unit is an excellent fertilizer for your rose bushes.

FLOWERING BUSHES

To rid your flowering bushes of a collection of bugs, spray liberally with diluted *Sol-U-Mel*. Cover the bush with a plastic bag overnight. The bugs will disappear.

FRUIT TREES

See Trees

FUNGUS

See Aphids, Crepe Myrtles and Zinnias

GARDEN BEDS

See Bugs – Yard

GNATS

See Lawn Spray

GRASS

See Bugs – Yard

GREEN HOUSE

Spray your green house with *Tough & Tender* as a deterrent to the growth of mold.

An alternate solution would be to dilute 4-5 drops of *T36-C5 Melaleuca Oil* in a spray bottle of water and spray throughout the greenhouse.

HELIOPSIS

See Red Spider Mites

HOUSEPLANTS

If you have found little brown spots on your variegated green houseplants, which have caused the leaves to turn brown and sticky, wipe the leaves with a diluted solution of *Tough & Tender*. Then pour the same solution around the base of the plant.

Diluted *Tough & Tender* is also an excellent product to clean the leaves of other houseplants.

INSECT REPELLENT

A mixture of 3-5 drops of *T36-C5* and 1 cup of distilled or cold boiled water in a spray mister is very effective in ridding plants of parasites or insects. Continue to use the spray for at least a week after the infestations appears to be gone. Make sure that the immediate area and other plants surrounding the affected one are also treated for the duration. This prevents a recurrence of the challenge.

LAWNS
See Bugs – Yard

LAWN SPRAY
Spray your lawn with a diluted mixture of **Tough & Tender** in a lawn sprayer unit. It will kill the little gnats as well as mushrooms that grow in your yard.

MILDEW
See Mold

MITES
See Aphids

MOLD
With a 1:5 mixture of **Sol-U-Mel**, spray the moldy areas around the foundation of your house. This will also work well for mildew and the musty areas in your garden where mushrooms crop up.

It has also been suggested that a mixture of 3-5 drops of **T36-C5** blended with 1 cup of distilled or cold boiled water in a spray mister is very effective on mold and aphid infestation on rose bushes and other household plants. Shake the mixture vigorously and mist the plants on the tops and bottoms of the foliage and the soil. Make sure to totally mist the affected area.

MOLD SPORES
See Disinfectant and Green House

MUSHROOMS
See Lawn Spray and Mold

MUSTY AREAS
See Mold

PLANTS
See Trees

PLANT – INDOOR
Spraying your indoor plants with **Sol-U-Mel** is very effective.

PLANT SPRAYS
See Insect Repellent

RED SPIDER MITES
Mix 1 cup of **Tough & Tender** in a lawn sprayer unit and fill with

water. Spray the plants thoroughly and saturate the ground surrounding the plants. This works especially well on Heliopsis or "Summer Sun" plants.

RHUBARD

Spray diluted *Tough & Tender* on your rhubarb and get rid of all of the aphids without harming the plant.

ROSE BUSHES

See Fertilizer and Aphids

SCALE

See Trees

SHRUBS

See Trees

SLUGS

Sol-U-Mel blended into a diluted spray will rid your garden of slugs and other bugs. It does not work as fast as salt, but it does not hurt the plants and is far cheaper and safer than pesticides.

SOIL SURFACTANT

Tough & Tender is an excellent soil surfactant. Putting it in the ground before you plant your garden in the summer will help the water stay in the ground when it gets hot and there is no rainfall.

SPIDERS

See Aphids

SUMMER SUN

See Red Spider Mites

TOMATOES

Add ⅛ cup of *Tough & Tender* to a 5-gallon water can and water the soil around the tomato plants every other day. They will need about three applications. Not only will it get rid of the blight, but also you will have delicious tomatoes from your "mini forest." (Spraying the tomato plants themselves does not seem to work.)

TREES

Mix *Tough & Tender* in your lawn sprayer unit and spray on the aspen trees to prevent scale and other bug challenges.

Use *Sol-U-Mel* in a 1:5 solution to spray your fruit trees, shrubs, plants and grass. It wipes out the aphids, ants, and all the other bugs that you do not want eating your garden.

See the section on *Bugs – Yard* in this book.

WEBWORMS

Tough & Tender is a very effective spray for webworms. Spray them liberally and be sure that the pressure of the spray breaks into the web. Your yard will smell much better and be a great deal safer than those sprayed with pesticides.

ZINNIAS

Spray diluted *Sol-U-Mel* directly on the leaves of your zinnias. They will usually show improvement in one day. This will even work on leaves that have been slightly affected by the fungus and restore them to their green color.

CHAPTER EIGHTEEN

ALTERNATIVE USES

For Melaleuca Products

This is the "fun" chapter. When we asked our creative reader's for unique uses of Melaleuca products we received all kinds of ideas. Most of them had already been included or were added to previous chapters where they obviously belonged. Some of them belonged here. All of them are real but you may not believe it! Have fun! Keep reading and enjoy.

AROMATHERAPY

Add a few drops of *T36-C5* to an aroma light, or to a small pan of boiling water to keep annoying insects away from your house. For your own benefit, add a drop or two to your pillow before you go to bed at night.

ART PROJECT

This art project requires very few materials, but give your kid's imagination a great workout! Use empty *Koala Pals* bottles; mix 2 parts of *Lemon Brite Dishwashing Liquid* to 1 part of powdered tempera paint. Blend until creamy. Mix up several different colors, then give your child a large brush and let him/her paint imaginative pictures on a window. This special paint mixture washes off easily with a wet sponge. It's a great project to do with it is cold or rainy outside.

ATTAIN SHAKES

Here are some new ways to enjoy your *Attain* shakes:

Root Beer Float
$\frac{1}{2}$ cup diet root beer
7 oz. skim milk or water
1 scoop *Attain Vanilla Shake Mix*
Mix all ingredients in a blender and enjoy this "old-fashioned" low-fat snack.

Pina Colada
6 pieces of canned pineapple
1 T. coconut flakes

2 oz. coconut juice
1 T. 100% pineapple juice
7 oz. crushed ice
7 oz. water
1 scoop *Attain Vanilla Shake Mix*
Mix all ingredients in a blender and enjoy this fruity, tropical treat.

Banana Wonder
½ ripe banana
2 T. non-fat vanilla or banana yogurt
7 oz. non-fat milk
1 scoop *Attain Vanilla* or *Milk Chocolate Shake Mix*
Mix all ingredients in a blender and top with the other half of the banana.

BANDAGES

T36-C5 is excellent for removing the "goo" on bandages. And, it doesn't mess up your nail polish! It is good for both the skin and the injury as well.

BILGE CLEANERS

Mix *Tub & Tile*, *Sol-U-Mel* and *MelaMagic* together to use as a bilge cleaner in place of the usual caustic substances.

BUBBLE BATH

When all else fails and you are ready for that bubble bath, try soaking in *Tough & Tender*. It's a wonderful bubble bath.

CAR PARTS

Oily car parts can be easily cleaned with a mixture of 4 ounces of *MelaMagic* and 1 capful of *Sol-U-Mel* in a 16 ounce bottle of water. Generously spray the surfaces and wipe away the oil.

CAT REPELLENT

Clear Power, used as directed, is an excellent cat and kitten repellent. It seems the cats hate the smell and stay off of the areas sprayed with *Clear Power*.

CONVERTIBLE TOPS

Rustic Touch is an excellent choice for convertible tops and car interiors. It makes them shine and contains no alcohol.

CUTICLES

Apply *Melaleuca Oil* (*T36-C5*) to dry and cracked cuticles. Follow this with *Moisturizing Hand Creme*. For prevention of the damaged cuticles, wash your hands thoroughly with the *Gold Bar* and apply a thin layer of **Renew Intensive Skin Therapy** before beginning the activity that is so damaging to your skin.

An alternative solution would be to use the **Sole to Soul Revitalizing Foot Lotion** as a hand cream.

It has also been suggested to use **Melaleuca's Lip Balm** on your damaged cuticles. It will soften them right up.

DETOXIFICATION

G'Day Melaleuca Herbal Tea is the most soothing, healing detoxifier there is. Drink at least 8 glasses of tea each day for one to two weeks to detoxify. The **G'Day Melaleuca Herbal Tea** will detoxify without making you sick.

Another effective detoxifier is **Kiwi Lime Shower Gel**. Not only does it detoxify, but because it contains the extract of arnica, it will aid in eliminating inflammation, swelling and pain.

It has also been suggested to take a long soaking bath in **Tough & Tender**. It, too, will help to detoxify the body.

DOGS

During your daily walk in the woods, or elsewhere, your dog may decide to roll in something that resembles the smell of dead fish. If bath time is not handy, trying wiping off the brown color with paper towels and **Tough & Tender**. Follow this with Sol-U-Mel to remove the remainder and especially the smell. It works great.

DOG HAIR REMOVAL

Sol-U-Mel is very effective in removing the dog smell and dust from old sofas and chairs. In five minutes or so you should be able to clean, deodorize and remove all the dog hair. Just spray with diluted **Sol-U-Mel** and wipe with a paper towel. The old sofa will look new again and it is easy to do every day.

Another solution might be to keep the dog off the couch!

EAR INFECTIONS

To relieve the pain and pressure from ear aches, infections and even fluid in the ear:

Take a paper towel and rip it in half. Fold it into a square about 2" in diameter. Take a small juice glass (4 oz. size) and stuff the paper towel into the bottom of the glass. Slightly dampen the paper towel with water (do not saturate it), and then put 5-6 drops of **T36-C5** on the towel. Microwave the glass for 20-30 seconds. Take the glass (you'll see the steam coming up from the paper towel) and put the mouth of the glass completely around your child's ear. It works best to have your child sitting down, and just have them tilt their head over the mouth of the glass. You child can hold the bottom of the glass, as it is not hot. Have them hold it for at least 5 minutes. Repeat 1-2 times each day until the problem clears up. (This treatment has been known to prevent the insertion of ear tubes.)

EYEGLASSES

An alternate use for *Rustic Touch* is to clean your eyeglasses. Spray one squirt 8-10 inches from the lenses and buff with a soft cloth. This will keep your eyeglasses dust free and quick and easy to clean the next day.

EYEBROW COLOR

Nicole Miller's Enhance Eye Shadow comes in colors very close to eyebrow color. Try using a small brush and lightly touching the eyebrows with your favorite eye color. It will give you the most natural color enhancement ever.

ELEPHANT FEET

Melaleuca Oil (T36-C5) has become a preferred treatment for nail infections in elephant feet. It is being recommended to zoos and circuses with similar challenges.

FACIAL CLEANSER

It has been suggested to try *Clear Defense* to clean the faces of people challenged with pimples.

Another solution is to clean your face with *Sole to Soul Revitalizing Foot Scrub*. It gives your skin the benefit of opening the pores and thus a thorough cleaning. Less pimple and blackhead challenges have been noticed and it does not leave your face feeling "pinched".

FEET – SOOTHING

Try using *Clear Defense* to cool and soothe your feet after long hours at work or shopping. The anti-bacterial aspect is also beneficial and it won't dry out your feet.

FINGERNAILS

When working in the garden and other particularly dirty areas, sometimes it is very challenging to clean your nails. Try washing them with *MelaBrite*. They will come clean almost instantly and remain snow white.

If your nails have a tendency to split and break, try rubbing them with *Mela-Gel* or *Triple Antibiotic Ointment* (which ever is handy), 2-3 times each day. Within a month you should see a significant difference and they should be very healthy by the end of two months. This can even be used on top of *Nicole Miller's Nail Color*. The *Mela-Gel* and *Triple Antibiotic Ointment* will penetrate right on into your nails.

HAIR GROWTH

It has been suggested that Anti-Bacterial Liquid Soap be used on your hair (scalp) to promote hair growth. It couldn't hurt. What have you got to lose?

HAND SOAP

When your *Advanced Expressions Styling Foam* bottle is empty. Rinse the bottle out and put in about 2 tablespoons of *Anti-Bacterial Liquid Soap*, and add about ⅔ cup of water. (Leave room for air at the top of the bottle.) Tip the bottle over a few times until the soap dissolves in the water. Don't shake it because you don't want bubbles in the bottle. This will provide you with a great soap pump. The soap comes out foamy and the kids love it and you also don't have to worry about them using too much of it like they frequently do from the regular soap pump. Your *Anti-Bacterial Liquid Soap* will last twice as long!

By the way, the label on the styling foam bottle will peel off very easily and leave you with a nice looking bottle to use in the bathroom, kitchen or any other place you need hand soap.

Another idea is to fill the *Anti-Bacterial Liquid Soap* bottle with *Tough & Tender* when you run out. Kids seem to like it and it's a pretty blue, too.

JEWELRY

Use a mixture of *PreSpot Plus* and water to soak your rings. They will sparkle!

If you have difficulty removing your rings and/or tight fitting bracelets, just spray *Clear Power* on the fingers and/or the top of the hand and the items will slip off like magic!

KITCHEN SINK

Try using a small amount of *Denti-Clean Extra-Whitening Toothpaste* on an old toothbrush to remove stubborn stains from your kitchen sink. It even works on very old sinks!

LAUNDRY

If your washer does not have a rinse dispenser, trying putting a capful of *MelaSoft* on an old rag or bath cloth and throwing it in with the clothes in the dryer. Every so often throw it in the washer of clothes and it will not only work in there but you will have a clean cloth to start over with. This will also work with a sponge.

An alternate solution would be to take a 100-count box of coffee filters, place them in a large bowl, and pour the entire pint of *MelaSoft* into it. Let the filters soak up all of the *MelaSoft* and "presto", dryer sheets at ¹⁄₁₀ of the cost.

LAUNDRY WHITENER

Save your old gallon container of *MelaPower* and the pump. It works great for this *Laundry Whitener.*

½ to ¾ cup of *Diamond Brite Gel*
¼ cup of *Tub & Tile*
¼ cup of *MelaMagic*
1 pint bottle of *PreSpot Plus*
Pour in the gallon container and fill the rest of the way with water.

Shake well before using. Use 2 to 3 pumps of the *Laundry Whitener*, in place of bleach, per large load of whites.

LEATHER

Use a cotton ball and full strength *Sol-U-Mel* to clean your good leather purses. (Try it on the bottom first just to be safe.) It will usually take off blue jean stains, pen marks, dirt etc. and look like new!

"LICE" BULLETIN BOARD NOTICE

"Dear Parents: Did you know that the leading lice shampoo contains a potent pesticide called LINDANE, which has been known to cause vomiting, diarrhea, convulsion, liver damage and many other health issues in kids? LINDANE has been banned in 18 countries and severely restricted in 10 others. Why are we using it on our kids' heads? The health of our kids is at stake. Don't let them be exposed to this sometimes deadly treatment when there is a natural, safe, non-toxic, chemical-free and effective way to prevent and treat lice infestations. Let us get rid of these pests once and for all in our community! LET'S DO IT FOR OUR KIDS!! For more information call...(Insert your name and number). "

MANURE

Try a diluted mixture of *Tough & Tender* to get manure out of clothes. Just spray it on and wash in *MelaPower Laundry Detergent, MelaBrite* and *MelaSoft* as usual.

MOSQUITO BITES

Try putting the *Melaleuca Lip Balm* on your mosquito bites. It works like magic! It will stop the itching almost instantly and you will rarely have to repeat the process. Besides it is convenient as you should have the *Lip Balm* in your pocket or purse at all times.

MUSICAL INSTRUMENTS

Tub & Tile is great for cleaning the strings on musical instruments. It makes them work better, it shines them and it makes them last longer.

NAIL POLISH REMOVER

Melaleuca nail polish remover has been in most of our homes for years. It is *Sol-U-Mel*. Use the *Sol-U-Mel* full strength on a cotton pad and hold it on the coating for a moment. Gently rub to remove the polish. It takes longer than the toxic forms of fingernail polish remover but it is much safer and even helps to condition and heal the nails, bed and cuticles. Follow the polish removal with *Clear Defense* and your nails won't even know that they had polish on them. It works!

PAINT

When oil based paint has attacked your skin for whatever reason, gently rub a small amount of full strength *Sol-U-Mel* onto the area. It will come out.

Try applying the *Sol-U-Mel* to paint stained clothes as well. They will usually come out of the laundry with no paint on them.

PAINT BRUSHES

When your brushes dry with paint in them, soak them in ½ strength *Sol-U-Mel* for a few hours. You should then be able to strip out the dried paint and reuse a soft and pliable brush.

PERMANENT MARKER

Try using *PreSpot Plus* to remove red Sharpee permanent marker from Formica countertops. It will probably work on other colors too. At least it is worth a try.

RAZOR BLADES

Use *T36-C5* on your razor blades occasionally. It will help if you have sensitive skin or get razor rash. Of course, continue to use your shaving cream.

RING AROUND THE COLLAR

If ring around the collar is a challenge for your washday, try pumping some *MelaPower Laundry Detergent* full strength directly on the dirty area. Rub the material together and throw it in the wash.

SHIN SPLINTS

Shin splints can be quite painful. Try massaging *Pain-A-Trate* into the sore area a couple of time during the day and at bedtime. The pain and discomfort will generally be gone by morning.

SHOESHINE

Try *Rustic Touch* when you want a quick and easy shoeshine. It is also very effective when shining leather purses.

SKIN CANCER

It has been suggested that *Triple Antibiotic Ointment* be put on a small skin cancer every morning and every night before going to bed. In several cases the skin cancer simply fell off in about three weeks. (Make sure to see your doctor if you suspect skin cancer.)

SLIME

This is a recipe that kids will love whether for Halloween or whenever. Although Mom might not appreciate the aesthetic value, at least she'll know that there are no chemicals and the kids won't be harmed if it is ingested.

2 tablespoons of *FiberWise*

1¼ cup of water

Food coloring (green makes a pretty gross concoction!)

Mix the *FiberWise*, water, and coloring until dissolved. Microwave on high for 5 minutes. Let it cool. If the mixture is not "gooey" enough, microwave an additional minute or two. Store in Tupperware-like containers or empty margarine tubs. ENJOY!

STATIC CLING

Spray your nylons with *Advanced Expressions Styling Spray* before you put them on and you won't have static cling on any of your clothes. If you get dressed and find that you have static cling, use *Moisturizing Hand Crème* and your static cling will disappear.

SUPER GLUE

If you have ever glued your fingers together with super glue, you will really appreciate this suggestion. Apply a couple of drops of *Melaleuca's T36-C5* to the glued area and rub for a couple of minutes. Voila, the glue comes off and the skin stays on. (This works for crazy glue, too.)

SUSTAIN MUFFINS

Make a batch of these delicious muffins and freeze them. A quick turn in the microwave will give you a fresh muffin every morning.

1 scoop *Sustain* (any flavor)
2 cups flour]
½ t. salt
¼ cup butter
½ cup juice (orange, pineapple, etc.)
1 egg
1 T. baking powder
¼ t. baking soda
2 T. milk

Heat oven to 350 degrees. In a small bowl combine flour, baking powder, *Sustain*, salt and baking soda. In a large bowl beat sugar and butter than add milk and egg. Gradually add the dry mix and blend well. Pour into muffin cups and cook 15-18 minutes.

TEA STAINS

Try using *PreSpot Plus* to clean the tea stains out of a pan. Simply spray the inside surface and let it stand for several minutes. Then wipe it clean.

WINDOWS

Try *Lemon Brite* to clean your windows, especially if you live near the ocean. The sheeting action seems to help with the salt residue.

An alternate solution is to add a few drops of *Lemon Brite* to your *Clear Power.* Not only does it seem to help with heavy residue, but the windows seem to stay cleaner longer.

APPENDICES
TEA TREE OIL RESEARCH

Altman, P.M. "Australian Tea Tree Oil," *Australian Journal of Pharmacy*, 69, 276-78, 1988.

Altman, P.M. "Australian Tea Tree Oil – A Natural Antiseptic," *Australian Journal of Biotechnology*, 3:4, 247-8, 1989.

Altman, P.M. "Australian Tea Tree Oil – An Update," *Cosmetics, Aerosols & Toiletries in Australia*, 5:4, 27-9, 1991.

Anon, "A Retrospect," *Medical Journal of Australia*, 85-89, 1930.

Anon, "Tea Tree Oil," *Australian Journal of Pharmacy*, 274, 1930.

Anon, *Journal of the National Medical Association*, (USA), 1930.

Anon, "Ti-trol Oil," *British Medical Journal*, 927, 1933.

Anon, "An Australian Antiseptic Oil," *British Medical Journal*, I, 966, 1933.

Australian Standard, "Essential Oils, Oil of *Melaleuca* Terpinen-4-ol Type," AS 2782 1985, Australian Standards Association, Sydney, 1985.

Bassett, I.B., Pannowitz, D.L. and Barnetson R.St.C. "A Comparative Study of Tea Tree Oil Versus Benzoyl Peroxide in the Treatment of Acne," *Medical Journal of Australia*, 153:8, 455-458, 1990.

Belaiche, P. "Treatment of Chronic Urinary Tract Infections with the Essential Oil of *Melaleuca alternifolia*-Cheel," *Phytotherapy*, 15, 9-12, 1985.

Belaiche, P. "Treatment of Vaginal Infections of *Candida albicans* with the Essential Oil of *Melaleuca alternifolia*-Cheel," *Phytotherapy*, 15, 13-14, 1985.

Belaiche, P. "Treatment of Skin and Nail Infections with the Essential Oil of *Melaleuca alternifolia*-Cheel," *Phytotherapy*, 15, 15-18, 1985.

Beylier, M.F. "Bacteriostatic Activity of Some Australian Essential Oils," *Perfumer and Flavorist International*, V4, 23-5, 1979.

Bishop, C.D. "Anti-viral Activity of the Essential Oil of *Melaleuca alternifolia* (Maiden & Betche) Cheel (Tea Tree) Against Tobacco Mosaic Virus," (Research Report) *Journal of Essential Oil Research*, 7, 641-644, 1995.

Blackwell, A.L. Tea Tree Oil and Anaerobic (Bacterial) Vaginosis. *The Lancet* 337-300 (1991).

Blamann, A. and Melrose, G.J.H. 4-Terpinenol. *Perfumery Essential Oil Record*. 50, 769 (1959).

Brophy, J.J., et al. "Gas Chromatographic Quality Control for Oil of *Melaleuca* Terpinen-4-ol Type Australian Tea Tree," *Journal of Agriculture and Food Chemistry*, 37, 1330-1335, 1989.

Buck, D.S., Nidorf, D.M. and Addino, J.G. "Comparison of Two Topical Preparations for the Treatment of Onychomycosis: *Melaleuca alternifolia* (Tea Tree Oil) and Clotrimazole," *Journal of Family Practice*, 38, 601-5, 1994.

Carson, C.F. and Riley, T.V. "Antimicrobial Activity of the Essential Oil of *Melaleuca alternifolia* (A Review)," *Letters in Applied Microbiology*, 16, 49-55, 1993.

Carson, C.F. and Riley, T.V. "The Antimicrobial Activity of Tea Tree Oil," *Medical Journal of Australia*, 160, 236, 1994.

Carson, C.F. and Riley, T.V. "Susceptibility of *Propionibacterium acnes* to the Essential Oil of *Melaleuca alternifolia*," *Letters in Applied Microbiology*. 19, 24-25, 1994.

Carson, C.F., Cookson, B.D., Farrelly, H.D. and Riley, T.V. "Susceptibility of Methicillin-resistant *Staphylococcus aureus* to the Essential Oil *Melaleuca alternifolia*," *Journal of Antimicrobial Chemotherapy*, 35:3, 421-4, 1995.

Carson, C.F., Hammer, K.A. and Riley, T.V. "Broth Micro-dilution Method for Determining the Susceptibility of *Escherichia coli* (*E coli*) and *Staphylococcus aureus* to the Essential Oil of *Melaleuca alternifolia*," Microbios 82:332, 181-185, 1995.

Carson, C.F. and Riley, T.V. "Antimicrobial Activity of the Major Components of the Essential Oil of *Melaleuca alternifolia*," *Journal of Applied Bacteriology*, 78:3, 264-9, 1995.

Carson, C.F. and Riley, T.V. "Toxicity of the Essential Oil of *Melaleuca alternifolia* (or Tea Tree Oil)," (Letter) *Journal of Toxicology-Clinical Toxicology*, 33:2, 193-4, 1995.

Carson, C.F., Hammer, K.A. and Riley, T.V. "In-vitro Activity of the Essential Oil of *Melaleuca alternifolia* against *Streptococcus Spp.*" *Journal of Antimicrobial Chemotherapy*, 37:6, 1177-8, 1996.

Carson, C.F., Riley, T.V. and Cookson, B.D. "Efficacy and Safety of Tea Tree Oil as a Topical Anti-microbial Agent," (editorial) *Journal of Hospital Infection*, 40:3, 175-8, 1998.

Coutts, M. "The Bronchoscopic Treatment of Bronchiectasis," *Medical Journal Australia,* 1937.

Dabbous, K.H., Pippin, M.A., Pabst, K.M., Pabst, M.J. and Haney, L. "Superoxide Release by Neutrophils is Inhibited by Tea Tree Oil," College of Dentistry, UT Memphis, Unpublished 1993.

Davies, P. "Ti-Tree Oil for an Adult with Chicken Pox," *Aromatherapy Quarterly,* 12, 1986.

Elsom, G. "Susceptibility of Methicillin-resistant *Staphylococcus aureus* to Tea Tree Oil and Mupirocin," *Journal of Antimicrobial Chemotherapy,* V43, 427-428, 1999.

"Essential Oils – Oil of Melaleuca, Terpinen-4-ol Type." Standards Association of Australia. Standards House, 80 Arthur St. North Sydney, N.S.W. 1985.

Feinblatt, H.M. "Cajeput Type Oil (Tea Tree oil) for the Treatment of Furunculosis (boils)," *Journal of the National Medical Association* (USA), 52: 32-4, 1960.

Goldsborough, R.E. "Ti-Tree Oil," *The Manufacturing Chemist,* 57-60, Feb 1939.

Guenther, E. "The Essential Oils," *Van Nostrand NY,* V4, p526, 1950.

Guenther, E. "Tea Tree Oils," *Soap and Sanitary Chemicals,* Aug/Sept. 1942.

Guenther, E. "Australian Tea Tree Oils," *Perfumery and Essential Oil Record,* Sept. 1968.

Halford, A.C.F. "Diabetic Gangrene," *Medical Journal of Australia,* 2, 121, 1936.

Hammer, K.A., Carson, C.F. and Riley, T.V. "Susceptibility of Transient and Commensal Skin Flora to the Essential Oil of *Melaleuca alternifolia* (Tea Tree Oil)," *American Journal of Infection Control,* 24:3, 186-9, 1996.

Hammer, K.A., Carson, C.F. and Riley, T.V., "In-vitro Susceptibility of *Malassezia furfur* to the Essential Oil of *Melaleuca alternifolia,*" *Journal of Medical and Veterinary Mycology,* 35:5, 375-7, 1997.

Hammer, K.A., Carson, C.F. and Riley, T.V. "In-vitro Activity of Essential Oils, in Particular *Melaleuca alternifolia* (Tea Tree Oil and Tea Tree Oil Products) against *Candida spp.,*" *Journal of Antimicrobial Chemotherapy,* 42:5, 591-5, 1998.

Hammer, K.A., Carson, C.F. and Riley, T.V. "In-vitro Susceptibilities of *Lactobacilli* and Organisms Associated with Bacterial Vaginosis to *Melaleuca alternifolia* (Tea Tree oil)," (Letter) *Antimicrobial Agents and Chemotherapy,* Jan 1999.

Humphrey, E.M. "A New Australian Germicide," *Medical Journal of Australia,* I, 417-418, 1930.

International Standard, "Essential oils – Oil of *Melaleuca* Terpinen-4-ol Type Tea Tree Oil," ISO 4730:1994 & 1996, International Standards Organization, Geneva, 1996.

Laakso, P.V. "Scientae Pharmaceuticae," *Czechoslovak Medical Press-Prague,* 485-492, 1966.

Laakso, P.V. "Fractionation of Tea Tree Oil." *25th Congress of Pharmaceutical Science,* Prague. 1,485-492, 1965.

Lassak, E.V. and McCarthy, T.M. "Australian Medicinal Plants," Sydney, NSW. Methuen Australian Pty Ltd. (Publishers).

Low, D., Rowal, B.D. and Griffin, W.J. "Antibacterial Action of the Essential Oils of Some of Australian Myrtaceae," *Planta Medica,* 26, 184-189, 1974.

MacDonald, V. "The Rationale of Treatment," *Australian Journal of Dentistry,* 34, 281-285, 1930.

Maruzzella, J. and Ligouri, L. "The in vitro antifungal activity of essential oils." *Journal of the American Pharmaceutical Association.* 47,250-4 (1958).

McCulloch, R.N. and Waterhouse, D.F. "Laboratory and field tests of mosquito repellents." *Australia Council of Science and Industry Research Bulletin.* 213,9-26 (1947).

McDonald, L.G. and Tovey, E. "The Effectiveness of Benzyl Benzoate and Some Essential Oils as Laundry Additives for Killing House Dustmites," *Journal Allergy and Clinical Immunology,* 1993.

Merry, K.A., Williams, L.R. and Home, V.N. "Composition of Oils from *Melaleuca alternifolia, M. Linariifolia* and *M. dissitiflora.* Implications for the Australian Standard, Oil of *Melaleuca* Terpinen-4-ol type. In Modern Phytotherapy – The Clinical Significance of Tea tree Oil and Other Essential Oils." *Proceedings of a Conference 2/12/1990 Sydney and a Symposium 8/12/1990 Surfers Paradise,* II, 107-104, 1990.

Murray, K.E. "The essential oils of five western Australian plants." *Royal Australian Chemical Institute Journal and Proceedings. 17,*398-402 (1950).

Nenoff, P., et al. "Antifungal Activity of the Essential Oil of *Melaleuca alternifolia* (Tea Tree oil) Against Pathogenic Fungi In-vitro," *Skin Pharmacology,* 9:6, 388-394, 1996.

Oleum Melaleuca; *British Pharmaceutical Codex,* 597-98, 1949.

Olsen, M.W. "Control of *Sphaerotheca fuliginea* on Cucurbits with a 1.5% Dilution of an Oil Extracted from the Australian Tea Tree," *Phytopathology,* 78:12, 1595, 1988.

Peña, E.F. "Melaleuca alternifolia: Its Use for *Trichomonal vaginitis* and Other Vaginal Infections," *Obstetrics and Gynecology,* 19:6, 793-795, 1962.

Penfold, A.R. "The Essential Oils of *Melaleuca linariifolia* and *Melaleuca alternifolia,*" *Journal Proceedings of the Royal Society of NSW,* 59, 318-325, 1925.

Penfold, A.R. "Essential oil of Melaleuca alternifolia," *Perfumery Essential Oil Record,* 25,121 (1934).

Penfold, A.R. and Grant, R. "The Germicidal Values of Some Australian Essential Oils and Their Pure Constituents," *Journal Proceedings of the Royal Society of NSW,* 59:3, 346-50, 1925.

Penfold, A.R. and Morrison, F.R. "Some Notes on the Essential Oil of *Melaleuca alternifolia*," *Australian Journal of Pharmacy*, 18, 274-5, 1937.

Penfold, A.R. and Morrison, F.R. "Australian Tea Trees of Economic Value," *Technological Museum Sydney*, 1:3, Bulletin 14, 1946.

Penfold, A.R. and Morrison, F.R. "Australian essential oils in insecticide and repellents." *Soap, Perfumery and Cosmetics.* 25,933-4 (1952).

Penfold, A.R., Morrison, F.R. and McKern, H.G. "Studies in the Physiological Forms of the Myrtaceae' Part 2, The Occurrence of Physiological Forms in *Melaleuca alternifolia* (Cheel), (Research on Essential oils of the Australian Flora)," *Museum of Technology and Applied Science*, 18-19, 1948.

Pickering, G.B. "Cedarwood Oil Compounds, Silica Gel Separation and Tea Tree Oil as Nutmeg Substitute," *Manufacturing Chemist*, 27, 105-6, 1956.

Priest, D. "Tea Tree Oil in Cosmetics-The Promise and the Proof," (Technical paper) *Cosmetics, Aerosols & Toiletries in Australia*, Main Camp Tea Tree Oil, 9:4, 1995.

Shapiro, S., Meier, A. and Guggenheim, B. "The Anti-microbial Activity of Essential Oils and Essential Oil Components Towards Oral Bacteria," *Oral Microbiolog. Immunology* (Denmark), 9:4, 202-8, 1994.

Shemesh, A. and Mayo, W.L. "A Natural Antiseptic and Fungicide," *International Journal of Alternative and Complementary Medicine*, Dec. 1991.

Small, B.E.J. "Tea Tree Oil," *Australian Journal of Experimental Agriculture and Animal Husbandry*, V21, 1981.

Southwell, I., Markham, J. and Mann, C. "Why Cineole is Not Detrimental to Tea Tree Oil," *Rural Industries Research and Development Corporation, Research Paper Series* 97/54, 1997.

Swords, G. and Hunter, G. "Composition of Australian Tea Tree Oil (Melaleuca alternifolia)," *Journal of Agriculture and Food Chemistry*, 26:3, 734-5, 1978.

Tong, M.M., Altman, P.M. and Barnetson R.St.C. "Tea Tree Oil in the Treatment of Tinea pedis," *Australian Journal of Dermatology*, 33:3, 145-9, 1992.

Van Hulssen, C.J. and Meyer, T.M., "Ethereal oils from Melaleuca alternifolia and Melaleuca bracteata," I*norganic Nederland-Indie*, 8, VII, 84-7 (1941).

Veal, L. "The Potential Effectiveness of Essential Oils as a Treatment for Head Lice, Pediculus Humanus Capitis," *Complementary Ther. Nurs. Midwifery*, 2:4, 97-101, 1996.

Walker, M. "Clinical Investigation of Australian *Melaleuca alternifolia* Oil for a Variety of Common Foot Problems," *Current Podiatry*, April 7th to 15th, 1972.

Walsh, L.J. and Longstaff, J. "The Antimicrobial Effects of an Essential Oil on Selected Oral Pathogens," *Periodontology*, V8, 11-15, 1987.

Williams, I.R, Home, V.N., Zhang, X. and Stevenson, I. "The Composition and Bacteriocidal Activity of Oil of *Melaleuca alternifolia* (Tea Tree oil)," *International Journal of Aromatherapy*, 1:3, 15-17, 1988.

Williams, L.R., Home, V.N. and Asre, S. "Antimicrobial Activity of Oil of Melaleuca alternifolia. Its Potential Use in Cosmetics and Toiletries," *Cosmetics, Aerosols & Toiletries in Australia*, 4:4, 1990.

Willix, Dr. Robert D. "A Must for Your Medicine Chest," *Health for Life*, 3:5, 4-5, May 1996.

DISINFECTANT PROPERTIES

of T36-C5™ Compared to Other Agents

The following table is a summary of clinical research and is based upon direct contact of the agent with the organism. Standard concentrations were used. This demonstrates the disinfectant ability of Melaleuca alternifolia oil which contains at least 37% terpenols and less than 7% cineol. Please note that although many organisms show sensitivity to certain agents, mutant strains are developing which resist control. Many disinfectants are toxic or cause damage to skin when used over a prolonged time period. For these reasons, a number of these agents are no longer used clinically.

Disinfectant Agent	S	E	B	F	V	C	TOXIC?
Isopropyl Alcohol	K	K	O	P	P	O	
Phenolics	K	K	O	P	O	P	
Chlorine Solution	K	K	O	P	P	P	Yes
Iodine Tincture	K	K	O	P	O	P	
Acetaldehyde	K	K	P	K	K	K	Yes
Mercury Salts	K	P	K	K	K	K	Yes
Hexachorophen	K	P	O	K	O	O	
Quaternary Ammonium	K	P	O	P	O	O	
Boric Acid	P	P	O	O	O	O	
Cidex	K	K	P	K	K	K	
T36-C5	K	K	K	K	K	K	

K = Kills organism
P = Partially effective
O = Does not kill organism

S = Staph Aureus
E = E. Coli
B = Bacteria Spores
F = Fungi
V = Viruses
C = Candida Albicans

MELALEUCA OIL

and Healthy Skin

Healthy skin produces many different essential oils to maintain equilibrium with the environment. Each cell of the body has a double fatty envelope that makes up its membrane. This is what separates the cell from its environment. It is the character of this envelope to allow highly selected gases, nutrients, vitamins, minerals, hormones, and water into the cell while excreting wastes with a precision unique to life itself.

When *Melaleuca alternifolia* oil is put in contact with healthy cells, only the Creator of both could describe the complex interactions which take place. Several things are known about plant oils and human skin. Incompatible ones such as oils of Poison Ivy activate a response to flush the substance away from the system. Essential oils are absorbed and mix delicately with the equilibrium and further the harmony of health.

Bacteria have an electrical charge on their surface, much like the electric polarity of a battery. Friendly bacteria have a similar electrical charge to the skin cells they protect. Essential oils, such as found in *Melaleuca alternifolia* oil, encourage the growth of these friendly bacteria. Potentially dangerous bacteria have a lower electrical charge and are destroyed by these oils. Viruses do not carry any appreciable electrical charge and their protective lipid coats are dissolved by essential oils, allowing them to be chemically destroyed by the body's natural defenses.

What do we understand about *Melaleuca alternifolia* oil and this symphony of life at the molecular level? Actually, not much more than what the native Australian people shared with Captain Cook—try it and see what its properties can do for you.

Drawing of Healthy Skin

TECHNICAL INFORMATION

Although there are over 300 known species of tea trees (*Melaleuca*) in Australia, only one, the *Melaleuca alternifolia*, is known to have substantial therapeutic properties. The most closely related species to Melaleuca alternifolia is the *M. linarifilia* that yields an oil that is somewhat bacteriostatic, but is too high in Cineole, a natural skin irritant.

The pure oil of *Melaleuca alternifolia* is known to contain at least 48 compounds. A few of these compounds are not yet identified. A unique compound, viridiflorene, is found only to exist in oil of Melaleuca. Two other compounds, Terpinen-4-ol and Cineole, are regulated by the Australian Standards Association to designate therapeutic quality.

In Australia, the minimum amount of Terpinen-4-ol allowed is 30%, and the maximum amount of Cineole is 15%. Terpinen-4-ol is one of the more important therapeutic ingredients in the oil. Therefore, one would want oil high in Terpinen-4-ol. And since Cineole is caustic to the skin, the higher quality oil is low in Cineole. High quality oil should have at least 35% Terpinen-4-ol and less than 10% Cineole.

Since pure oil of *Melaleuca* is entirely natural and the genetics of one tree varies slightly from the other, the quality of oil from one grove of trees may vary substantially from another. In fact, much of the oil that has been distilled from *Melaleuca alternifolia* trees does not meet the minimum standards of quality oil.

Much research still needs to be done to determine exactly why *Melaleuca oil* works as it does and what extract proportion of each of the 48 compounds produces the most effective blend of oil.

In order for any product to give repeatable, expected results, it must be consistent from batch to batch. For this reason, we strongly recommend that anyone purchasing products labeled as or containing oil of *Melaleuca* do so from a reputable firm that has its source of oil and quality of oil well documented.

The following lists the 48 known compounds in pure *Melaleuca alternifolia* oil.

48 Known Compounds of Pure *Melaleuca alternifolia* Oil

1. a-Pinene
2. Camphene
3. ß-Pinene
4. Sabinene
5. Myrcene
6. a-Phellandrene
7. 1,4-Cineole
8. a-Terpinene
9. Limonene
10. 1,8-Cineole
11. g-Terpinene
12. p-Cymene
13. Terpinolene
14. Hexanol
15. Allyl hexanoate
16. p,a-Dimethyl-styrene
17. (a Sesquiterpene)

18. a-Cubebene
19. (a Sesquiterpene)
20. a-Copaene
21. Camphor
22. a-Gurjunene
23. Linalool
24. (a Sesquiterpene)
25. (unidentified)
26. 1-Terpineol
27. 1-Terpinene-4-ol
28. ß-Elemene
29. Caryophyllene
30. (a Sesquiterpene)
31. Aromadendrene
32. ß-Terpineol
33. Alloromadendrene
34. (unidentified)

35. Humulene
36. (unidentified)
37. g-Muurolene
38. a-Terpineol
39. Viridiflorene
40. Piperitone
41. a-Muurolene
42. Piperitol
43. (unidentified)
44. a-Cadinene
45. 4,10-Dimethyl-7-isopropyl bicyclo [4.4.0]-1,4-decadiene
46. Nerol
47. 8-p-Cymenol
48. Clamenene

PRODUCT PRICE COMPARISON
WalMart VS. Melaleuca
Survey Date: August 27, 2002 (WalMart in Fort Worth, Texas)

WALMART	Size/Use	No. of Uses Per Purchase	Ratio* to Melaleuca	Cost of Each Pkg.	TOTAL COST
Tide Liquid	50 oz.	12	5.33	$ 4.47	$ 23.83
Downy Care Fabric Softener	60 oz.	60	1.60	4.74	7.58
Windex	32 oz.		1.50	2.47	3.71
Tilex	32 oz.		2.00	3.27	6.54
Pro409 Degreaser/All Purpose	32 oz.		32.0	2.24	71.68
Listerine	8.5 oz.		2.35	2.47	5.80
Scalpicin Medicated Shampoo	1.5 oz.		5.00	5.24	25.85
Lamisil Antifungal	42 oz.		1.19	8.87	10.56
Tylenol PM	50 caplets		1.00	6.27	6.27
Glide Dental Tape	27.4 yds.		2.01	3.24	6.51
	SUB TOTAL				$ 168.33
	Tax(8.25%)				$ 13.89
	WALMART TOTAL				**$182.22**

MELALEUCA	Size/Use		No. of Uses Per Purchase	Ratio* to Melaleuca	Cost of Each Pkg.	Total COST
MelaPower Laundry Soap	64 oz.	=	64 loads	1	$10.49	$ 10.49
MelaSoft Fabric Softener	32 oz.	=	96 uses	1	7.34	7.34
Clear Power Glass Cleaner	8 oz.	=	48 oz.	1	3.23	3.23
Tub & Tile Bathroom Cleaner	16 oz.	=	64 oz.	1	4.47	4.47
MelaMagic Heavy Duty Cleaner	32 oz.	=	1024 oz. (8gal)	1	4.47	4.47
Breath-Away Mouthwash	4 oz.	=	20 oz.	1	3.99	3.99
Naturals Shampoo	7.5 oz.			1	6.99	6.99
Dermatin Antifungal Creme	.5 oz.			1	6.32	6.32
CounterAct PM	50 caplets			1	3.99	3.99
Exceed Dental Floss	55 yds.			1	2.99	2.99
	SUB TOTAL					$ 54.28
	Shipping (3.90 + 4% of order total)					6.07
	Tax (8.25%)					4.98
	Less Advantage Rewards (Preferred Customers)					–4.30
	MELALEUCA TOTAL					**$ 61.03**

WALMART TOTAL = $182.22
MELALEUCA TOTAL = $61.03

*For example it takes 5.33 50 oz. bottles of Tide Liquid to equal 1/2 gallon of Melaleuca's MelaPower AND it takes two 32 oz. bottles of Tilex to equal one bottle of Tub & Tile.

BOOK ORDERING INFORMATION

THE
MELALEUCA
WELLNESS GUIDE

BOOK PRICES

*(prices are in US dollars and
include shipping and handling)*

Quantity	Price Each
1-4	12.50
5-9	10.75
10-19	9.50
20-49	8.25
50-99	6.95
100+	5.75

IF ORDERING BY PHONE

We accept all major credit cards and ship most orders the same day we receive them. Smaller orders are shipped by First-Class Mail or Priority Mail. Larger orders are shipped by United Parcel Service. Call:

TOLL-FREE 1 (888) 209-0510

Local (303) 224-0277

Fax (303) 224-0299

IF ORDERING BY MAIL

We accept checks or money orders. All Canadian checks must be in U.S. funds. We usually ship mail orders the day after we receive them. Smaller orders are shipped by First-Class Mail or Priority Mail. Larger orders are shipped by United Parcel Service. Send order to:

RM BARRY PUBLICATIONS
PO BOX 3528
LITTLETON, CO 80161-3528